MICHIGAN WETLANDS – YOURS TO PROTECT

A Citizen's Guide to Wetland Protection
third edition
by Wilfred Cwikiel

©2003 Tip of the Mitt Watershed Council
Cover photograph © John & Ann Mahan
ISBN# 1-889313-08-4

The interpretations and conclusions presented in this publication represent the opinions of the author. They do not necessarily represent the views of the C.S. Mott Foundation, the SFC Charitable Foundation, the Frey Foundation, the Wege Foundation, the Offield Family Foundation, the U.S. Environmental Protection Agency, the Michigan Department of Environmental Quality, the sponsors, the individuals who served as reviewers, or any of the organizations listed in the text or appendices of this document.

The purpose of this document is to promote citizen involvement in wetland protection. If you would like to reproduce this book or portions of it for reasons consistent with this purpose, please contact the publisher:

Tip of the Mitt Watershed Council
426 Bay Street
Petoskey, MI 49770
phone: (231) 347-1181
fax: (231) 347-5928
web address: www.watershedcouncil.org
e-mail: info@watershedcouncil.org

This book shall be cited as follows:

Cwikiel, Wilfred. *Michigan Wetlands – Yours to Protect: A Citizen's Guide to Wetland Protection (Third Edition)* 2003. Tip of the Mitt Watershed Council, Petoskey, MI 49770

Funding for this project was made possible by grants from the U.S. Environmental Protection Agency to the Michigan Department of Environmental Quality (Federal Grant # CD995523-01-0), the C.S. Mott Foundation, SFC Charitable Foundation, Frey Foundation, Wege Foundation, Offield Family Foundation, and sponsorships by dozens of organizations involved in protecting Michigan's wetlands.

TABLE OF CONTENTS

iii

ACKNOWLEDGMENTS

The most important acknowledgment for the book goes to the thousands of citizens who have gotten involved in protecting Michigan's wetlands. Their experiences–both successes and failures–have served as the base upon which this document is drawn. Several of these local wetland advocates are featured in the wetland protection spotlights included in each chapter.

This book was made possible by the financial support of many entities. Support for compiling the text of this document was provided by the U.S. Environmental Protection Agency and the Michigan Department of Environmental Quality (through the Wetland Protection State Development Grant Program), as well as the C. S. Mott Foundation and SFC Charitable Foundation. Printing of this document was paid for by the Frey Foundation, the Wege Foundation, and Offield Family Foundation. The organizational sponsors listed on the next page contributed to the project and will play an important role in distribution of this document across the state.

This project was a long time in coming. Some individuals deserve special note for making this document a reality. I thank Colleen O'Keefe of the Michigan Department of Environmental Quality for her patience and determination. I am indebted to the entire staff of the Tip of the Mitt Watershed Council. Gail Gruenwald, Executive Director, was essential to the project in many ways, from writing the first edition to providing valuable editing and oversight of this edition. Scott McEwen, Water Resource Program Director provided valuable text review. Rachel Martin, Water Resource Specialist, contributed greatly to the research and writing of the wetland protection spotlights and the public lands and organizing chapters. Chuck Robbins, of Dragonfly Websites, has done a wonderful job of translating this book to the Internet (www.michiganwetlands.org). Special thanks also to Sheryl Hildebrand Marsh of Supergirl Designs for the final design of this document. But truly, this book would not have been possible without T. Jones, Watershed Council program assistant who coordinated the final editing, layout, and printing.

An important part of this publication were the comments provided by individuals who are experts in the various aspects of citizen involvement in wetland protection, restoration, and enhancement. Although their comments improved the text of this document, it is important to note that they did not necessarily endorse every opinion expressed in this document. The staff of what was previously the Land and Water Management Division of the DEQ deserve special note. In the midst of budget cuts and several re-organizations, these folks took time to review the text and provide comments: Peg Bostwick, Colleen O'Keefe, Lynn Dancy, Rob Zbiciak, Amy Lounds, John Arevalo, Dina Klemans, and Barry Horney. Comments provided by the following individuals were greatly appreciated during the creation of this document: Libby Harris, East Michigan Environmental Action Council; Carla Clos, Ingham County Deputy Drain Commissioner; Al Puplis, Wetlands Conservation Association; Bill and Cheryl Collins; Steve Sadewasser, retired DNR/DEQ wetland guru; Bob Kavetsky, U.S. Fish and Wildlife Service; and Dave Dempsey, Michigan Environmental Council. A heartfelt thanks goes to these folks and others who have helped to improve this document. The blame for any mistakes that I'm sure still exist within these pages rests squarely on my shoulders.

And I thank you, the reader, for picking up this book and using it to protect Michigan's valuable wetlands. I hope you find something in here useful!

Wil Cwikiel, January 2003

ORGANIZATIONAL SPONSORS

Bear Creek Watershed Council
Center for Applied Environmental Research
Center for Environmental Study
Central Lake Superior Watershed Partnership
Citizens Against Pollution
Clean Water Action
Clean Water Fund
Clinton River Watershed Council
Detroit Audubon Society
Ellen J. Kohler, PLC
Flintsteel Restoration Association
Friends of the Crystal River
Friends of the Rouge
Galien River Watershed Council
Grand River Environmental Action Team
Grand Traverse Regional Land Conservancy
Huron River Watershed Council
Izaak Walton League of America, Michigan Division
Keweenaw Land Trust, Inc.
Lake Erie Advisory Committee
Lake St. Clair Advisory Committee
Leelanau Conservancy
Little Traverse Conservancy
Michigan Association of Conservation Districts
Michigan Environmental Council
Michigan Lake and Stream Association
Michigan Natural Areas Council
Michigan United Conservation Clubs
National Wildlife Federation, Great Lakes Natural Resource Center
Northern Michigan Environmental Action Council
Oakland Land Conservancy
Partnership for the Saginaw Bay Watershed
Sierra Club - Mackinac Chapter
Southeast Michigan Land Conservancy
Southwest Michigan Land Conservancy
Superior Land Conservancy
Thumb Bioregional Alliance
Upper Peninsula Environmental Coalition
Wetlands Conservation Association
With The Grain

INTRODUCTION

Starting with its official formation in 1979 (the same year the Goemaere-Anderson Wetland Protection Act was originally passed) the Tip of the Mitt Watershed Council has focused on wetland protection. In 1987, the Tip of the Mitt Watershed Council published the first edition of *Michigan Wetlands - Yours to Protect: A Citizen's Guide to Wetland Protection*. That guidebook was the compilation of experiences gained during a three-year wetland protection project focusing on the Northern Michigan counties of Charlevoix, Emmet, and Cheboygan. In 1992, the second edition of *Michigan Wetlands* was published.

Since then, while continuing its wetland protection work in Northern Michigan, the Watershed Council has initiated and coordinated the Great Lakes Wetlands Policy Consortium and served as the coordinating body of the Michigan Wetland Action Coalition (MWAC). The Consortium, a bi-national group of environmental and conservation organizations, was instrumental in developing policy recommendations to increase wetland protection at all levels of government in the United States and Canada. As a direct result of the Consortium, MWAC was initiated and has served to form a network of individuals and organizations to promote wetland protection in Michigan. In the decade since MWAC was formed, individual citizens and conservation and environmental groups have advocated for maintaining a strong wetland protection program. At the same time, substantial modifications have been made to state and federal wetland protection programs.

This edition of *Michigan Wetlands - Yours to Protect: A Citizen's Guide to Wetland Protection* builds on past efforts and translates the experiences gained into a tool that will serve to empower citizens across Michigan to get involved in wetland protection. The guidebook has been completely revised and expanded. With chapters that focus on the range of wetland protection activities from education to reviewing permit applications, there is valuable information here to assist concerned citizens, local governments, conservation organizations, landowners, and others in their efforts to initiate and implement wetlands protection activities.

This guidebook has been "published" in two forms–the print copy you have in front of you and a web-based version. The print copy provides you with an easy-to-use guidebook that you can take into the field or hand to a neighbor. The web-based version provides all the information in the book, plus the most recent updates on laws and additional appendix materials. The web-based version has been designed to be easily down-loaded so you can print out copies of chapters or graphics for your wetland protection purposes.

The Watershed Council hopes that you find the information presented here useful in your efforts to protect wetlands in your backyard and throughout Michigan. If you find that you need more information, consult Appendix A, Michigan Organizations Involved in Wetlands Protection, and contact one of the organizations that serves your geographic area, or contact the Tip of the Mitt Watershed Council for information about how you can get involved in the Michigan Wetland Action Coalition.

Good luck in your efforts to protect Michigan's wetland resource. In addition to the benefits you will enjoy, the future generations of Michiganians that benefit from the functions and values of Michigan's wetlands will appreciate your efforts.

JENNIFER M. GRANHOLM
GOVERNOR

STATE OF MICHIGAN
OFFICE OF THE GOVERNOR
LANSING

JOHN D. CHERRY, JR.
LT. GOVERNOR

January 6, 2003

Dear Michigan Citizen:

This book is in your hands because you care. Wetlands are some of our most valuable resources – they provide homes for wildlife, maintain water quality, and protect us from floods. They are places of beauty that contribute greatly to the overall health of our environment. Notwithstanding the important functions wetlands serve for our communities, they do not have a voice of their own. Unfortunately, wetlands continue to be lost.

That's where you come in.

Citizen involvement is critical to wetland protection in Michigan. Citizen input is an important part of the state and federal wetland laws. In addition to participating in state wetland permitting, citizens and non-governmental organizations are the foundations for wetland education, wetland restoration, purchase of wetlands, and wetland regulation and management by local governments. Simply put, Michigan's citizens are the voice of Michigan's wetlands.

Some pundits have claimed that citizen involvement is waning. I don't believe that to be true in Michigan. We are at the heart of the Great Lakes Basin. We know we have a responsibility to ourselves and the rest of the world to take care of our land and water . . . and we know that sound wetland protection is important to our economy, our quality of life, and our future.

It doesn't matter if you are motivated by the need to protect clean water, the sight of a great blue heron hunting among the cattails, a flight of ducks at sunset, the promise of catching a big largemouth bass, or the desire to prevent flooding. The important thing is that you get involved. This book – and more than 100 organizations and agencies listed in the appendices – is here to help you ensure that Michigan's wetlands are restored, enhanced, and protected.

Please get involved. I, your neighbors, and future generations will thank you.

Sincerely,

Jennifer M. Granholm
Governor

Chapter 1   A Call to Action

When asked why wetlands are important, a 32-year-old computer programmer responded, "Cattails make good swords." To explain, he told of how he and his grade school companion would venture into the only wilderness around his suburban home—a small wetland on a played-out farm that had escaped the drainer's tile and the dozer's blade—and of the adventures and daring-do experienced there. His most memorable image was of swashbuckling with cattails. His voice dropped as he told how the farm had been sold to grow a strip mall and the wetland was converted to a fenced storm water pond. Cattails might make good swords, but they are no match for backhoes and bulldozers.

The story of this man's boyhood has little to do with water quality protection, erosion control, flood storage, wildlife habitat, or any of the other "scientific" reasons why it's important to protect wetlands. It does, however, have a lot to do with why wetlands are important to our families and our communities.

Because everyone in the community benefits from the functions performed by healthy wetlands, wetlands are community resources. Whether it is through water quality protection, wildlife habitat, or places to experience nature, healthy wetlands promote healthy communities.

In order to ensure the protection and restoration of healthy wetlands, and therefore the maintenance of healthy communities, we must all be involved.

One measure of the success of our democracy is the quality of our shared environment. How we treat the environment is an indicator of how we treat each other. The ability to act on our desire to protect healthy wetlands so that we may have healthy communities is based on the bedrock values and processes of democracy. Since protecting wetlands benefits everyone in the community, protecting wetlands is an act of civic service. Democracy is not something that we just "have," it is something that we must "do." We must accept our responsibilities as citizens and stand up for the wetlands that provide our kids with places to play, protect us from floods, clean our water, and serve as homes for wildlife.

Thanks to the scientists, hunters, anglers, and citizen activists who have studied, used, and fought to protect wetlands over the last 100 years, our society has a better understanding of wetlands and their values. We know that each of us benefit from the water quality protection, flood storage, and wildlife habitat that wetlands provide. This recent understanding runs counter to our cultural heritage, however. Although the mountain of scientific evidence that documents the important functions and values of wetlands is massive, the old conception of "wetlands as wastelands" is a current that still runs deep.

As citizens who appreciate the functions and values of wetlands, our task is not easy. The growing understanding over the last century and the last few decades of regulatory protection pale in comparison to the potency of thousands of years of western culture's imaginative understanding of wetlands and the hundreds of years of our efforts to convert wetlands on this continent. Words used to describe wetlands—Swamp, Bog, Muskeg, Mire—evoke images of mystery and intrigue. Movies like "The Swamp Thing" tap into deep-rooted fear of what might be hidden in a wetland. If nothing else, today these words convey annoyance—who among us has not been "mired," "bogged down," or "swamped?"

In addition to this historic aversion to wetlands, another major threat to wetlands is the concept of individual property rights taken to the extreme—that notion held by some property rights advocates that the individual's right to do whatever he or she chooses on their property supersedes any concern for how that activity might impact the health, safety, and general welfare of others.

So it is with this backdrop that the campaign to protect Michigan's wetlands is waged. Despite this cultural context, advocates for wetland protection have made great strides forward. Wetland functions are widely acknowledged and appreciated. Wetland regulations at the federal and state levels, and in some local communities, provide a process to avoid and minimize impacts while creating a mechanism that affords an opportunity for citizen involvement. Citizens are involved in restoring formerly degraded wetlands across the state. The growth of the local land trust movement has created an opportunity for the preservation of many important wetlands. And, on the philosophical front, even the "negative" image of wetlands is being appreciated for its value as a metaphor for the unknown and unpleasant side of human existence.

But we still have a long way to go. Thousands of permits to degrade wetlands are applied for in Michigan each year, and the vast majority of them are permitted. Hundreds, perhaps thousands (nobody knows), of wetlands are lost or degraded each year outside of the regulatory process altogether. Some of these are due to loopholes in the law, others are flagrant violations of the law.

Everyone benefits from the multitude of functions and values that Michigan's wetlands provide. Because everyone shares the benefits of clean water, flood protection, healthy fish, and abundant wildlife, everyone has a stake in how wetlands are protected and managed. As citizens who value and benefit from the functions that wetlands provide, we are responsible for their protection.

3

There are many different opportunities to get involved in wetland protection. Because the stated intent of wetland regulations is to protect the public interest in the functions and values that wetlands provide, citizens are provided with the opportunity to participate in the permit

decisions that will impact wetlands. Participating in the wetland regulatory process is but one example of meaningful involvement. Citizens are crucial to protecting wetlands through raising money to purchase them and promoting conservation easements or other land protection methods. Citizens have also been essential to the efforts to restore wetlands that have been degraded in the past and help raise the level of awareness of the importance of wetlands. In fact, the strength of

The Pillars of Wetland Protection

There are many opportunities to get involved in wetland protection. Because each of us benefit from the valuable functions that wetlands provide, we have a responsibility to get involved. The numerous opportunities can be grouped into six categories. Some of the categories of activities will appeal more to you than others. However, like the pillars holding up a building, each one is important. Even if you don't have the patience for school-aged education, or don't like the potential controversy over commenting on dredge and fill permit applications, it's important to realize that only by having citizens working to strengthen each of these pillars will we ever have any hope of protecting Michigan's wetlands.

Education - The opportunities to share your knowledge and enthusiasm about wetlands are endless. Everything from taking local 1st graders on a wetland walk to talking with your neighbor about wetlands helps to raise awareness in the community. As our communities become more aware of wetland functions and values, so too will the interest in protecting them increase. An important part of education is continually educating ourselves about wetlands and how to protect them.

Advocacy - Notwithstanding their beauty, power, and mystery, wetlands do not have a voice that is heard in our political or economic system. In order to protect wetlands, we need strong advocates who are willing to speak on behalf of the resource. Because wetlands provide us with so many benefits, when we speak for wetlands we speak for the greater good of our communities.

Advocacy means everything from commenting on individual dredge and fill permits to reporting violations to lobbying to ensure that effective wetland regulations are on the books and being implemented and enforced.

Protected Lands - There are over 7 million acres of public land in Michigan. There are thousands of acres of wetlands protected by private nonprofit conservancies. Citizens can play a critical role in ensuring that public lands are managed wisely.

Individual citizens and conservancies are on the cutting edge of expanding the base of protected wetlands across the state. Your role can be as involved as commenting on proposed actions on federal land as part of the NEPA review to contributing to the land purchase efforts of a local conservancy.

Stewardship - The word steward comes from the Norse language and means "the keeper of the house." Stewardship means expanding our definition of "the house" to include the natural world. Wetland stewardship can happen on many levels, from protecting and wisely managing wetlands on your own property to encouraging good stewardship activities on public lands. On a broader context, each of us can be a good steward of resources wherever we live. As a result, our watersheds will be healthier and so too will the wetlands that occur in the watershed.

Restoration - Michigan has lost over 50% of its original wetland base. If we are to have any hope of regaining the diminished functions and values, we must work to restore wetlands. Citizens can play a very important role in encouraging landowners and public land managers to restore formerly degraded wetlands. Citizens can also play a critical role in identifying drained wetlands that could be potentially restored. The act of restoration also has a rejuvenating effect on the individual who does the work. There is nothing more gratifying than to see a thriving ecosystem where there was once a manipulated or degraded landscape.

Research - As citizen activists, we rely on good research in order to ensure that our efforts are based on sound technical information and policy analysis. We can also participate in meaningful efforts to help advance the state of wetland science. For the hunter, participating in harvest surveys provides critical information on wildlife populations. In addition, there are numerous programs that rely on citizens to monitor and report wildlife populations (such as MDNR's spring frog and toad survey and National Audubon Society's Christmas Bird Count).

4

wetland protection efforts in Michigan depends on citizens actively engaged in many different protection approaches, from permit review and comment to raising money to purchase wetlands.

Just as there are a multitude of wetland functions, so too are there a multitude of opportunities to protect them. What will motivate you to get involved? Is it the childhood memory of exploring the wilderness of a wetland? Is it the promise of bountiful fish or game? Is it the sight of a rare and beautiful orchid? Is it the knowledge that less flooding means lower taxes? Is it the desire to swim in clean waters? Or is it the conviction that each generation should have wild places for swashbuckling adventures in which swords can readily be crafted from cattails?

Regardless of what it takes to motivate you to get involved in protecting wetlands, it is essential that you do get involved. Wetlands are being degraded as you read this. There are millions of acres of drained wetlands waiting to be restored. The time to take action is now. If not you, then who?

Wetland Protection Spotlight

Alan Puplis and the Wetlands Conservation Association

"Wetland protection is like running a race. A wetland activist needs to determine what kind of runner they want to be—a half-miler, miler, or marathoner. The best advice I can give is to be a marathoner, and stick with the race. There'll be hills, and sweat, and tears. But there will be victories."

– Alan Puplis

Alan Puplis moved to Southwest Michigan from Midland in 1984. Being an avid duck hunter, he started two local chapters of the Michigan Duck Hunters Association. Alan and a friend, also with the Duck Hunters Association, became very interested in the permit applications that were being sent to the group by the Michigan United Conservation Clubs (MUCC). They would review the permits, submit comments, request hearings, and identify drained and filled wetlands. "I became involved in protecting wetlands when I came to appreciate the full value that they provide to our society; flood control, wildlife habitat, food values, natural beauty–wetlands are just awesome!"

But the Association seemed more interested in placing wood duck boxes and tearing out old blinds than getting involved in permit review. "There were just the two of us trying to convince them that if they didn't take a better stance on wetland protection, and work to prevent wetland loss, they would have no place to put their wood duck boxes," Alan recalled.

Seeing the need to get more people involved, they got the idea of starting a new group that would focus on protecting habitat so that all values of wetlands could be realized. "If they wanted to argue about hunting vs. anti-hunting, they could do so outside of meetings," said Alan. Thus the Wetlands Conservation Association (WCA) was born.

A year after the WCA's beginning, a Michigan Department of Transportation (MDOT) highway construction project threatened a valuable wetland known as Blue Creek Fen. The fen is a "Noah's Ark" of rare species. It contains the second highest population (of 19 remaining populations in the world) of the endangered Mitchell Satyr Butterfly, the highest recorded number of Eastern Box Turtles (a species of special concern) in Michigan, as well as Yellow-Spotted Turtles (a threatened species), and Blandings Turtles. Blue Creek is spring fed and runs from a tamarack swamp through the fen, and into the Paw-Paw River.

WCA was particularly concerned about the impacts the bridge would have on the Mitchell Satyr Butterfly. At the time the butterfly was stranded on the waiting list to be officially designated as a federal endangered species. Not much was known about the life cycle of the insect, making the situation even more difficult. Given the situation, the U.S. Fish and Wildlife Service emergency-listed the butterfly.

After a disappointing "stakeholders meeting" and afraid that the bridge would permanently harm the ecological integrity of the fen and its endangered inhabitants, the WCA decided to make the case for protection based on sound science. The group contacted university scientists who studied the fen (at a very low cost.) Armed with this information, Alan and his group were able to prove that the bridge construction, as proposed, would harm the endangered species. This information helped the U.S. Fish and Wildlife Service to make a "jeopardy call" on their biological opinion, meaning this project could substantially reduce the chance of recovery for the butterfly. The opinion dictated that if the bridge were constructed, it would have to be specially designed to insure that the wetland would not be harmed. The Fish and Wildlife Service stated that had Alan and his group not brought this information to their attention, the project may have been approved as proposed. Currently, MDOT is carefully weighing the expense of the specially-designed bridge and is investigating other alignments that would avoid the fen altogether.

Alan's involvement in this issue had a profound effect on him. "It makes you realize that you can take on anything. It teaches you to deal with problems and look for resources to solve the problems. It gives you a lot of confidence. But what is most important, you learn the importance of a team," said Alan.

Today, Alan's group is taking the time to enjoy the places they have been working to protect. They're still commenting on permits and looking for illegal fills, and they've also started working to educate folks about the importance of wetlands.

Alan's final advice to others still shows that he's in it for the long run: "Keep an open mind, and evaluate all ideas from everyone. It has to be a true team effort to succeed. And have some fun too!"

For more information about the WCA, contact:
Alan Puplis
Wetlands Conservation Association
P.O. Box 133
Stevensville, MI 49127-0133
Phone: (269) 429-1862

Chapter 2 A Valuable Resource

What are wetlands? Why are wetlands important? When this country was first settled by Europeans, few of the functions of wetlands were recognized, let alone valued as important to society. Prior to the mid-1970s, the destruction of wetlands through dredging, draining, and filling were accepted practices. As a result, according to the U.S. Fish and Wildlife Service, Michigan has lost approximately one-half of its wetland resources since European settlement. Now, through the work of scientists, hunters, anglers, naturalists, and land managers, we understand the importance of wetlands better than ever before.

Terms Used to Describe Wetlands

Aquatic Bed: Areas of shallow permanent water that are dominated by plants that grow on or below the surface of the water.

Bog: A peat-accumulating wetland that has no significant inflow or outflow of ground or surface water and because of its acidic nature, supports acidophilic vegetation, particularly *Sphagnum* mosses.

Bottomland: Lowlands (usually forested) along streams and rivers that are periodically flooded.

Estuary: A marsh system associated with the drowned mouth of a large river.

Fen: A peat-accumulating wetland that receives some inputs of ground water or drainage from surrounding mineral soils which typically results in alkaline waters and usually supports grass-like vegetation.

Interdunal Swale Wetland: A wetland dominated by grass-like vegetation that occurs in the low areas between sand dunes or beach ridges along the Great Lakes shoreline.

8

WHAT ARE WETLANDS?

Wetlands are unique and varied ecosystems that are too wet to be considered upland, and too dry to be considered "deep water" habitats. An old farm adage, "Too thick to drink and too thin to plow," gives a hint both at the nature of wetlands as a transitional zone between upland and aquatic habitats, and lack of value attributed to them in the past. Michigan is fortunate to contain a diversity of wetland types ranging from broad expanses of coastal marsh to small isolated bogs. Although each wetland is unique, wetlands are typically differentiated from upland areas by three common characteristics:

1) The presence of water at or near the land surface for a frequency and duration long enough to exert a controlling influence on the type of vegetation that can grow there (wetland hydrology);

2) The presence of plants adapted to living in saturated soil conditions (hydrophytic vegetation); and

3) The presence of distinctive soil types which develop under saturated conditions (hydric soils).

These three characteristics serve as the scientific and regulatory basis for identifying and delineating wetlands, and are more fully described in Chapter Three.

Although numerous terms have arisen over the years to describe different types of wetlands across the United States, Michigan's wetland regulatory statute clumps the many different wetland types into three categories: marsh, swamp, and bog (northern peatland).

Marsh

When people hear the term wetland, they most commonly think of a marsh. Marsh is a term that represents a broad array of wetlands that are dominated by grass-like vegetation. Typical marsh plants include rushes, reeds, sedges, cattails, and grasses. They are wet areas which can be periodically covered by standing or slow-moving water and are usually associated with ponds, rivers, streams, inland

Marsh: A frequently or continually inundated wetland characterized by grass-like and other emergent vegetation adapted to saturated soil conditions.

Muskeg: Large expanses of peatlands.

Peatland: A generic term for any peat-accumulating wetland.

Poor Fen: A peat-accumulating wetland that is transitional between a true bog and a true fen.

Pothole: A shallow pond dominated by grass-like vegetation.

Slough: A swamp or shallow lake system.

Swamp: A wetland dominated by trees or shrubs.

Vernal Pool: An ephemeral wetland usually in a forested area.

Wet Meadow: Grassland with saturated soil near the surface but without standing water for most of the year.

Wet Prairie: Intermediate between a marsh and a wet meadow.

lakes, and the Great Lakes. Although some marshes have sandy soils, marshes usually have finer textured, nutrient rich soils with a high content of organic matter.

There are many types of wetlands that are dominated by grass-like vegetation and fall into the general category of marsh. One that deserves special note occurs in swales between beach ridges, wind blown depressions, and small embayments along the Great Lakes shoreline. These wetlands (referred to as interdunal swale wetlands), depend on the Great Lakes for their water source. As such, their water table and period of saturation fluctuates with Great Lakes water levels. Because of the highly variable ecosystem characteristics, and the fact that they exist nowhere else on earth, interdunal swale wetland/upland complexes support many endangered or threatened species such as the Piping Plover, Pitcher's thistle, Lake Huron tansy, and Houghton's goldenrod. Due to a combination of the natural fragility of interdunal wetlands and the loss of shoreline habitat due to development along the Great Lakes shoreline, these habitats are threatened.

9

Another type of marsh-like wetland that deserves special note is the wet meadow. Wet meadows contain grass-like vegetation and saturated soils, but seldom have water standing on the ground surface. Many wet meadows occur in the former lake-plain of the Great Lakes, especially in southeast Michigan and the Saginaw Bay watershed. Because these areas are relics from a former geologic epoch, they provide habitat for many plant species rare in Michigan that are typically adapted to prairies. Unfortunately, a large percentage of these wet prairies (as they are sometimes called) have been severely degraded or converted to agriculture or housing.

Marshes comprise the most biologically productive ecosystems in Michigan. The lush vegetation and rich invertebrate and insect life provide excellent habitat and breeding grounds for water birds such as ducks, geese, swans, and herons. The common loon, bald eagle, and osprey also utilize marshes for feeding or nesting areas, as do numerous species of song birds. Marshes are also home to many mammals, such as muskrat and mink, and are important spawning grounds for many fish species.

Swamp

Swamps do not have the best public image. Movies like "The Swamp Thing" and place names like "The Great Dismal Swamp" convey a foreboding landscape. However, the term swamp simply refers to a wooded wetland. Based on dominant vegetation, Michigan's swamps can generally be divided into three different types: a conifer swamp with tree species such as tamarack, cedar, or balsam fir; a hardwood swamp with tree species such as red maple, black ash, American elm, or balsam poplar; or a shrub-scrub swamp with shrub species such as tag alder, willows, or dogwoods.

Swamps are usually inundated or saturated periodically at some point during the growing season. Some types of swamps, such as a red maple floodplain forest, are associated with lakes, rivers, or streams: others are associated with areas where the ground water is near the soil surface. The soils in swamps are usually rich in nutrients and organic matter. This is due to silt and organic matter deposited by flood events and the accumulation of organic matter (dead trees and other vegetation) over time.

A unique type of wetland that occurs in forests, but may not be recognized as a swamp due to its small size, is a vernal pool. Vernal pools are small isolated wetlands that only hold water for a short time during the spring. After snowmelt, amphibians congregate in vernal pools to create another generation of frogs, toads, and salamanders. By midsummer, the water is gone from this important, yet ephemeral, wetland.

Swamps provide very important habitat for a wide array of wildlife throughout the year, including deer, bear, raccoons, bobcats, eagles, songbirds, and other small animals. The dense vegetation and proximity to surface water (especially along rivers) allow for high nutrient exchanges between land and water ecosystems. These factors also contribute to the value of swamps as cover and food sources for many animals.

Northern Peatlands

Northern peatlands, commonly referred to as bogs, occur as thick peat deposits in old lake basins or as blankets of peat across the landscape. Their formation is due to the combination of cool temperatures and adequate rainfall in northern temperate regions around the earth. Michigan's northern peatlands are usually divided into two categories: bogs or fens. In scientific terms, the main difference between a bog and a fen is based on the connection of the peatland to a source of ground water or mineral-rich surface water. Bogs form in lake basins that are isolated from sources of ground water. Because normal rain water (the only water source for true bogs) is slightly acidic, bog water tends to be slightly acidic. The acidic nature of bogs supports acid-loving (acidophilic) vegetation, especially *Sphagnum* mosses, and contributes to a deficiency in available plant nutrients. As a result, many plants, animals, and microbes have special adaptations. An example of a unique adaptation can be found in vegetation such as the pitcher plant and sundew,

which attain nutrients by catching and "digesting" insects. Other vegetation adapted to the highly acidic and nutrient poor conditions include black spruce trees; shrubs such as leather-leaf, blueberries, and cranberries; and sedges such as cotton grass.

11

Although bogs can form in a number of ways, the most common in Michigan is the development of a "quaking bog." Typically, this successional process involves a small isolated lake basin (most likely a depression created when a large block of ice melted after the glaciers retreated) that is gradually taken over by the accumulation of organic matter formed from the life and death of thousands of generations of plants growing on the edge of the basin. Since the production of plant material outstrips decomposition, the dead plants at the water's edge accumulate to form a floating mat of peat. Over many thousands of years, a mat of mosses, reeds, sedges, grasses and other herbaceous plants develops along the leading edge of the floating mat. The older peat is then colonized by shrubs and eventually trees such as tamarack and spruce which form concentric rings around the advancing floating mat. When one ventures out onto this floating mat, the ground underfoot "quakes" with every step.

If a true bog is at one end of the northern peatland spectrum, then a calcareous (alkaline) fen is on the other. A calcareous fen (sometimes called a true fen) receives water that has passed through mineral soils rich in limestone. The ground cover in these peatlands is usually dominated by grasses, sedges, or reeds instead of *Sphagnum* moss. A poor fen lies somewhere between a true bog and a true fen on the peatland spectrum. Due to the accumulation of peat over time, a gradual reduction in ground water flow through the fen occurs, and the water chemistry becomes more and more acidic. The resulting system is dominated by a combination of plants typically found in both bogs and fens, including sedges, *Sphagnum* moss, leather-leaf, tamarack, bog laurel, bog birch, and other plant species typically associated with bogs like sundew and pitcher plants.

WHY ARE WETLANDS IMPORTANT?

Wetlands are complex ecosystems that provide many ecological functions that are valued by society. In Michigan, these functions become increasingly significant as we continue to lose wetlands. The valuable ecological functions of wetlands and the aesthetically pleasing open space they provide help to enhance the quality of life for Michigan residents and visitors. When discussing the importance of wetlands, the terms "wetland functions" and "wetland values" are often used. Wetland functions are natural processes that continue regardless of their perceived value. Society does not necessarily attach value to all wetland functions. Value is usually associated with wetland goods and services that benefit individuals in some tangible way.

Wetland Functions

Wetlands are known to be the most biologically productive ecosystems in the temperate regions of the earth. Their biological productivity rivals that of tropical rainforests and involves complex nutrient and energy cycles. Many wetland functions are a direct result of the biological activity that occurs in wetlands.

Fish and Wildlife Habitat

Fish and wildlife habitat is the most widely celebrated and actively enjoyed wetland function. In fact, it was this particular function that first inspired individuals and organizations like Ducks Unlimited and the Audubon Society to promote wetland protection in the early part of the 20th century. Some species spend their entire lives in wetlands, while others utilize them intermittently for feeding or rearing their young. Simply put, wetlands provide critical habitat for Michigan's wildlife.

Most freshwater fish are considered wetland dependent. Fish feed in wetlands or on food produced there. Wetlands serve as nursery grounds for many species whose young take cover there, and many important sport fishes spawn in or near wetlands.

Like fish, many bird species are dependent on wetlands for either migratory resting places, breeding or feeding grounds, or cover from predators. It is estimated that more than one-third of all bird species in North America rely on wetlands for at least one of these purposes.

Nearly all of Michigan's amphibians are wetland dependent, especially for breeding. Amphibians are sensitive to changes in wetland quality and quantity. Many scientists correlate declines in amphibian populations with wetland degradation worldwide.

Wetlands serve as the preferred habitat for many mammals such as muskrat, beaver, otter, mink, and raccoon. In Northern Michigan, cedar swamps are critical to white-tailed deer for many reasons, including winter browse (northern white cedar sustains deer in the absence of other foods) and important thermal cover during harsh winters.

12

Threatened and Endangered Species Habitat

Wetland habitats are critical for the survival of threatened or endangered species. Endangered species are those that are in danger of becoming extinct. Threatened species are those that are in danger of becoming endangered. These species represent a unique element of Michigan's valuable natural heritage. More than one-third of all threatened or endangered animal species in the United States live in wetland areas or depend on wetlands for some part of their life cycle. This is especially critical considering that wetlands comprise only about five percent of the lower 48 United States. Examples of Michigan's threatened or endangered animals that rely on wetlands include the bald eagle, osprey, common loon, and king rail. According to the Michigan Natural features inventory, of Michigan's total 395 threatened, endangered, rare, and special concern plant species, 194 of them are found in wetland habitats. Thus, nearly 50% of Michigan's plants of management concern reside in less than 15% percent of Michigan's surface area.

13

Water Pollution Control

A major function of wetlands is the preservation of water quality. In a sense, wetlands function like living filters by trapping polluting nutrients and sediments from surface and ground water. Although less well-known than providing fish and wildlife habitat, this wetland function is important to the integrity of aquatic ecosystems and can influence all other functions.

Excess inputs of nutrients such as phosphorus and nitrogen can cause severe problems in aquatic ecosystems. You might say, "But I thought nutrients were good?" Nutrients such as phosphorus are necessary, but can be a classic example of how "too much of a good thing is bad." Excess nutrients can cause an undesirable increase in algae and aquatic plant growth. The result is water that is reminiscent of pea soup, weed-choked lakes, depleted dissolved oxygen levels, and the rapid aging or "eutrophication" of a lake. This in turn impacts other functions such as use for recreation and fish and wildlife habitat.

In the Great Lakes Region, the massive algae blooms and depleted dissolved oxygen levels of Lake Erie in the early 1970s is a classic example of what happens to an aquatic system under the strain of too many nutrients. Wetlands retain or remove nutrients in four ways: 1) uptake by plant life, 2) adsorption into sediments, 3) deposition of detritus (organic materials), and 4) chemical precipitation. The most significant of these is the uptake of nutrients by plants (which occurs primarily during the growing season, the same time that lakes and streams are most sensitive to nutrient inputs) and adsorption into sediments.

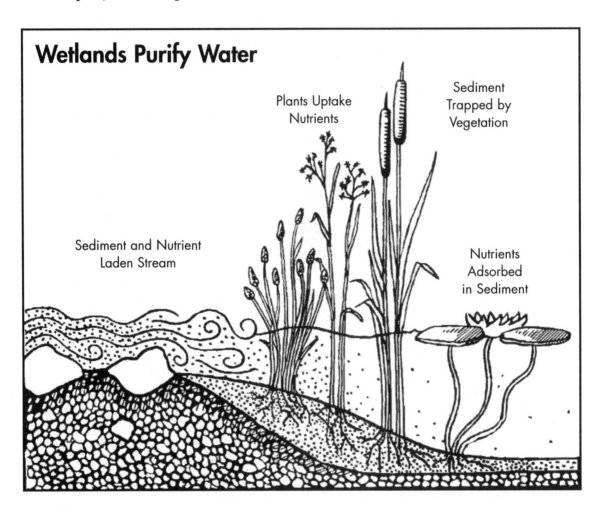

Wetlands Purify Water

Plants Uptake Nutrients

Sediment Trapped by Vegetation

Sediment and Nutrient Laden Stream

Nutrients Adsorbed in Sediment

Sediment Control

As sediment-laden water flows through a wetland from the surrounding watershed, the sediments are deposited in the wetland. This reduces siltation into lakes, rivers, and streams. A combination of wetland vegetation and generally flat topography serves to slow water flow and increase deposition of silt and organic matter (carbon compounds). Because of the soil chemistry in wetlands, carbon compounds that are deposited in wetlands decompose very slowly. In this manner, wetlands serve as a relatively permanent resting place for carbon compounds. This function of wetlands can help to trap carbon that would otherwise accumulate in the upper atmosphere and contribute to global climate change. Furthermore, there is a strong tendency for heavy metals and other toxic chemicals to attach to the sediment particles found in surface water runoff. Wetlands can trap these human-induced pollutants and remove them from the water column. However, when the natural ability of a wetland to function as a filter is overstressed from human inputs, the wetland and its functions can be destroyed. In fact, when overloaded, wetlands can actually become sources of pollutants, exporting materials that have been filtered and stored for centuries.

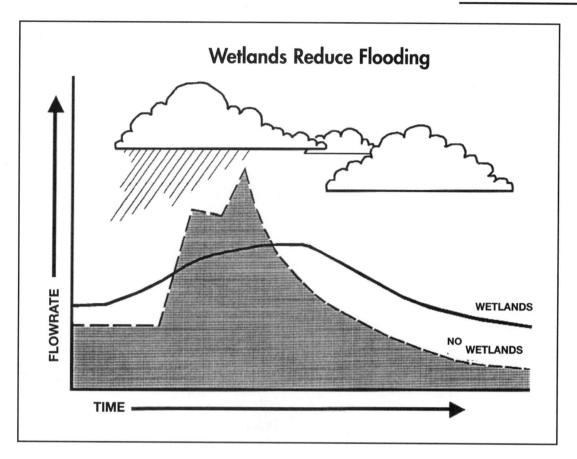

Wetlands Reduce Flooding

FLOWRATE

WETLANDS

NO WETLANDS

TIME

15

Barrier to Waves and Erosion

In their natural condition, wetlands function as a barrier to erosion along shorelines. The root systems of wetland plants stabilize soil at the water's edge and enhance soil accumulation at the shoreline. Wetland vegetation along shorelines reduces erosion by dampening wave action and slowing current speed.

Water Supply

Wetlands are usually found where the ground water table intersects or is close to the land surface. They are usually sites of springs or seeps where ground water is discharged and are very important for providing high quality water for our lakes and streams. However, some wetlands are found where ground water seeps back into the earth and recharges aquifers. The recharge potential of a wetland varies according to a variety of factors, including wetland type, geographic location, subsurface geology, soil type, and precipitation.

Flood Storage and Conveyance

Wetlands act as a hydrologic sponge, temporarily storing flood waters and releasing them slowly, thus reducing flood peaks and protecting downstream property owners from flood damage. Wetlands and adjacent floodplains often form natural floodways that convey flood waters from upland to downstream points. These functions become increasingly important in urban areas where development has increased the rate and volume of runoff.

Wetland Values

Since practically every wetland function has some value to individuals and society, wetland values closely correspond to wetland functions.

Hunting, Fishing, and Trapping

According to the American Sportfishing Association, more than 35 billion dollars is spent annually by an estimated 50 million people on fishing. These expenditures generate over one trillion dollars of economic output. In Michigan alone, anglers spend more than $1.5 billion on their sport and generate nearly $3 billion in total economic output. Hunting and trapping also generate significant economic output, especially in rural areas of the state.

Since nearly all sport fishes, many popular game animals, and most fur-bearing animals depend on wetlands for their survival, healthy and functioning wetland ecosystems are necessary to maintain the resource base for this segment of the economy.

16

Water Quality Maintenance

Whether it is used for recreation, drinking water, or industrial processes, everyone needs clean water. For example, the value of wetlands for maintaining water quality can easily be seen if we look at the problem of municipal water supply and treatment. On the delivery side of the water equation, clean water resulting from the water quality maintenance function of wetlands helps to keep water treatment costs low. Ground water is vulnerable to contamination at many recharge areas. The filtering capacity of wetlands and the absence of pollution-generating uses in wetlands serve to protect vulnerable aquifers. On the treatment side of the water use equation, the pollution treatment functions of natural wetlands have been mimicked in artificial wetlands constructed to serve as wastewater treatment systems and to reclaim areas degraded by strip mining. As alternatives to typical engineered systems, created wetlands provide a cost-effective approach to meeting human needs.

Water Supply

Because wetlands store water and slowly release it, they are often very important for maintaining base flow in streams. Wetlands are also very important for water storage during drought conditions. In severe drought years, the only vegetation lush enough to cut for hay may be from wetland areas.

Food and Fiber Production

Wetlands support many commercial activities. In addition to the revenue generated by hunting, fishing, and trapping wetland species, wetlands provide a variety of natural products including blueberries, cranberries, and wild rice. Wetland grasses are hayed in many places for winter livestock feed. Forested wetlands, such as cedar swamps, can provide sustained yields of valuable timber if harvested with careful management and planning. It must be noted that many commercial activities, such as peat mining, logging, livestock grazing, or cranberry cultivation can severely degrade wetlands and a majority of their values if not done on a small scale with the utmost of care.

Flood Protection

Each year, many Michigan communities experience severe flooding and hundreds of millions of dollars in damage is caused by flooding across the United States. Due to below market cost of federal flood insurance and other forms of federal assistance to help flood victims, the American taxpayer bears the majority of the financial burden of flood damage. The flood storage and conveyance functions of wetlands can help to prevent flooding, resulting in substantial savings to the taxpayer. In the 1990s, in an effort to avoid a repeat of the devastating damage cause by flooding of the upper Mississippi River watershed, federal, state, and local agencies coordinated restoration of thousands of acres of wetlands. This move was reminiscent of the 1970s, when the New England District of the U.S. Army Corps of Engineers concluded that natural wetland protection was the most cost-effective means of floodwater control for the Charles River near Boston. As a result of that finding, instead of expensive engineered dikes, dams, and levees which all degrade wetlands, the Corps acquired nearly ten thousand acres of wetlands in the Charles River watershed for permanent protection.

17

Sedimentation and Erosion Control

Controlling erosion and sedimentation into our lakes and streams can be expensive, especially when considering the high cost of shoreline property. Many riparian landowners experience erosion along the shore of their lake or stream. Often, this is a result of landowner activities that result in making the shoreline more susceptible to erosion (e.g., vegetation removal) or other human-caused circumstances (e.g., excessive boat wake). Maintaining or restoring wetland vegetation at the shore can be a cost-effective means of protecting the property from erosion and protecting the lake or stream from sedimentation.

Historic and Archeological Values

Some wetlands are important for historic, archeological, or paleontological reasons. Because wetlands served as a good source of food, early Native American settlements were often located in or near wetlands. Well-preserved remains of prehistoric mammals and Native American artifacts have been found in Michigan's wetlands. Bogs, due to the extremely slow rate of decomposition resulting mainly from anaerobic conditions and their acidic nature, were used by pre-historic residents of Michigan to store meat— mastodon meat!

Education and Research

Wetlands serve as wonderful outdoor classrooms, providing excellent opportunities for discovery and living examples of nearly all ecological principles. Boardwalks and observation platforms have been constructed in many wetlands across the state to facilitate educational activities.

Cultural, Philosophical, and Psychological Values

For thousands of years our cultural imagination has used wetlands as a metaphor for mystery and intrigue. Movies like "The Swamp Thing" tap into deep-rooted fear of what might be hidden in the wetland. Words used to describe wetlands–Swamp, Bog, Muskeg, Mire–evoke images of the dark and unpleasant side of human existence. Although on the surface negative, the evocative nature of wetlands is important to our psyche. In this age where the landscape is nearly completely controlled by the hand of our culture, wetlands provide rare opportunities to experience the wild force and the fecundity of nature. The existence of this wilderness, even though not everyone may choose to physically enter it, is psychologically important. Some philosophers and writers feel that without the real presence of wetlands on the landscape–intact wetlands in all their magnificent mystery, beauty, and fecundity–the power of the metaphor, and its meaning to our culture, would be lost.

18

Recreation and Aesthetic Values

The richness of the plant and animal communities found in wetlands make them some of Michigan's most beautiful natural environments. Bird watching is quickly becoming a popular pastime and wetland-rich communities, such as the Les Cheneux area in Michigan's Upper Peninsula, are beginning to realize the economic benefits of promoting this activity. Rare, threatened, and endangered plant and animal species provide added interest for naturalists. Wetlands provide valuable open space for visual and recreational enjoyment. Throughout the state, protected wetlands have been shown to enhance the value of neighboring properties due to these factors. Perhaps the most valued function of wetlands is the space they provide for introspection, quiet reflection, and the opportunity to experience wildness.

QUANTIFYING WETLAND VALUES

Although it is obvious that wetlands provide many important values, it is difficult to place a dollar value on the range of ecological functions that wetlands serve. This difficulty is due to many inherent problems associated with evaluating the dollar value of wetlands, three of which are discussed below.

First, wetlands are valuable for many different reasons. Each wetland performs many different functions, the value of which often depends upon the person making the evaluation. Some functions are relatively easy to quantify (e.g., the value of the standing timber in a cedar swamp), while others are nearly impossible (e.g., the value of seeing a bobcat stalk a snowshoe hare in the same swamp). Complexity is added when one attempts to compare the value of the wetland in its natural state to the value of the wetland converted to a farm field or other non-wetland use.

Second, many wetland functions provide services that benefit the public as much (if not more) than the person who owns the wetland. It is precisely because wetland functions are valued by society that regulations have been passed to protect them. Some wetland functions, such as the flood storage capacity provided by a wetland located in the headwaters of a major river system, benefit downstream property owners more than the actual landowner. For another example, consider the owner of a large marsh adjacent to a lake. The landowner does not economically benefit from the bass, pike, and other wetland-dependent fish that are caught in the lake by other anglers.

Third, and perhaps the most critical problem with attempting to quantify wetland values, is the issue of time frame. Wetlands provide ecological functions in perpetuity. Private entrepreneurs typically expect to recoup their investments within 10 to 30 years. Comparisons between short-term high economic yield projects and long-term ecological functions are inappropriate because economic analysis typically discounts the future value. Because of this, the decision regarding whether to convert a wetland based on a short-term economic analysis (assuming the absence of regulations) will typically favor wetland destruction. It is important to remember that the destruction of wetlands by permanent conversion (e.g., house construction, filling, or draining) removes the ecological functions forever. On a related front, the economic evaluation of wetland conservation versus wetland conversion has an intergenerational component. Future generations do not compete in the "marketplace," and therefore decisions that affect the natural resources that they will inherit are often made without their regard.

WETLAND LOSSES

Although the functions that wetlands provide make them our most valuable landforms, Michigan and the United States have lost alarming amounts of wetlands. Since European settlement, the lower 48 states have lost over 53% of their original wetlands. According to a study by the U.S. Fish and Wildlife Service, Michigan has lost approximately 50% of its original wetlands. Other Great Lakes states and parts of Ontario have fared worse—it's estimated that only 30% of the original wetlands remain in the Great Lakes watershed.

There have been no comprehensive studies to assess and document the overall ecosystem impacts of these significant wetland losses. However, one only needs to look at the increases in flood damage, the degraded

or impaired lakes and rivers, number of species that are threatened with extinction, and a myriad of other indicators of poor ecosystem health to get an idea of the impacts. Another way to visualize the impacts of wetland conversion in Michigan is to consider that we now only have one half of the functions and values that wetlands provide—one half of the flood protection, one half of the wetland habitat, one half of the water quality protection, and so on.

Wetlands continue to be converted or degraded today. Each year, the Michigan Department of Environmental Quality and the U.S. Army Corps of Engineers receive a greater number of permit applications to authorize activities that further degrade Michigan's wetlands. The vast majority of these permits are issued. On top of this intense pressure, there are numerous other activities that degrade wetlands without any regulatory and protection oversight, including county drainage projects, illegal dredging and filling, polluted runoff, and activities (like logging) that don't require a permit. This continued threat to Michigan's wetlands underscores the critical importance of citizen involvement in protecting them.

In summary, wetlands provide many ecological functions that are valuable to our quality of life, including recreational opportunities, flood storage, erosion control, and water quality maintenance. For many reasons, as with other natural resources, the monetary value of wetland functions is difficult to quantify. As we continue to lose wetlands, the functions that they provide will continue to increase in value. If we accept our responsibility as citizens to get involved in wetland protection, future generations will be able to experience (and surely find value in) the leap of a largemouth bass on the end of their line, the opportunity to watch a great blue heron stalking frogs, wild places in which to get lost (and maybe find themselves), abundant game in marshes and swamps across the state, and high quality water resources for a variety of uses.

Wetland Protection Spotlight

Assessing Mill Creek's Wetlands

Southeast Michigan has experienced a tremendous historic loss of wetlands. Ever-increasing development pressure threatens those that remain. What is a wetland worth to a community? How can local units of government, landowners, and environmentalists know which specific functions a particular wetland performs and integrate that into their decision-making?

In 1997, the Huron River Watershed Council (HRWC) initiated a project that would seek to answer these questions and stem the tide of wetland loss in Southeast Michigan. The HRWC, in conjunction with the Clinton River Watershed Council, decided to develop a program that demonstrated how assessments of wetland functional values may be utilized by local governments, community organizations, and landowners to support protection and restoration of wetlands. This project, known as the Advanced Identification (ADID) Functional Assessment project is funded by the U.S. Environmental Protection Agency as part of their grant program to support state and local efforts to protect wetlands.

The initial step in the ADID Functional Assessment project was to develop a methodology to assess wetlands that could be completed quickly by staff or volunteers with a minimal amount of wetland technical experience. The "Rapid Wetland Assessment Method," developed by Tilton and Associates, was selected because of its ease of implementation and its previous use in Southeast Michigan.

21

The method starts with locating the wetlands within the watershed to be assessed. A Geographical Information System (GIS) is used to combine information from National Wetland Inventory maps, County Soil Survey maps, and MIRIS maps to create a map of potential wetlands. Where two or more of the information layers intersect to form a polygon, the polygon is considered to be a wetland. Once wetlands are identified, the method involves measures to record wetland characteristics and assess the degree to which each wetland provides certain functions. The functions assessed in this method include: floral diversity and wildlife habitat; fishery and herpetile habitat; flood and stormwater storage; runoff attenuation; water quality protection; shoreline and streambank protection; and aesthetics and recreation.

Once the method was selected and the maps were made, it was time to field test it. The project team selected the North Branch Mill Creek watershed, which lies in the northwest corner of Washtenaw County and flows into the Huron River. Areas of this watershed, particularly between the Villages of Chelsea and Dexter, have come under extreme development pressure in recent years. In addition to high development pressure, this particular watershed was chosen because of the receptivity of the project by local government officials and citizens, and it would complement other programs in the watershed such as a Mill Creek fishery restoration project.

The initial wetland map contained over 700 wetlands in the subwatershed. Realizing that there was no way to assess all these wetlands in one field season, the project team prioritized those in areas that were under greatest threat or had the greatest support for their protection. They used several methods to complete the fieldwork and analyze the functions, including "windshield" reviews, on-site assessments, and aerial flights.

The initial results provide some interesting insights. All of the wetlands assessed were found to perform at least one function; 90 percent of the wetlands performed at least three functions; and nearly one-half performed five or more functions. The most common functions fulfilled by the wetlands investigated included water quality protection, flora and wildlife habitat, and aesthetic and recreational values. Of the 338 wetlands evaluated in the North Branch of Mill Creek, 229 were found to have no protection under existing state law.

Now that the data has been gathered, the project team is working to apply the information in a way that fosters wetland protection in the Mill Creek subwatershed. The wetland maps and functional assessment data have been presented at a community visioning forum in Chelsea and are being used with private property owners, elected officials, and planning commissioners to illustrate the important functions and values that wetlands provide. Potential future applications of the information include developing a model site analysis for anticipated developments and developing and implementing local wetland ordinances and management plans.

The lessons learned from the ADID Functional Assessment of Mill Creek's watershed can be applied to other areas of the state. While the Huron River and Clinton River Watershed Councils are well-staffed organizations, the methodology could be applied by smaller groups or by individual municipalities in a cost-effective manner. In addition to learning more about the values a particular wetland provides, the assessment program has effectively identified hundreds of valuable wetlands that go unregulated. Such information can be used by wetland advocates to protect these valuable resources through local ordinances and help private landowners make better decisions during the development process.

**For more information about the
ADID Functional Assessment Project, contact:**
Elizabeth Worzalla
Huron River Watershed Council
1100 N. Main, Suite 210
Ann Arbor, MI 48104
Phone: (734) 769-5123
Fax: (734) 998-0163
e-mail: eworzalla@hrwc.org
e-mail: staff@hrwc.org

Chapter **3** Identification and Delineation

It is useful for citizens working to protect or restore wetlands to have a clear understanding of what constitutes a wetland and be able to determine with some degree of accuracy if an area is indeed, or was at one time, a wetland. This information is invaluable in identifying potential sites for wetland restoration, recognizing and reporting wetland violations, responding to dredge and fill public notices, and educating others about wetland functions and values. This chapter is designed to provide a general background regarding the science and practice of wetland determination and delineation, not as a manual to be used when conducting formal wetland delineations.

A SHORT HISTORY OF WETLAND DELINEATION

Wetland determination (sometimes called identification) is simply the determination of whether an area is a wetland or not. Wetland delineation is the actual determination and establishment of wetland boundaries. The science of wetland delineation is directly linked to wetland regulation. Although ecologists and biologists had been studying wetlands long before laws were passed to protect them, there was little need to determine the precise boundary of a wetland until

Where are Wetlands Usually Found?

Wetlands are typically found in depressions, the lowest portion of the landscape, or adjacent to lakes, rivers, or streams. Landscape position, climate, and soil type all influence wetland formation. You can expect to find wetlands in the following places:

- In low areas with a high water table

- On slopes where ground water breaks out as springs or seeps

- Near rivers, streams, lakes, and the Great Lakes

- In flat areas where clayey soils or bedrock close to the surface form an impervious layer that creates a "perched" water table

- In abandoned ditches or stream channels

24

certain activities in wetlands were regulated. As the realization of the importance of wetlands grew, so too did the federal programs designed to protect them. In addition to laws that regulated activities in wetlands, laws were passed that created incentives for farmers to avoid wetlands and for landowners to protect them. From all perspectives—the regulated community, the regulators, and the citizens interested in wetland protection—the regulations and incentive programs created an acute need to identify and delineate wetlands in a scientifically sound and reliable manner.

In the 1980s, substantial scientific effort was committed by the various federal regulatory agencies charged with implementing wetland regulations. As part of their statutory authority, the U.S. Environmental Protection Agency (EPA), the U.S. Army Corps of Engineers (Corps), the U.S. Fish and Wildlife Service (FWS), and the Natural Resources Conservation Service (NRCS—formerly the Soil Conservation Service) all played a role in delineating wetlands. Interestingly, they all had slightly different methods of defining wetlands and delineating their boundaries. Not surprisingly, the variations in definition and delineation methodology created controversy.

In response to criticism from the regulated community regarding contradictions between the various federal methods, scientists from the four federal agencies involved with wetland regulation formally adopted a joint manual for identifying and delineating jurisdictional wetlands in 1989. The manual sought to develop a methodology that would allow regulatory staff to delineate wetlands based on the definition of wetlands in the Clean Water Act:

...[wetlands are] those areas that are inundated or saturated by surface or ground water at a frequency and duration sufficient to support, and that under normal circumstances do support, a prevalence of vegetation typically adapted for life in saturated soil conditions.
(Section 404 of the Clean Water Act, 33 CFR 328.3)

The method developed presented the concept of three mandatory criteria (hydric soils, hydrophytic vegetation, and wetland hydrology) to delineate wetland areas (with some exceptions).

Even though it was well-researched and heavily documented, the manual came under political attack. The controversy came to a head in 1991 when several bills backed by opponents of wetland protection were introduced that would have created a "political" (as opposed to a scientific) definition of wetlands. According to federal agencies charged with field testing the proposed delineation methodology, only 50% of Michigan's remaining wetlands would have been determined to be jurisdictional wetlands. With the scientific, regulatory, and environmental communities opposed to the changes, Congress sought a way out of the battle by requiring that federal agencies utilize the Corps 1987 manual (which was very similar to the 1989 manual) and commissioning a report from the National Academy of Sciences (NAS). The 1995 report by the NAS reaffirmed the scientific validity of wetland delineation methods that investigate vegetation, hydrology, and soils, and acknowledged that these three indicators are inter-related and, with few exceptions, present in undisturbed wetland areas.

In the meantime, the Land and Water Management Division of the Michigan Department of Natural Resources (now the Michigan Department of Environmental Quality) developed their own manual in 1989–The Michigan Department of Natural Resources Wetland Determination Draft Manual for Field Testing. The purpose of this manual is to formalize the process used to delineate wetlands as they are defined by state law:

> *"Wetland" means land characterized by the presence of water at a frequency and duration*
> *sufficient to support, and that under normal circumstances does support, wetland*
> *vegetation or aquatic life, and is commonly referred to as a bog, swamp, or marsh...*
> *[Section 30301(d), Part 303, Wetland Protection, Act 451 of 1994]*

This manual drew heavily on the 1987 manual, and for all practical purposes, created a consistent methodology. The manual was finalized by MDEQ staff in 2001. Like the federal method, the Michigan methodology involves investigating vegetation, hydrology, and soils. However, under Michigan's delineation methodology, soils are used as an indicator of hydrology instead of a stand-alone criterion.

The MDEQ is responsible for determining wetland boundaries pursuant to Michigan's Wetland Protection statute. The Corps of Engineers is responsible for determining wetland boundaries pursuant to the federal Clean Water Act. According to state law, all local units of government in Michigan must use the MDEQ's definition of wetlands. Although using slightly different methods, these various agencies delineate wetlands in a consistent manner.

When you consider the variety of wetlands that occur in Michigan and that wetlands are ecosystems subject to fluctuating natural influences (e.g., rainfall, temperature, or lake levels), it is easy to understand that the actual "line" between upland and wetland is not always clear. State and federal agency staff sometimes disagree slightly on wetland boundaries. In addition, agency staff sometimes disagree with delineations conducted by wetland consultants. Often, the resolution of disputed wetland boundaries requires site visits with both parties. It is important to remember that the state and federal regulatory agencies have the ultimate authority over boundaries of wetlands regulated by state and federal statute.

ENVIRONMENTAL INDICATORS OF WETLANDS

Since nearly all wetlands in Michigan fall under state jurisdiction, the discussion here will focus on wetland determination and delineation procedures used by the Michigan Department of Environmental Quality. As noted above, this method is consistent with that practiced by the Corps and wetland consultants.

According to Michigan's wetland delineation methods, there are two primary indicators of wetlands:

1) The predominance of plants adapted for living in saturated conditions (hydrophytic, or wetland, vegetation); and

What's A Wetland Indicator Status?

The U.S. Fish and Wildlife Service, in cooperation with other agencies and professional botanists, developed the following categories to help determine if a vegetation community would be considered to be adapted to wetland conditions:

Obligate Wetland Plants (OBL)— Species in this category are estimated to occur in wetlands more than 99 percent of the time.

Facultative Wetland Plants (FACW)— Species in this category are estimated to occur in wetlands approximately 99-67 percent of the time.

Facultative Plants (FAC)— Species in this category are estimated to occur in wetlands approximately 66-34 percent of the time.

Facultative Upland Plants (FACU)— Species in this category are estimated to occur in wetlands approximately 33-1 percent of the time.

Obligate Upland Plants (UPL)— Species in this category are estimated to occur in wetlands less than 1 percent of the time.

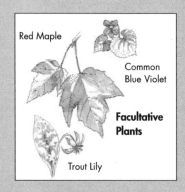

2) The presence of water at or near the land surface throughout the year or for some portion of the year (wetland hydrology), which is commonly indicated by the presence of distinctive soils which develop under saturated conditions (hydric soils).

As noted above, the 1995 report by the National Academy of Sciences clearly states that these indicators are inter-related, and with few exceptions, are present in undisturbed wetland areas.

Hydrophytic Vegetation

Hydrophytic (water-loving) vegetation is plant life that is adapted to grow in areas where the frequency and duration of inundation or saturation is sufficient to exert a controlling influence over the plant species present. Among other things, all plants need oxygen and water. There is a point at which the frequency and duration of water in the soil causes at least periodic deficiencies in oxygen in the root zone. This is because water replaces air in the spaces between the soil particles in saturated conditions. In order to survive the stress of low oxygen levels in the root zone, hydrophytic plants have structural and functional adaptations to allow them to thrive in these areas. As a result, they can out-compete other plants that are not adapted to living in saturated conditions. An example of a common adaptation that allows wetland plants to survive in wet conditions can be easily observed by cutting a cattail near its base. The air-filled tissue that you see in the cross-section transports air to the roots of the plant so that it can live in inundated areas.

For the wetland plant criteria to be met in determining that an area is a wetland, a predominance of wetland vegetation must be present—not just the occurrence of a single wetland plant. In other words, a wetland will have a community of plants that are adapted to survive in wet conditions. To help wetland delineators determine if a plant community is adapted to wetland conditions, the U.S. Fish and Wildlife Service (in cooperation with the Corps, the EPA, and the NRCS) has published a list of plant species that occur in wetlands for each state and region. The list separates plants into five basic groups, ranging from plants which almost always occur in wetlands to plants which almost never occur in wetlands. These five categories are referred to as wetland indicator statuses or wetland fidelity ratings. Typically, an area is considered to have a wetland plant community when more than 50 percent of the dominant species in each layer of vegetation (e.g., tree layer, shrub layer, or herb layer) have wetland indicator statuses of FAC, FACW, or OBL (see sidebar for wetland indicator status definitions and examples).

 27

Wetland Hydrology

Wetland hydrology refers to the specific hydrologic conditions that are required to form and maintain wetlands. Saturation at or near the surface, or inundation, for approximately 14 consecutive days or more during Michigan's growing season typically creates the necessary conditions in the soil to form and maintain wetlands. Wetland hydrology, hydric soils, and hydrophytic vegetation are all linked. Hydrophytic vegetation and hydric soils result from wetland hydrology; and conversely, the presence of hydrophytic vegetation and hydric soils indicate wetland hydrology.

Of the indicators used for wetland identification, wetland hydrology is the most variable and often the most difficult to observe directly. Numerous factors influence hydrology, including precipitation, topography, soil permeability, and plant cover. The technical wetland hydrology criteria looks at the distance to the water table based on soil drainage and permeability characteristics. Depending on the soil type, an area can have wetland hydrology even if the ground surface is never

Common Field Indicators of Wetland Hydrology

In the absence of hydrologic data or direct evidence of hydrology, the following field indicators can be used to assess wetland hydrology.

Drift lines: Drift lines consist of debris (remnants of vegetation, sediment, litter, etc.) that was deposited as a result of water movement. Most common adjacent to streams or other sources of water flow, debris is usually deposited parallel to the direction of water flow. However, because shallow water can extend beyond where the debris is deposited, drift lines do not represent the maximum level of inundation.

Water marks: Water marks are commonly found on woody vegetation. They often occur as stains on bark or other fixed objects such as bridges or pilings. Plants and other vertical objects often have thin layers, coatings, or depositions of mineral or organic matter after inundation.

Oxidized root channels (rhizopheres): Some hydrophytic plants transport oxygen to their root zone. Although iron in anaerobic environments is usually in a reduced state, the oxygen that is transported through the root channels allows it to oxidize (rust) along the root or rhizome and form iron oxide concretions (orange or red-brown in color) along the length of the root channel.

Water-stained leaves: Forested wetlands that are inundated in the spring will frequently have water-stained leaves on the forest floor. These leaves are generally grayish or blackish in appearance from being under water for significant periods.

Surface scoured areas: Surface scouring occurs along floodplains where overbank flooding erodes sediments. The absence of leaf litter from the soil surface is also sometimes an indication of overbank flooding or prolonged inundation.

Watermarks from spring floods

covered with water, so long as the water table is close enough to the surface to influence the root zone and cause the development of a wetland plant community.

Evidence of wetland hydrology can come from a variety of sources. When available, recorded hydrologic data or aerial photographs can be useful. Perhaps the best evidence is the direct visual observation of inundation or soil saturation. Saturated soils may be detected by digging a hole at least 18 inches deep and observing the water table after it has had a chance to stabilize in the hole. In the absence of reliable hydrologic data or direct evidence of hydrology, field indicators have been developed for assessing wetland hydrology. These indicators are useful during the drier portions of the growing season when visual evidence of inundation or saturation is not possible. Some of the most common field indicators for hydrology include oxidized root channels, water marks, or surface scoured areas. Under Michigan's wetland delineation method, perhaps the most useful hydrology indicator is the presence of a hydric soil.

Hydric Soils

Hydric soils have physical and chemical indicators of repeated and prolonged saturation at or near the soil surface. These indicators are a direct result of the lack of oxygen in the upper part of the soil caused by the presence of water in the spaces between soil particles (which forces air out of the soil). In Michigan and most of the temperate regions of the United States, hydric soils are flooded, ponded, or saturated for about 14 consecutive days during the growing season.

The U. S. Department of Agriculture has developed a basic system of soil classification and coordinates mapping of soils on a county-by-county basis across the nation. There have been 10,500 types of soils, called soils series, identified in the United States. The National Technical Committee for Hydric Soils has developed criteria for hydric soils as well as a list of the nation's hydric soils, of which there are approximately 2,100 in the United States. Sometimes, a list of hydric soils is developed locally for individual counties. Generally, the county list is more reliable due to recent updating and local knowledge.

Hydric soils are usually divided into two categories: organic and mineral. Organic soils are so named because they are made up of partly decomposed organic matter (from dead plants) that forms peats and mucks. Almost all organic soils are considered hydric soils. The mineral soils that are hydric are set apart from other mineral soils because of their poor drainage characteristics or susceptibility to ponding and flooding. Because of these features, there is often a layer of muck that forms above the mineral component of the soil. There are several field indicators that can help in determining if a soil would be considered hydric, including organic surface layers, sulfidic materials, and soil color.

Field Indicators of Hydric Soils

There are several field indicators that can help in determining if a soil would be considered hydric, including:

Organic Soils: Organic soils, also known as histosols, are easily recognized as thick peats and mucks. Mucks feel greasy when rubbed between the fingers. Partially decomposed plant remains can be identified in peats.

Organic Surface Layer: Organic surface layers often form above the mineral substrate in hydric mineral soils due to the greatly slowed decomposition of the organic matter as a result of soil saturation and inundation.

Sulfidic Material: Soils that emit an odor of rotten eggs indicate permanent saturation and the presence of sulfidic material. Such permanent saturation causes anaerobic conditions that cause the sulfidic material to be chemically reduced to form hydrogen sulfide.

Iron and Manganese Concretions: Under the chemical conditions of hydric soils, iron and manganese are sometimes segregated into concretions or soft masses. These accumulations are usually black or dark brown.

Soil Color: Due to the presence of water in the soil column creating very low oxygen conditions, hydric mineral soils often form diagnostic colors. The two main categories of hydric soil colors are gleyed and low chroma/mottled soils. Gleying (bluish, greenish, or grayish colors) is an indication of a soil that is saturated for prolonged periods. Low chroma (dull) colors and mottles (bright splotches of color in a dull matrix) indicate soils that are saturated for substantial periods during the growing season, but unsaturated for some amount of time. Accurately identifying soil colors usually requires comparing the soil to standardized color charts made specifically for that purpose.

Dark Vertical Streaking: In sandy soils with an organic surface layer, organic matter is moved downward through the sand as the water table fluctuates. This often occurs more rapidly in some sections of the soil than in others. As a result, a cross-sectional view of the soil as revealed in a soil pit will appear to be vertically streaked. (It is important to note that vertical streaking can be observed in some non-hydric soils as well.)

Exceptions

Although these wetland indicators are routinely used by consultants and agency staff, it is important to note that there are several situations in which wetlands will not show direct evidence of all three environmental indicators. These areas include wetlands that have been disturbed (human intervention may have removed one or more of the indicators), newly created wetlands (hydric soils or hydrophytic vegetation may not have had a chance to fully develop), interdunal swale wetlands (hydric soils or wetland hydrology may be difficult to identify), and wetlands on sloping glacial till (wetland hydrology may not be evident). In addition, there are some cases in which wetlands can become dominated by facultative upland species. Although this is not a comprehensive list, it does provide examples of situations where the basic indicators of wetlands would not be readily evident.

Disturbed Areas

Disturbed areas are those which have been altered either recently or in the past in some way that makes wetland identification difficult. In Michigan, most disturbances are a direct result of human activity. However, in some cases, wetlands are disturbed by catastrophic natural events (such as tornados) or by ongoing processes such as erosion and sedimentation (these are most severe when exacerbated by human activity). Unfortunately, there have been many cases where those wishing to convert a wetland have purposefully altered one or more of the wetland indicators in an effort to avoid the regulatory process. These activities have included regulated activities such as draining a wetland and non-regulated activities such as cutting and clearing vegetation.

Cutting and clearing vegetation, especially trees, deserves special note. Since cutting vegetation is a non-regulated activity, some landowners are under the mistaken impression that one "legal" way to avoid wetland laws is to cut and clear a forested wetland to "dry it out" and convert it to upland. In fact, just the opposite usually happens. The trees in a wetland move water from the ground into the air through evapotranspiration and intercept rainfall allowing it to evaporate faster from the leaves and branches. The processes of increased evaporation due to interception and evapotranspiration transport many times more water into the air than simple evaporation from the ground surface. In one case on Lake Charlevoix, a landowner cleared all the trees in their sloping "yard" except for the birches. With the removal of the cedars and spruce trees, the ground became more wet. After only one season the birches were showing stress from too much water (birches have a facultative upland indicator status). After two growing seasons, the birches were dead due to increased ground water. By the third growing season, what was once a mixed forest of species dominated by FACU, FAC, and FACW plants was dominated by cattails and sedges (obligate wetland plants (OBL)).

In addition to clearing vegetation with the misguided hope of making the site dryer, others have also attempted to change vegetation by planting non-wetland plants on the site. Because of the stress on the plants caused by excessive water, these efforts are usually unsuccessful. Either way, efforts to alter a wetland so that it does not appear to be a wetland can indeed change the character of the land and create a challenge for anyone wanting to identify or delineate wetland boundaries.

When attempting to determine if a wetland occurred on an altered site or to delineate wetland boundaries, the first task is to understand the nature of the alteration and what impacts it may have had on the three wetland indicators. Depending on the nature of the disturbance, it may be difficult to directly observe evidence of the three indicators. If the area has been disturbed by fill, digging through the fill may reveal buried plants and the original soils. If the disturbance was due to clearing and vegetation change, then aerial photographs may provide evidence of the site before disturbance. Sometimes, the best approach is to find a nearby undisturbed wetland that is likely to have similar soils, vegetation, and hydrology as the altered site prior to disturbance. This wetland can serve as a reference site that provides vital information on the nature of the disturbed wetland.

OFFSITE WETLAND DELINEATION

The most reliable way to collect evidence for these three parameters is through onsite investigation. If you can access the site in question to sample vegetation and dig pits to investigate the soils and

Desktop and Windshield Identification: What to Look For

- Indication of wetland on National Wetland Inventory Map, USGS topographical map, MIRIS map, local wetland inventory, or other wetland map

- Indication of hydric, poorly, or very poorly drained soil on the USDA County Soil Survey

- Depressions in the land where water pools on the ground surface in the spring

- Ditches or natural swales that drain an area

- Differences in vegetation community

- In farmed areas, crop stress due to excessive water

sub-surface hydrology, by all means do so. In situations where wetlands are being degraded illegally, or an individual has applied for a dredge and fill permit and wants to avoid citizen opposition, permission for on-site investigation may not always be granted. In these cases, wetland advocates must be able to determine if an area is a wetland with off-site information.

There are two types of offsite wetland identification—"desktop" and "windshield." Desktop identification employs a variety of resources—maps, surveys, personal experience of old timers, etc.—that all come short of actually looking at the area. Sources that can provide information related to hydrology, soils, and vegetation are available throughout the state. Not only are these information sources invaluable to understanding a wetland when visual access is denied, they are extremely helpful in providing additional information for onsite and windshield investigations. Organizations and individuals concerned about wetland protection should have the resources listed in the following pages on hand for their region.

Because all "remote" sources of information (maps, surveys, etc.) have their limitations, it is recommended that you get as close as legally possible to the site in question so that you may confirm the information provided by the "desktop" review and glean additional information. "Windshield" investigations involve getting as close as possible to the wetland via public roads, public waters, or from adjacent lands. Much information can be gathered from a road right of way, including the presence of standing water, differences in vegetation, and earth moving activity. A good pair of binoculars can help tremendously. In cases where access to adjacent properties is

granted, soils, vegetation, and hydrology characteristics similar to the subject property may be present. In these cases, the wetland protection advocate can reliably document evidence of the three parameters. Soil pits should be dug to confirm wetland soils. Vegetation should be identified and the dominant vegetation should be analyzed in regards to its wetland indicator status. Evidence of wetland hydrology should also be noted.

It is important to remember that you must respect the rights of the property owner and not enter private property without permission. Although nothing compares to investigating the wetland onsite, when permission to enter land is denied, "desktop" and "windshield" investigations can provide enough information for wetland advocates to know if the site in question is likely to be a wetland, the general type of wetland, and (in the case of violations) if the activities occurring on the site are regulated. In addition, these offsite methods can be used to identify likely areas for wetland restoration (for example, wet areas that suffer crop stress in fields may indicate the location of formerly drained wetlands which could be restored to wetlands).

WETLAND IDENTIFICATION RESOURCES

There are numerous resources that are available to help you identify wetlands in your area. The resources listed below are extremely useful in providing information to help citizens protect wetlands. Some, such as the USDA County Soils Surveys, the Hydric Soils list, National Wetland Inventory maps, and USGS Topographic maps are essential tools for conducting offsite wetland determinations. It is important to note that all of these resources are best used in conjunction with onsite (or at least windshield) visits.

MDEQ Wetland Identification Manual: A Technical Manual for Identifying Wetlands in Michigan: In 2001, the MDEQ finalized their manual for wetland delineation which was originally developed in 1989. This manual is meant to serve as a methodology for MDEQ and local government staff and environmental consultants. Citizens will find it extremely useful as a source of information about the rationale and methodology of wetland delineation. To order, contact the MDEQ wetland program.

33

Natural Resource Conservation Service Soil Surveys: The U.S. Department of Agriculture's Natural Resource Conservation Service (NRCS) has conducted surveys of the soils in most counties of the state. The soil surveys contain a wealth of useful information, including soil maps, engineering suitability ratings, soil profile descriptions, and hydrologic characteristics. This information is extremely valuable in determining if a hydric soil occurs on a site. Keep in mind that the detail and quality of soil surveys vary between counties. Due to map scale and the fact that the maps are based on aerial photos, the maps are not accurate enough to show precise boundaries of a soil series. For this reason, it's always advisable to dig a soil pit and compare what you see on the ground to the soil description in the book. Soil surveys are available from your county Soil and Water Conservation District or your NRCS District Conservationist.

Hydric Soils of the State of Michigan: The Natural Resources Conservation Service, in cooperation with the National Technical Committee for Hydric Soils, has compiled a list of hydric soils in Michigan. This is the definitive resource for determining if a particular soil is considered hydric. This list should be used in conjunction with county soil surveys to locate areas where wetlands might occur. This publication is available from your county Soil and Water Conservation District or your NRCS District Conservationist.

Michigan Resource Information System (MIRIS) Current Use Inventory Maps: These maps are compiled by the Michigan Inventory Program of the Michigan Department of Natural Resources. The maps contain inventories of 60 different land use classifications, of which approximately 12 relate to wetlands. Specific classes of wetlands include wooded, scrub/shrub, aquatic bed, emergent, and mud flats. In addition, there are other classes which are not classified as wetland in the MIRIS system, but more than likely would be considered jurisdictional wetlands. These include lowland hardwood and lowland conifer forest classifications. The wetland boundaries shown on these maps are meant to identify approximate boundaries. To see if your county has a completed MIRIS inventory, call your county planning and zoning department or regional planning office.

National Wetlands Inventory (NWI) Maps: On these maps, created by the U.S. Fish and Wildlife Service, wetlands are delineated based on features shown on aerial photographs. NWI maps are used to show the approximate extent of a wetland and its association with other wetland and non-wetland areas. Due to the scale of the aerial photography used and the lack of ground verification, NWI maps cannot be used as the sole basis for determining whether an area is a wetland. To order NWI Maps, call 1-888-ASK-USGS. Select NWI maps that have been digitized are available on the Internet at www.nwi.fws.gov.

United States Geological Survey (USGS) Topographic Maps: These maps are available in several different scales and provide landmark features including towns, roads, bridges, streams, buildings, water bodies, etc. that are not commonly found on road maps. The topographic lines and elevations are helpful in determining drainage patterns and watersheds. These maps should not be used to delineate wetland boundaries, as the scale is too small to make the boundaries accurate, and not all wetlands are indicated. However, those areas that are marked as wetlands are most likely wetlands unless they have been altered since the map was made. To order USGS topographic maps, call 1-888-ASK-USGS. USGS topo maps, as well as depth charts of inland lakes and NOAA nautical charts of the Great Lakes, can also be ordered from MUCC by calling 1-800-777-6720.

Natural Resource Conservation Service Mapping: As part of their administrative responsibilities under the conservation provisions of the Farm Bill, the NRCS delineates wetlands on agricultural lands enrolled in agricultural conservation programs. Although NRCS delineation maps do not define jurisdiction for wetland permitting under Michigan's law, they can provide useful information. The Farmed Wetland and Prior Converted mapping classifications can be especially helpful in identifying wetland restoration and enhancement sites. Contact your NRCS District Conservationist to see if these maps are available for your area.

Local Wetlands Maps and Inventories: Many local organizations or municipal governments have developed wetland maps for their service areas. Although they vary greatly in terms of scale and quality, they can serve as excellent resources.

County Plat Maps: County plat maps are essential pieces of information to determine land ownership patterns and current local road names. Both are important when trying to locate a particular property or to identify a landowner. Depending on the scale of the map, small parcels may not include the names of property owners. In that situation, the names of property owners can be found at the county property tax equalization office.

Wetland Plants of the State of Michigan: The U.S. Fish and Wildlife Service, as part of the National Wetlands Inventory Program, has compiled a wetland plant list for Michigan. This plant list includes a comprehensive list of the plants that occur in wetlands, including their wetland indicator status. This plant list is essential for determining if an area meets wetland vegetation criteria. To order this publication, contact the U.S. Fish and Wildlife Service Field Office in Lansing. (See Appendix B for address.)

Floristic Quality Assessment with Wetland Categories and Computer Application Programs for the State of Michigan: Developed by the Michigan Natural Features Inventory (MNFI), this document describes the use of Floristic Quality Assessment (FQA) as a tool to assist environmental decision-makers in assessing the floristic, and implicitly, the natural significance of any given area throughout Michigan. The assessment method is not intended for use as a stand-alone method, but to complement and corroborate other methods of evaluating the natural quality of a site. This document also contains an expanded list of wetland plants that includes non-wetland plants and information relevant to FQA. To order, contact the MNFI at (517) 373-1552.

Wetland Trends in Michigan since 1800: A Preliminary Assessment: Developed by the Michigan Natural Features Inventory, this document describes the potential locations of Michigan's original wetlands based on surveyors' notes taken as part of the original survey of Michigan between 1816 and 1856. The report provides information on the original landscape vegetation, wetland extent, and wetland type on a county-by-county basis. The companion map (available separately) to this report provides a broad scale look at the presettlement wetland resource in Michigan. To order, contact the MNFI at (517) 373-1552.

Plant Identification Guidebooks: The precise identification of vegetation to the species level is necessary to determine if an area has a hydrophytic vegetation community. For example, identifying a tree as a "maple" is not very helpful, as there are six species of the maple family in Michigan, with wetland indicator statuses ranging from FACW to FACU. There are numerous excellent plant guidebooks to choose from, including *Michigan Trees* by Barnes and Wagner, *Ferns of Michigan* by Billington, *Michigan Wildflowers* by Smith, and the three-volume *Michigan Flora* by Voss. In addition, there are several guidebooks specific to wetland plants, including *Great Lakes Wetlands: A Field Guide* by Hoagman, and *A Great Lakes Wetland Flora* by Chadde.

Aerial Photography and Satellite Images: With the advent of the Internet, aerial photography is only a mouse-click away. Aerial photography or other remote sensing data can be very helpful in identifying patterns of plant communities. In the case of reviewing disturbed sites, historic aerial photographs can be used to determine when an impact occurred. There are many sources of aerial photographs, and the photos from each source have various scales. Contact your county planning department to see what aerial photos they have available. Your NRCS District Conservationist should also have aerial photos of your county as part of their administration of the Farm Bill. Also, the soil surveys noted above contain aerial photographs that can be very useful. USGS digital orthophoto quadrangles have been downloaded and featured on the Internet by Microsoft's TerraServer. To access (view, download, and print out) aerial photos on the Internet, point your browser to www.terraserver.microsoft.com.

Local Knowledge: In addition to these published resources, information about the wetlands in your area may be available from hunters, anglers, former landowners, or long-time residents.

MDEQ's WETLAND ASSESSMENT PROGRAM

In response to requests from landowners and members of the development community, the Michigan Department of Environmental Quality began implementing a Wetland Assessment Program in 1998. This program is authorized by Michigan's wetland law and administrative rules, and is intended to serve landowners and developers in identifying wetland and upland areas on their property.

Although designed to serve landowners and developers, this program also benefits citizens working to protect wetlands. Level 1 Assessments can be requested on any piece of property in the state. This is essentially a "desktop" review conducted by an MDEQ wetland technician. Citizens can encourage landowners and developers to take advantage of the program to establish wetland boundaries early in the land planning process, making it easier to avoid and minimize impacts to wetlands. This program can serve wetland advocates in another way too. Once the MDEQ conducts an assessment, the results of the assessment can be requested (in writing) by the public under the Freedom of Information Act.

The types of services available and associated fees (as of November, 2002) are outlined below:

Level 1 Assessment: In-Office Review

MDEQ personnel will conduct an in-office review of readily available information on an identified area of land, including maps showing the approximate location of wetlands in the given area. This service includes copies of available maps, a general interpretation of the maps, and other helpful information. The fee for this service is $50.

Level 2 Assessments: On-Site Determination

Level 2 Assessments involve an on-site assessment of an identified area of land to determine the presence and location, or absence, of wetlands. On-site determinations must be requested by the landowner or be conducted with written permission by the landowner if requested by someone other than the landowner. A written report of findings, including a map showing the apparent location of wetland and upland areas, and information regarding the regulatory process will be provided. The report will include a statement that the MDEQ lacks wetland jurisdiction over those areas classified as uplands for three years from the assessment date. This service does not require delineation or marking of the wetland boundaries prior to the MDEQ's assessment, but does require marking the area to be assessed. The fee is $200 for areas of one acre or less and $50 for each additional acre of land to be assessed.

Level 3 Assessment: On-Site Wetland Boundary Confirmation

The purpose of this service is to confirm specific wetland boundaries established by a wetland consultant. Trained MDEQ staff will review the staked and/or flagged boundaries and submit a written report of their findings. This service will provide the specific location of wetlands on the subject property, as well as provide a three-year guarantee that the MDEQ lacks wetland jurisdiction over those areas identified as uplands. This service requires that wetland boundaries be delineated, marked, and mapped prior to the MDEQ's assessment. Again, this service must either be requested by the landowner or someone with written permission of the landowner. The fee is $150 for areas of one acre or less, and $15 for each additional acre of land to be assessed.

Fees and Application Process

As with private consultants, the MDEQ staff will only be able to perform the assessment service during times of the year and under conditions that will provide reliable information. In the event that winter weather conditions prohibit MDEQ staff from conducting a thorough site assessment, inclusive of evaluating vegetation, soil, and hydrologic information, the assessment will be delayed until weather conditions permit the collection of all pertinent information to make an accurate assessment. If recent disturbances (e.g., lack of vegetation, disturbed soils, drainage diversion, etc.) do not allow for making an assessment, a report specifying the reasons will be submitted to the applicant. The report will also include a description of the information needed to make a final assessment.

In addition to using this service to gain valuable information about a particular wetland, citizens can play a key role in encouraging landowners and developers to use this service. By knowing the location of wetlands boundaries in the early stages of the development process, developers are better able to protect wetlands by avoiding impacts and integrating them into a good conservation design. Citizens interested in assessment services will be required to submit an application to the MDEQ indicating the level of service desired, a description of the area to be assessed, and the associated fee. Wetland Assessment Program applications are available from the MDEQ. See Appendix B for address and phone number.

CONCLUSION

As you can see even by this greatly condensed description of wetland delineation, the scientific basis for wetland delineation is complicated. This chapter is not meant to serve as a wetland delineation manual. Rather, its purpose is to provide you with enough information to understand the scientific basis for wetland determination and delineation. Although nothing compares with reviewing soils, hydrology, and vegetation onsite, it is possible to get a good understanding of a particular wetland from offsite information resources. By understanding what goes into wetland identification and delineation, you will be more effective in your efforts to protect and restore them. For example, as part of the public review of dredge and fill permit applications, you have the opportunity to review and comment on wetland boundaries submitted by private consultants as part of the application. The more you know about wetland delineation, the better your ability to interpret a consultant's findings. Remember, regulatory agency staff have the final authority in determining jurisdictional wetland boundaries. To become more familiar with the three basic characteristics of wetlands, take some time to visit wetlands in your area and investigate the indicators of hydric soils, hydrophytic vegetation, and wetland hydrology. If you want to become trained in wetland delineation, several consulting firms across the country offer formal wetland delineation training courses.

Chapter 4 — Activities that Impact Wetland Functions

I n order to influence decisions that impact wetlands, it is important to understand what activities will impact wetlands and how. Understanding the implications of wetland degradation will help you make your case when commenting on wetland dredge and fill permits, deepen the knowledge you can share in your educational efforts, and strengthen your commitment to land preservation. This chapter briefly describes some of the activities that impact wetlands and alter the functions they provide. The next chapter discusses some management practices to help you advocate for wetland protection and encourage wetland stewardship.

Assuming that the wetland you are working to protect has not undergone changes such as dredging, filling, topsoil removal, draining, or other major changes that would severely alter its type and function (in other words, "normal" conditions exist at the site), it is providing valuable functions that contribute to the health and well-being of the surrounding landscape. Some of the activities listed below, such as dredging, filling, draining, and construction in wetlands, are regulated and require permits from the appropriate agency before being conducted. For these, citizens play an important role in protecting wetlands through the regulatory process. Others, such as cutting vegetation are not regulated, and therefore citizens working to protect wetlands from these activities must work directly with the landowner (whether public or private) and try to convince them to avoid the activity.

HYDROLOGIC MODIFICATIONS

Water is the lifeblood of wetland ecosystems. The term hydrology (literally the study of water) refers to all the various parameters that can be used to characterize water in a particular location, including water levels, water table, fluctuations, inputs and outputs, etc. Maintaining the natural hydrology of a wetland is the key to protecting it. Activities that alter hydrology of a wetland can severely degrade it. Even small changes in hydrology, like changing the amount of surface water entering and leaving a wetland or changing the ground water table a few inches either up or down, can have dramatic impacts on the way a wetland functions, including how much flood protection a wetland provides, how much sediment and pollutants it can remove, what sort of vegetation can live there, what wildlife habitat the wetland provides, and how the wetland relates to other bodies of water. Ironically, some of these activities are done with the intention of improving wetlands. A few specific activities that influence wetland hydrology are addressed below.

Flooding

Impounding water behind a dam, or conveying additional water to a wetland, results in the raising of surface and ground water levels in and around that wetland. Often such projects are undertaken to create wildlife floodings. Although floodings have created additional wetland wildlife habitat in former uplands, they have also resulted in dramatic changes to the original wetlands that existed in the area that was flooded. Often, the analysis of the benefits of flooding projects depends on the perspective of the person making the assessment. Regardless of who is making the assessment, it is clear that either impounding water or otherwise increasing the water that enters a wetland can cause changes in the vegetation community, the animals that live there, water quality maintenance functions, and flood storage and conveyance. These changes need to be understood and determined if they are indeed in the best interest of the resource.

Not all flooding is caused by human-induced factors. Beaver dams are one of nature's ways of creating a wetland, but also of flooding existing wetlands. As with human-induced impoundments, beaver dams can dramatically change wetland systems. From an objective perspective, beavers and their dams and lodges have both positive and negative impacts.

On the positive side, in areas where beavers have long been a part of the landscape and wetland vegetation communities have formed in response to long-term beaver activity, their activities provide a beneficial service to many other species. Mink, raccoons, and green-backed herons utilize beaver-created wetlands when hunting for frogs, crayfish, and other prey. The beaver lodge and dam serve as good basking areas for snakes and turtles, and frogs and salamanders breed in the shallow waters that are created. The dead trees that result from beaver activity harbor insects that serve as food for insectivores such as nuthatches and pileated woodpeckers. The woodpecker holes in turn provide habitat for cavity nesting birds such as the wood duck and hooded merganser.

On the negative side, beaver dams cause flooding which results in changes in natural vegetation communities, siltation of the stream upstream of the dam, and an increase in water temperature. In areas that are developed, beavers may cause property damage by saturating roadbeds, flooding basements, and downing prized trees. As discussed below, the removal of beaver dams can sometimes cause more harm than good. To make sure that any beaver management activities are conducted in a way that maximizes benefits, it is important to analyze all positive and negative aspects of beaver dams on a case-by-case basis. A recommended approach to beaver management is included in Chapter Five.

Draining

The flipside of flooding a wetland is draining it. The United States has a long history of draining wetlands. Since the early years of this country, there have been governmental programs to fund the draining of wetlands. In fact, the Michigan Drain Code still provides a mechanism to tax landowners in a watershed to pay for drainage activities, many of which adversely impact wetlands. Although some drainage activities related to agriculture and the maintenance and operation of existing designated county drains by Drain Commissioners are exempt from wetland permit requirements, all other drainage activities are regulated by Michigan's wetland laws because of the adverse impacts on wetland functions. It is important to note that a loophole in the federal wetland program allows wetland drainage.

41

Activities which result in draining wetlands include ditch construction, the laying of field tiles (sub-surface pipes with holes that collect water from the soil and convey it to a lower point), and the removal or alteration of structures that impound water (beaver dams, roads, etc.). Drainage has many adverse effects on wetlands and the surrounding watershed. The wetland itself undergoes dramatic vegetation changes as less water-tolerant species colonize the area. As a result, wetland dependent insect, amphibian, reptile, bird, and mammal species are lost and other animals suited to uplands take their place. Drainage also severely impacts water quality. Instead of the wetland trapping sediment and nutrients, thus protecting the receiving waters from pollutants, the soils in the wetland are exposed to air and rapidly oxidize the organic material that had been trapped. The result is that thousands of years of accumulated organic materials are released into the water system and atmosphere.

The removal of dams (human-made or beaver-made) can have severe downstream impacts beyond the effects of increased nutrients released from oxidizing organic soils. Dam removal (even small scale beaver dam removal) typically results in an increase of downstream flow which can cause bank erosion, streambed scouring, and the release of silt and sediment that had been trapped behind the dam.

The combination of erosion, scouring, and increased sediment load can have devastating effects on the ability of a stream to support desirable aquatic life.

Due to the presence of contaminants in Great Lakes fish, dam removal that allows passage of "toxic" salmon can also negatively impact the aquatic ecosystem upstream from the dam. In addition to the food-chain contamination considerations of Great Lakes fish in streams, when anadromous fish such as salmon and steelhead (which are, in fact, introduced species to the Great Lakes) are in the early stages of their life in their "nursery" stream, they compete for food with resident fish and native brook trout. Successive generations of salmon and steelhead in the stream result in lower populations of resident trout. Removal of dams can also open up the watershed to sea lamprey, which use high quality streams for spawning. Thus, although dam removal is often done in the name of trout habitat improvement, it can sometimes cause more damage than good to the aquatic system.

42

LAND USE CHANGES

Land use changes in the watershed can dramatically affect wetland hydrology. The most typical land use changes are those which involve the conversion of natural vegetation or farmland to areas in which much of the land surface is covered with impervious surfaces (roofs, pavement, etc.). The changes to wetland hydrology are twofold: 1) a reduction in the amount of precipitation that can percolate into the soil and then be discharged slowly into a wetland as ground water, and 2) a dramatic increase in the amount of water that flows into a wetland via surface water. Both of these combine to create a situation where the major inputs of water become "flashy," causing the amplitude of the fluctuations between high water and low water in the wetland to become more extreme. An additional concern is the presence of sediment, nutrients, and other pollutants in stormwater runoff. Although wetlands do serve as natural filters, the amount and type of pollutants associated with urban stormwater runoff is typically more than what wetlands can handle. This degraded water quality can severely impact wetland functions. Like other changes in wetland hydrology, the result is a change in vegetation community, wildlife habitat, and the ability of the wetland to serve critical functions such as flood storage and water quality protection.

Dredging

Dredging activities are those in which the soil surface in a wetland is changed by the removal of soil. This can involve such large-scale projects as the dredging of a ditch, canal, or harbor, or such small-scale projects as mechanical vegetation clearing or grading an undulating wetland for the purpose of landscaping a lawn. All dredging activities, regardless of the size of impact, are regulated. Dredging removes and disturbs the vegetation and soil of a wetland. This topographic change (albeit minor in some cases) essentially changes the hydrology of the wetland by making the surface either closer to the water table or under deeper water. Since dredging involves removal of organic accumulations and exposure of the underlaying subsoil, dredging activities usually result in a wetland substrate less able to support vegetation and other aquatic life. Again, the result is a change in vegetation community, wildlife habitat, and other functions. In addition, by disturbing wetland soils, especially those in direct contact with water bodies, dredging activities release sediment into receiving waters. This can be especially damaging in cases where the soils contain contaminants.

A common dredging activity in intact wetlands is the creation of a pond or open water in an otherwise pondless wetland. This is commonly done with the intent of improving or "enhancing" wetlands. Although a vegetated shallow pond is a type of wetland (aquatic bed), it does not follow that all wetlands should have ponds, or that a pond is always an enhancement to an existing wetland. When a pond is dredged in a wetland that does not otherwise have open water, some functions associated with the original wetland are changed or lost. Therefore, this "enhancement" is not always an environmental enhancement. In some cases, where wetlands have been degraded by past activities (such as intensive livestock grazing and subsequent invasions by nuisance species), dredging may be a valuable management activity. Dredging an upland area near an existing wetland to create a pond is an excellent way to accomplish the dual goal of wetland protection and habitat enhancement. To serve as effective wildlife habitat, ponds associated with wetlands should be shallow with gently sloping sides, an undulating bottom, and a sinuous edge. All spoils from pond construction should be moved to a suitable upland site and stabilized to control erosion.

Filling

Past wetland filling activities in Michigan have ranged from large-scale filling of wetlands to provide suitable conditions for constructing buildings, to small-scale filling for landscaping. The result of both activities is essentially the same: change in the soils, hydrology, and vegetation of an area from wetland to upland. Accordingly, the wetland's natural functions are lost. Furthermore, unlike activities such as drainage which provide some opportunities for wetland restoration, once land is converted to upland by filling, it is very costly to restore and therefore represents a permanent change. Under both state and federal law, all filling activities are regulated in jurisdictional wetlands.

43

Most wetland advocates are aware of the impacts of large scale filling and "land balancing" (grading high spots into low spots) activities. However, the impacts of small-scale filling activities are often overlooked. Two small-scale filling activities that have substantial adverse impacts on wetlands, but are common throughout the state, include landscaping for lawns and building bulkheads.

Many landowners who construct a home on lakefront property desire to have a "lawn to the lake." If the property has wetlands bordering the lake, or other body of water, fulfilling this desire usually involves filling the wetland fringe (or at least grading the high spots into the low spots—essentially dredging and filling). Next, non-native turfgrass is planted and typically maintained with unnecessarily high doses of pesticides and fertilizers. The result is a loss of fish and wildlife habitat, a reduction in water quality due to the increase in polluted runoff and the destruction of the natural filtering capacity of the shoreline wetland, an increase in erosion potential due to the removal of shoreline wetland plants, and a loss of the aesthetic value of the wetland.

An activity often associated with creating a "lawn to the lake" is the creation of a bulkhead or seawall. In fact, most seawalls are proposed for the purpose of controlling erosion—erosion which many times is a direct result of destroying the natural vegetation along the shoreline. Wetlands along the shorelines of lakes, rivers, and streams (called riparian wetlands) are especially important nursery habitat for the early life stages of fish and other aquatic life. They also play an important role as the final pollutant filtering zone before runoff enters surface water. Bulkheads are typically proposed to be built right in this critical aquatic habitat zone. As a result, the important functions that these wetlands provide are directly lost because of the filling and construction associated with bulkheads. They are also indirectly lost as a result of the bulkhead's effect on wave activity and water flow patterns on adjacent and nearby shorelines (which can cause either deposition of sediment or erosion of the shoreline).

44

In addition to the mechanical filling described above, the lack of respect our society has given wetlands in the past can be seen by another type of filling—that of dumping rubbish into wetlands. Since wetlands have traditionally been viewed as wastelands, they have been used as dumps. Old cars, refrigerators, stoves, tires, bikes, and every other imaginable household waste item can be found in wetlands. In addition to the unsightly nature of this sort of filling, some of these items may have released toxic substances into the wetland.

Another common dumping practice is to throw lawn clippings, wood chips, and other yard waste into wetlands. This is often done without concern for environmental health, but sometimes done with the intent of slowly filling the wetland over time, perhaps to extend a lawn or garden area. Any kind of filling will result in a loss of wetland functions. Additionally, dumping yard waste can cause changes in a wetland's chemical balance. Yard waste is composed of natural materials that will eventually decompose. As they decompose, they release nutrients and any contaminants they may contain. Advocates can encourage wetland property owners to compost yard waste at a safe distance away from wetlands or other surface water to ensure that nutrient-laden runoff from the compost pile does not enter the lake.

Vegetation Cutting

Although vegetation cutting (including forestry activities) is technically exempt from wetland protection statutes, the effect on wetland functions can be extremely damaging. For the most part, the vegetation in a wetland provides the structure for wildlife habitat. Through evapotranspiration, nutrient uptake, and the physical structure of rooted plants, vegetation influences hydrology and is

critical to a wetland's ability to protect water quality, control soil erosion, and control floods. In addition, depending on the actual method and equipment used, vegetation cutting and timber harvesting activities can directly cause severe erosion and sedimentation into adjacent water bodies. As mentioned in Chapter Three, some landowners and developers clear vegetation because they think that it may dry the site out. In fact, because trees and other vegetation facilitate the removal of water through evapotranspiration, vegetation clearing can make the land more wet. Although the cutting of vegetation to the ground level is not regulated, mechanical land clearing (i.e., removal of trees or woody vegetation with bulldozers or other heavy equipment) is regulated as a dredging and filling activity because it removes roots and redistributes soil.

Humans are not the only animals that clear wetland vegetation. In many parts of the state, wetlands are used as summer pasture for cattle. When livestock graze in a wetland, the typical result is trampled banks, damaged vegetation, and direct addition of animal waste to the aquatic system. Such a degraded system quickly ceases to perform its natural functions and is ripe for being overtaken by such invasive species as reed-canary grass.

In some cases, vegetation removal can be a useful method to maintain a certain type of wetland. For instance, if there is a need to maintain a wet prairie for the purpose of providing habitat for threatened or endangered plant species, then active management techniques (e.g., controlled burn) to impede invasion by woody species (which would turn the prairie into a scrub-scrub swamp) may be desirable. Another example may be to cut "marsh hay" from a wetland to maintain its wet meadow character for the benefit of birds that use such areas for nesting, feeding, and safety cover.

Exotic Species Invasion

Introduction of exotic (non-native) plants has damaged ecosystems around the world. Invasive exotic plants choke out native vegetation and alter wetland functions. This can affect sediment removal, nutrient uptake, fish and wildlife habitat, and other functions. Exotic plants have been, and still are, introduced to wetlands either directly, as decorative additions, or indirectly through natural seeding from exotics placed in nearby lawns and gardens.

Purple loosestrife is the most striking example of an exotic plant introduced to wetlands. There are many problems associated with this beautifully colored but highly aggressive invasive plant. Due to its amazing reproductive capabilities (this perennial can spread by its

45

roots and each individual plant can produce between 100,000 to 2.5 million seeds each year), and the fact that it has no natural parasites or diseases in this country, it can literally take over wetland vegetation communities. Unfortunately, few wildlife species find purple loosestrife palatable. Wetlands that once contained diverse vegetation communities and provided excellent wildlife habitat for a range of wetland species are now monotypic stands of purple loosestrife and seemingly devoid of animal life. Because the large reddish-purple flower heads are admittedly beautiful, many people have purposefully planted purple loosestrife in their wetlands and flower gardens. Thus, people have actively facilitated its spread. Attempts to control the spread of this plant have met with very little success—especially in areas where it has become well established. In response to the impacts of this plant on the functions of Michigan's wetlands, the Michigan Legislature passed a law that outlaws the retail sale of purple loosestrife in Michigan.

Using Harmful Chemicals

Fertilizers, pesticides, and herbicides represent a potential threat to wetlands. If they are used on adjacent or upstream lawns or farmland, it is likely they will eventually enter local wetlands and waterways. For example, additional nutrients from fertilizers (especially phosphorus) can upset the natural balance in the wetland system and cause extensive plant and algae growth in adjacent water bodies. Likewise, pesticides and herbicides can upset the natural flora and fauna of a wetland by impacting the ability of some plants or animals to survive. Conversion of a formerly diverse vegetation community to a monotypical stand of cattails has occurred in marshes subject to inputs of nutrients from fertilizers and wastewater treatment plants. Broad scale herbicide use in wetlands can kill all herbaceous species, providing the opportunity for aggressive species such as purple loosestrife to easily take over the area. However, selective use of herbicides may have some use in controlling exotic species. An Aquatic Nuisance Control permit is required for the use of pesticides in any standing water, including inundated wetlands.

Recreational Overuse

Off road vehicles (ORVs)—dirt bikes, all-terrain vehicles, and mountain bikes—destroy soils, vegetation, and wildlife habitat within wetlands and adjacent uplands. The unwise use of motorboats and personal watercraft (i.e., "jet-skis") can disrupt wildlife and wetlands located along the shores of rivers, lakes, and estuaries. Excessive boat wakes (waves larger than what would typically be generated by normal conditions) can cause severe shore erosion in heavy recreational use areas.

Conclusion

This list of activities which impact the natural functions of intact wetlands provides a glimpse at the many threats facing wetlands. Concerned citizens are the critical link in efforts to defend wetlands from these threats.

Chapter 5

Promoting Wetland Stewardship

Most wetland advocates find themselves working to stop a proposed project or activity that threatens to harm wetlands. At the same time, there are many landowners and local units of government who want to manage their wetland in a way that protects or restores its functions. As an advocate, your knowledge of management practices to protect and enhance wetlands will be invaluable in your efforts to encourage wetland property owners and private land managers to manage their lands in a way consistent with community wetland protection goals. This chapter discusses some management practices to help you advocate for wetland protection and encourage wetland stewardship. How citizens can get involved in wetland restoration is addressed in the next chapter.

MANAGEMENT PRACTICES TO PROTECT WETLANDS

The simplest way to protect a wetland is to ensure that the activities discussed in the previous chapter don't occur there. Citizens involved in wetland protection have many tools available to ensure that these activities do not occur, including participating in the regulatory process, encouraging voluntary protection and stewardship, and

education. The management practices listed below are offered to help you promote positive stewardship activities that will help protect the integrity of wetland ecosystems. The intention is to provide you with enough information so that you can encourage environmental stewardship among landowners and developers to provide wetland management and protection that goes beyond that required by law. Because each wetland is different, to ensure success with these activities, you may want to encourage the landowner or developer to obtain additional information on how to implement them. For example, the information below only provides enough information to explain the importance of establishing a greenbelt to control erosion and enhance habitat, actually designing and installing it will take additional expertise.

Nesting Boxes and Platforms

One popular reason why people own wetlands is because of the bountiful wildlife habitat they provide. People relate to wildlife and one of the chief motivations for wetland protection has always been to provide for wildlife habitat. Citizens can help encourage landowners to protect wetlands by helping them enhance wildlife habitat. Construction and installation of nesting boxes and platforms also provides great opportunities to engage youth groups in wetland management and protection.

One of the most critical components of wildlife habitat (especially waterfowl) is the availability of safe nesting areas. For ground nesters such as the mallard, wetlands that have no upland buffer provide little opportunity for nesting. For cavity nesters such as the wood duck and hooded merganser, the removal of large trees and snags adjacent to and in wetlands has severely limited

Waterfowl Nesting Box Plan

nesting opportunities. You can provide nesting areas for these and other species by building nest boxes, cylinders, and platforms and placing them in appropriate locations in a wetland. Installing nest boxes involves a commitment to the birds using them. Unless there is a way to maintain nest boxes or cylinders annually (clean out and replace wood shavings), it is best not to install them at all.

Nesting platforms and boxes placed in the water should be at least 50 feet from the shoreline to reduce predation (preferably 300 feet). Boxes on posts or trees should be placed four to five feet above water surfaces and 15 to 30 feet above land surfaces. Boxes should be placed so that the entrance hole is visible to ducks on the water. They should be more than 100 feet apart and can be placed up to 300 feet into the woods away from the water. Ducks using boxes are more prone to predation than those using natural cavities. Human scent on trees and nest structures is an attractant to predators such as raccoons, opossum, and skunks. To ensure that the nest boxes that you put up do not serve to feed the local raccoon population, do not place nest boxes without using adequate predator guards, make sure they are placed the recommended distances apart, and always use a 3 inch x 4 inch oblong entrance which will exclude raccoons.

In addition to waterfowl, there are dozens of other birds that utilize wetlands for nesting cover. Tree swallows will readily nest in constructed boxes, and their aerial gymnastics are very entertaining. Because their main source of food is flying insects, they can also provide much appreciated mosquito control. The same is true for the several species of Michigan's flying mammals–bats. Construction plans for nest boxes can be found in your local library, bookstore, or wild bird feed store.

Establish and Maintain Buffers or Greenbelts

Perhaps the most effective management practice to protect wetlands from adjacent human activities is to establish and maintain a vegetative buffer (or greenbelt) around the wetland. A greenbelt is simply a strip of upland surrounding the wetland that is maintained in a natural vegetated state. On properties which have had the natural vegetation removed, establishing a greenbelt involves planting native trees, shrubs, and ground cover, ceasing use of fertilizers and pesticides, and only cutting or removing select vegetation.

Greenbelts around wetlands provide many valuable functions. The vegetation in the greenbelt protects the wetland by taking up excess nutrients and pollutants in overland flow. The vegetation also serves to slow the velocity of overland flow which helps to prevent erosion and creates a better opportunity for the water to percolate into the soils. This helps to reduce the "flashy" nature of runoff from urbanized areas. Greenbelts are very important from a wildlife standpoint. The greenbelt serves as a visual and noise barrier to the interior of the wetland, which is beneficial to wildlife sensitive to human disturbance. The greenbelt also serves as a habitat connector between the wetland and upland habitats, or as a protective pathway between different wetlands. Such wildlife corridors are very important to many animals, especially those with large ranges. In addition, greenbelts can be valuable habitat in their own right for animals that periodically use the wetland but spend most of their time in nearby uplands. Such habitat can be enhanced by select planting and maintenance without any adverse effect on the other functions of the greenbelt.

49

The ideal greenbelt ranges from 50 to 300 feet (or more) wide, depending on a variety of factors, including slope, soil type, quantity of water flowing through the greenbelt, size of the wetland, functions the wetland provides, activities in the watershed, and management goals (such as the desire to attract certain types of wildlife into the greenbelt area). Even if the landowners or developers with whom you are working cannot install a greenbelt of the ideal width, it is important to remember that a greenbelt of any width is better than none at all.

Protect and Enhance Adjacent Upland Habitat

The nature of a wetland is influenced by what happens in the adjacent upland. The establishment and maintenance of a greenbelt is considered the first line of defense against pollutant-laden stormwater and as a buffer against upland activity that might adversely impact the wetland. However,

What to Plant in a Greenbelt

If the area that you are working to establish a greenbelt is covered with only grass or other ground cover, simply not mowing will allow natural succession to begin. However, natural succession can take many years to reestablish an effective greenbelt. You can speed up the process by planting the following species. The plants listed below are native species adapted to upland and wetland sites. It is important to use native plants to reestablish greenbelts. Not all of these plants are available at your local nursery. They are however, available from specialty wildlife plant nurseries. Contact your county soil and water conservation district office or your MSU Extension county office for information on locally available native plant sources and specialty nurseries.

DRY, WELL DRAINED (UPLAND) SOILS

Trees	Woody Shrubs	Herbaceous Ground Cover
red pine	beaked hazelnut	baneberry
hemlock	mountain maple	large-leafed aster
sugar maple	striped maple	bunchberry
white birch	native honeysuckles	Canada mayflower
white spruce	staghorn sumac	black/raspberry
American beech	juniper	bearberry
red oak	ninebark	bracken fern
white pine	buffalo berry	wintergreen
aspen	flowering dogwood	partridge berry
		goldenrod

WET, POORLY DRAINED (WETLAND) SOILS

Trees	Woody Shrubs	Herbaceous Ground Cover
northern white cedar	red-osier dogwood	boneset
tamarack	silky dogwood	joe-pye-weed
red maple	willows	cordgrass
green ash	meadow sweet	sedges and rushes
black willow	winterberry	royal fern
balsam fir	American black currant	mint
balsam poplar	sweet gale	cattail
	button bush	Canada anemone
	high bush cranberry	blue flag iris
		virgins bower

50

just as a wetland can be over stressed by too much sediment and nutrient input, greenbelts cannot be expected to handle all the stormwater, sediment, and other pollutants that might result from poor land use management activities in the uplands.

Most wetland wildlife, including many waterfowl species, rely on upland nesting and feeding areas adjacent to wetlands. Ground nesting species such as mallard and black duck require either uplands adjacent to wetlands, nesting islands, or artificial platforms. Establishing native vegetation in the upland around your wetland can meet the needs of these and numerous other wildlife species. Songbirds, raptors (such as the threatened red-shouldered hawk and bald eagle), and game birds such as woodcock, pheasant, and ruffed grouse all benefit from undeveloped uplands adjacent to wetlands.

Managing stormwater runoff to protect water quality also benefits wildlife. Wetland animals such as frogs and other amphibians are very sensitive to changes in water quality—more so than most other wetland animals. Since amphibians are an important component in the wetland food web, activities that impact amphibians will impact other animals such as fish, herons, and mink.

Exactly how best to protect and enhance adjacent upland habitat will depend on the unique circumstances of the landowner or developer and the primary management goals (e.g., stormwater management or mallard duck nesting habitat). Accordingly, there is no practical way to address the wide range of options in this chapter. Regardless of what the landowner is planning to do in the uplands (e.g., nothing, farm corn, build homes, etc.), these "rules of thumb" will help them clarify appropriate management activities:

• Manage stormwater runoff so that its quantity and flow regimes are as close as possible to the original flow;

• Ensure on-site control of all pollutants (including sediment, fertilizer, parking lot oils, etc.) that might be generated from upland activities; and

• Determine what wildlife use the upland/wetland complex and consult wildlife habitat experts to determine how to manage the uplands to benefit these species without harming others.

51

Fencing

Both private and public lands can suffer from inappropriate use. In areas where livestock grazing or excessive human use or vehicle traffic is degrading wetlands, fencing is one of the simplest ways to protect a wetland area. This is especially critical in wetlands along streams and lakes where the degradation is directly impacting water quality through erosion and sedimentation. Even if the entire wetland can't be fenced, it is usually possible to fence off overused places where extra protection is necessary. There are several things to consider when determining what fencing is best. First, fencing should be placed as far from the wetland as is reasonably possible. In this way, the fenced area also includes a protective buffer between the activity and the wetland. Second, choosing the correct fence material for the purpose will save money and maintenance time. For example, a single-strand, high-tensile fence with flexible line posts will keep cattle out of an area, and will collect less debris and is less likely to be damaged during flooding than woven fencing. Although less aesthetically appealing, steel guard railing may need to be installed to control vehicle traffic.

Control Stormwater Runoff

Runoff is an important component of the hydrologic budget for most wetlands (bogs receive a negligible amount of runoff from surrounding lands). However, what stormwater picks up from the ground surface on its way to the wetland can be damaging, especially in urban areas. In an undeveloped vegetated landscape a majority of the precipitation that hits the ground soaks in. In areas that are urbanized, much of the ground is covered with surfaces such as roofs and concrete. The result is that the water flows along the top of the ground toward the lowest point. There are three primary questions related to stormwater runoff that citizens can raise when reviewing development proposals or encouraging improving existing systems: Have all efforts been made to minimize the amount of stormwater runoff? Where is the stormwater going to be conveyed and will it get there in the most environmentally sensitive way? Have all efforts been made to avoid activities that pollute stormwater runoff?

The best way to minimize the generation of stormwater is to minimize the area of impervious surface that covers the ground. For projects in which it is impossible to avoid runoff (like building the roof of a house), it is best to design the site to encourage the water to soak into the ground, thus minimizing the runoff that leaves the site and enters the wetland. At a minimum, detention or infiltration basins should be properly designed and maintained to handle a 10-year, 24-hour storm. If enough runoff is generated so that it must be conveyed somewhere, then the best option is to construct a grass-lined swale. The grass will help to slow runoff so it does not cause erosion, the living plants will take up nutrients, and the physical structure of the plants will help trap sediments. Any excess runoff, even if conveyed by a grass-lined swale, should not be conveyed directly to wetlands. Instead, runoff should be conveyed to a detention or infiltration basin that will allow some amount of natural treatment before the water enters the wetland. The specific design of a stormwater management structure will depend on slope, soils, and amount of runoff. Environmental consultants, civil engineers, or local soil conservation district staff can help in the design of a grass-lined swale, detention basin, infiltration basin, or other stormwater management structures based on site conditions. The *Guidebook of Best Management Practices for Michigan Watersheds*, available from the Michigan Department of Environmental Quality, and the Environmental Protection Agency's *Protecting Natural Wetlands: A Guide to Stormwater Best Management Practices* (EPA-843-B-96-001) both provide useful advice.

Septic Systems

Septic systems can be a source of pollutants to wetlands. Improperly located, malfunctioning, or inappropriately sized septic systems can be a source of phosphorus, nitrogen, chloride, and other substances which could upset the chemical balance of a wetland. Citizens can provide information to landowners and encourage proper septic system location, construction, and maintenance. Use of commercial products that claim to be a substitute for maintenance pumping is not recommended. Many of these products liquefy the sludge and cause it to enter the drainfield. This can increase the potential for contamination of ground water and nearby surface waters, as well as destroy the drainfield. Those on septic systems should avoid using chemicals such as drain cleaner and large amounts of bleach because they kill the bacteria that break down solid wastes in the septic tank.

Your local district health department is a great source of information on septic system construction and maintenance and they are also responsible for administering sanitary system regulations. Septic system regulations can help protect wetlands by ensuring that new systems are not sited in areas in which the ground water table is too close to the ground surface to ensure proper treatment of human waste. However, local sanitary appeals boards sometimes overturn septic permit denials, thus allowing construction and development in marginal areas and potentially threatening public health and environmental protection. Citizen involvement in these local decisions is very important.

Use Fertilizers and Pesticides Wisely

Citizens can play an important role in encouraging other community members to utilize the many safe alternatives to chemical fertilizers and pesticides around the home. Organic pesticide formulations, use of other insects to fight pests, and composting kitchen and yard waste to enrich soil have all been proven successful. The soil conservation district, your county MSU Extension agent, and many environmental organizations can recommend alternatives to using these products. Many homeowners use fertilizers when they do not need to. Before anyone decides to use lawn fertilizers, they should get their soil tested to see if it is even necessary. If it is determined that fertilizers or pesticides are necessary, manufacturers' directions should be followed carefully. Research into the technology and practice of Integrated Pest Management (IPM) has provided an excellent way to reduce reliance on heavy inputs of pesticides. Contact your soil conservation district or MSU Extension agent to find out about IPM practices in your area. In any case, the development of a chemical-free greenbelt to buffer the wetland from upland use of fertilizers and pesticides is very important.

Managing Recreation

Waves from motorboats can cause erosion damage to riparian wetlands. Although wetland vegetation serves to dampen wave energy, the waves from boats often generate much larger waves than the physical parameters of the water body would normally generate. One way citizens can protect these areas is to establish "No Wake Zones." Local lake associations can help in determining no wake zones. In other cases, it may be appropriate to limit the speed or motor size on an entire lake. For information on how to legally establish a no wake zone near your wetland or a speed limit on your lake, contact the marine division of your county sheriff's office. Because of the damage to soils and vegetation, the use of off-road vehicles such as dirt bikes, all-terrain vehicles, and even mountain bikes should not be permitted in wetlands.

53

Recreational activities such as hunting, fishing, hiking, canoeing, and bird watching are compatible with wetland protection as long as wildlife and their habitat are not disturbed by overuse. If a particular wetland is getting "loved to death," then you may need to advocate for limiting some uses during critical times such as breeding or nesting seasons. Accomplishing this might be as simple as a sign at access points or something more complicated like installing a fence or constructing a boardwalk to manage where people go in the wetland.

Pet Control

"Gentle" house pets can wreak havoc on wildlife populations that their owners are trying to help by protecting wetlands. Cats are very effective predators, especially on young animals. Dogs, especially small packs of them, can seriously harass wetland species. Declawing house cats can somewhat reduce their ability to kill small animals. Both cats and dogs should be restricted from wetlands during spring and summer bird nesting seasons. Keeping your dog on a leash allows access to the wetland yet reduces wildlife harassment.

Beaver Management

As noted above, beavers are an important natural component of wetland systems. Because human residential development throughout Michigan tends to concentrate around lakes and streams (preferred beaver habitat), beaver activities often conflict with human interests. This has been compounded in recent times by an increase in beaver populations. This increase is due to a variety of factors, including less trapping due to low fur prices, historic loss of natural predators, and forestry practices that favor beaver food sources (i.e., aspen). Accordingly, beavers have come to be regarded by many people as nuisances.

This nuisance quality of beavers tends to elicit dramatic response from those annoyed by beaver activities. When the response is to destroy the beaver dam, the resulting downstream sedimentation and scouring can sometimes cause more harm than good. Citizens can help educate landowners and various interest groups seeking to remove beavers about how to manage beavers in a way that doesn't cause additional problems. There are a variety of ways to manage beavers, including protecting prized trees, reducing beaver population through trapping, installing beaver foolers, and carefully (slowly) removing beaver dams.

54

The most important part of beaver management is population regulation. Beavers have one or two kits each year. An established beaver colony is usually composed of three generations: kits, yearlings, and a pair of adults. When the yearlings become two years old, they usually leave the parental colony to set up their own colony elsewhere, which makes room for the next litter of kits. An established colony of beavers can sustain the removal of several individuals each year. If fewer beavers are removed, then colonization of additional habitat will occur and the chances for nuisance beaver activity will increase. If the beaver population in your area has risen to nuisance proportions, encourage trappers to use the area during trapping season or contact the Michigan Department of Natural Resources (MDNR) Wildlife Division for information about nuisance beaver control permits.

The removal of established dams should be avoided unless it is determined necessary for the benefit of the river or stream system by a competent biologist and is authorized by appropriate permits. Those wishing to remove a beaver dam should contact their local MDNR Management Unit office to obtain a Wildlife Damage Investigation and Control Permit before attempting to remove the dam. Depending on the size of the dam and the amount of material to be removed, a permit from the Michigan Department of Environmental Quality may also be required. Even then, beaver dam removal should be done slowly and carefully to avoid downstream scouring from increased flows and to reduce downstream siltation. If done early in the beavers' construction process (before the dam spans the river and begins to impound water), beaver dams can be removed with little long-term impact on the stream. Any debris from dam removal should be disposed of in upland areas. It should also be noted that beaver dam removal will not solve the problems associated with beavers unless the activity is coupled with beaver removal. In other words, unless the population is reduced by trapping and maintained at an acceptable level, the beavers will simply rebuild the dam (and build others as the population expands), thus creating a never-ending cycle of dam building and removal which will result in recurrent siltation each time the dam is removed.

55

A different solution to ongoing beaver dam removal that avoids the negative impacts of stream siltation or bank scouring is the installation of a Clemson Beaver Pond Leveler. This simple device, also known as a "Beaver Fooler," is essentially a large tube (8-inch diameter, or larger, PVC pipe) that is placed through the beaver dam. Given that beaver dams are extremely well constructed, installing the beaver fooler is a lot of hard work. Typically, a notch is created in the dam and the fooler is dropped into the notch. The beaver fooler should be located so that it will still be under water when the water level achieves the desired level. Although installation will typically cause downstream siltation and some scouring, this only happens once (as opposed to recurrent dam removals) and can be minimized by drawing the level of the river down over several days. It is essential that the intake end of the pipe be protected by heavy wire fencing so that the beavers are not able to clog it. If the desire is to maintain some open water behind the dam, the beaver fooler can be constructed with an elbow on the downstream end to maintain a certain water level upstream of the dam. Due to atmospheric pressure, when the upstream level reaches the same elevation as the downstream end, water will stop flowing through the pipe. For large streams, two or more beaver foolers may be necessary in order to pass enough water through the dam to achieve the desired upstream water level. Placement of beaver foolers, or any other structure in a stream, requires appropriate permits from the MDEQ. Since beavers occupy streams and rivers that flow across lands owned by many different individuals, it is important to coordinate beaver management activities with neighboring landowners.

Often, the primary issue with beavers is damage to trees as a result of cutting and feeding activities. In instances where flooding from beaver dams does not threaten wetlands or water quality, nor threaten property other than by tree cutting, and there is no desire to reduce the population by trapping, the best option is to protect the trees. Desired trees can be effectively protected from beaver damage by fencing around the base of the trees with heavy wire mesh or hardware cloth. The fencing should encircle the tree, be at least three feet high, and staked about three inches away from the tree. Mesh size should be less than one inch in order to be effective.

Control Shoreline Erosion With Alternative Methods

In shoreline areas that are experiencing erosion, erosion control is very important. The first step in controlling erosion is to evaluate the nature and extent of the problem and determine if the problem is serious enough to warrant corrective action. There are two basic reasons for controlling erosion: to protect property and to protect the environment. Most shoreline erosion control activities require a permit from the MDEQ. Citizens can play an important role in reviewing and commenting on permit applications for erosion control activities. If the erosion is largely the result of natural processes that do not harm the environment nor threaten property, then erosion control may not be necessary. Assuming the nature and extent of the erosion warrant corrective measures, it is important to look at alternative methods of control and encourage the one that accomplishes the goals of the project with the maximum benefit to wetlands and water resources.

The traditional method of controlling erosion is to construct a bulkhead at the water's edge or armor the shoreline with rock rip-rap. Such activities often result in the loss of wetland habitat and can exacerbate erosion problems on adjacent properties. Researchers have developed an environmentally friendly, aesthetically pleasing, and effective method of controlling shoreline erosion that relies on the use of vegetation (both living and non-living) and is known as biotechnical erosion control (BEC). In its simplest terms, BEC involves the re-establishment of a diverse vegetation community that mimics a natural shoreline system. The vegetation at the shoreline, and in the water itself, binds the soil and provides increased protection against erosion. With careful vegetation trimming one can have a pleasing filtered view of the wetland, lake, or stream while still maintaining a naturally stable vegetated shoreline. By encouraging BEC, citizens can help restore natural shorelines and at the same time protect the interests of shoreline property owners.

Be Aware of Activities in the Watershed

Water is the lifeblood of wetlands. The quality of that lifeblood is dependent on the watershed. One of the most important roles for citizens is to be aware of proposed and ongoing activities in the watershed that could adversely impact its quality. If you identify a proposed activity that will impact wetlands, determine if the project will require any permitting at the local, state, or federal levels. Contact the person proposing it to find out more and encourage alternatives that would have less impact. If this is not successful, it will be necessary to participate in the decision-making process at the local, state, or federal level by going to meetings, providing public comment, and sharing your information with others. As mentioned in Chapter Six, the MDEQ posts a list of all permit applications submitted to the MDEQ. This is an excellent resource to find out about proposed activities that might impact the wetlands, lakes, and streams in your watershed.

Control Exotic and Nuisance Species

Management activities to control the spread or invasion of exotic or nuisance plant species that impact wetland vegetation communities and wildlife habitat vary depending on the size and type

The Purple Loosestrife Project

Michigan State University is working with K-12 teaching professionals, naturalists, property managers, and citizen groups to control purple loosestrife and foster stewardship of our natural resources. The Purple Loosestrife Project involves the rearing and releasing of natural enemies of this invasive exotic. There are many opportunities for citizens to get involved in this project that seeks to restore the health of Michigan's marshes.

Loosestrife Locator Survey

In order to ensure the most effective approach to purple loosestrife control, it is important to know where purple loosestrife has been established and identify new infestations. Concerned citizens can perform a valuable function by reporting sightings of purple loosestrife. Participation in the Loosestrife Locator Survey involves completing and returning a postcard, available on-line, that includes questions regarding location, size, and type of habitat the loosestrife is colonizing.

K-12 Learning Activities

This innovative project involves a diversity of educational activities for students of all ages. Projects include studying insect life cycles through rearing and releasing the insects, exploring local wetlands and watersheds by conducting surveys of loosestrife infestations, and learning about various ecological principles such as allopathic plant interactions and abiotic limits to plant growth.

Rearing and Release of Loosestrife's Enemies

Purple loosestrife's natural enemies are relatively easy to rear, requiring a modest amount of time and relatively inexpensive equipment. In order to produce enough beetles to be successful, hundreds of thousands of insects will need to be reared each year until viable naturally reproducing populations are established. The most effective way to accomplish this goal is to have dozens of rearing sites across Michigan. The picture window of your living room, or your child's classroom, is a potential rearing site.

If you are interested in getting involved in efforts to control the "purple plague," check out the Purple Loosestrife Project on the Internet at www.msue.msu.edu/seagrant/pp. Or contact:

Purple Loosestrife Project
Michigan State University
334 Natural Resources Building
East Lansing, MI 48824-1222

57

of the wetland, the invading species, the extent of the invasion, and the resources available. The most ubiquitous exotic and nuisance plants impacting Michigan's wetlands include reed canary grass, buckthorn (common and glossy), phragmites, and purple loosestrife. Although each of these plants looks different, they share many similarities. They have few pests, they form dense stands which crowd out native vegetation, and they have little value as food or cover for native wildlife.

The first and best line of defense is to minimize the opportunities for invasion by nuisance species. Everybody should refrain from growing invasive species in their yards or gardens and should discourage their neighbors from doing so also.

Given that plant seeds are transported by natural processes such as wind, flowing water, birds and other animals, etc., it will not be possible to stop all introductions of exotic and nuisance species into wetlands in your community. Accordingly, the next line of defense is to destroy those plants that are introduced and take root. If the introduced population is small, and they are recognized and removed early, there is a good chance that you can keep the wetland from being completely overrun. Removal methods include hand pulling or cutting the vegetation before the seeds set (and disposal of the plants away from the wetland) and cautious application of herbicides that effect broadleaf plant species. Hand pulling may require gently "teasing" the roots to facilitate pulling the entire plant. Although hand pulling involves the most time, some consider it the most effective way to eradicate new stands.

Vegetation cutting alone will limit seed production and dramatically slow the spread of a purple loosestrife or phragmites stand, but it will not remove it. This is because invasive plants like purple loosestrife can reproduce from the root stock. In addition, purple loosestrife can sprout from plant pieces. For this reason, it is important to be careful to remove all plant pieces from the wetland when hand pulling or cutting these species.

Perhaps the best method for the removal of small numbers of purple loosestrife plants is a combination of cutting and herbicide application. The MDNR Wildlife Division recommends cutting the vegetation near the ground and applying a broadleaf herbicide by "painting" it directly on the cut stem. Painting the herbicide directly on the stem minimizes potential impacts on non-target plants. The optimal time for this procedure is during the flowering stage but before the seeds set (July and August). It is important to realize that the application of any herbicide "over water" requires a permit from the MDEQ. However, by late July or August, most loosestrife stands are no longer in standing water (due to low summer water levels in the wetland).

Despite efforts to control purple loosestrife, by the early 1990s, it appeared that control by conventional methods (pulling, cutting, burning, digging, and poisoning) was difficult and impractical on a large scale. A promising alternative to halt the spread of this terrible beauty is a natural biological control that involves less-than-beautiful insects. In 1994, the Michigan Department of Natural Resources Wildlife Division released two species of a European leaf-eating beetle and a weevil as part of a field trial to test the biological control of purple loosestrife. The beetles (*Galerucella calmariensis* and *G. Pusilla*) have been shown to be highly selective for feeding on bud, leaf, and stem tissue causing defoliation and suppression of flowering and seed production. *Hylobius transversovittatus* is a weevil whose larvae mine in loosestrife root tissue weakening and ultimately killing the plant. While these natural enemies cannot eliminate purple loosestrife, experts believe that they are capable of reducing the density by 90% over most of its current range. Reducing purple loosestrife to this extent will allow reestablishment of native wetland plants and restore ecosystem health to many of Michigan's marshes.

We have all heard about the problems of introducing one exotic species to control another... and the dastardly chain of events that may be set into motion. In an effort to avoid such a happening with the loosestrife-eating beetles, the United States Department of Agriculture conducted extensive field and laboratory tests on the beetles used for loosestrife control. Based on this research, these exotic insects are believed to be safe.

The challenge is to establish viable populations of these natural enemies in Michigan watersheds where purple loosestrife occurs. In an effort to meet this challenge, the Purple Loosestrife Project at Michigan State University was initiated to couple biological control with an innovative outreach, education, and citizen involvement program. This program seeks to establish Cooperative Biological Control Sites which will be involved with the actual rearing and release of purple loosestrife's natural enemies, K-12 curriculum development, and citizen monitoring of purple loosestrife populations. If you are concerned about the spread of the "purple plague" in your wetlands, see the sidebar for information about how you can get involved.

Wetland Protection Spotlight

Living with Walloon's Beavers
The Walloon Lake Association

Walloon Lake's sapphire blue waters, healthy populations of trout and smallmouth bass, and long history of summer recreation (for example, Ernest Hemingway's boyhood cottage is now owned by his nephew) have elicited love from generations of residents and visitors. The Walloon Lake Association (WLA) sports membership from nearly 90% of the shoreline residents and dozens of citizens in the watershed. In an effort to "put their money where their heart is," the Walloon Lake Trust and Conservancy was formed to acquire lands that significantly contribute to the quality of the lake. Not surprisingly, over the years the Trust has acquired significant wetlands that border the lake's tributaries.

59

When the local population of beavers started expanding in the mid-1990s, old beaver dams were added to and new dams were built. The water levels in the wetlands on the Trust property, and on adjacent private lands began to rise. Prized trees along the shoreline were felled to feed the next generation of beavers. Rising water levels threatened the safe operation of septic systems. When the local county road commission removed a beaver dam on Trust property, releasing a large plume of sediment into the lake, the controversy came to a head.

The issue threatened to create a schism among the WLA members—all citizens concerned about the protection of the water quality and habitat of Walloon Lake. Some wanted to take a laissez-faire approach and allow the beavers to impact the resource in their own way. Others wanted to eradicate all beavers and remove any trace of them. In response to the need to develop a means of resolving the issues, the leadership of the WLA and the Trust decided to take a proactive approach to managing beavers in its watershed. And thus the Walloon Lake Association Beaver Management Committee was born in the summer of 1996.

The Committee included a representative cross section of the interests present in the WLA and the Trust membership, agency staff, and the Tip of the Mitt Watershed Council. The Committee's charge was to address concerns raised and develop a management plan to help guide the Walloon Lake Association in managing beaver populations in the Walloon Lake Watershed in a way that allows humans and beavers to harmoniously coexist.

First, the Committee developed the following goals to guide their work:

1) To involve the Walloon Lake Association and Trust, and Walloon Lake residents in a cooperative and pro-active management plan with the Road Commissions of Charlevoix and Emmet Counties, Michigan Department of Natural Resources Wildlife Division, Michigan Department of Environmental Quality Land and Water Management Division, and the Tip of the Mitt Watershed Council;

2) To develop an ecologically-sound lake-wide strategy to coordinate and maximize the effectiveness of beaver management activities;

3) To protect and enhance water resources in the Walloon Lake Watershed; and

4) To prevent or minimize property damage resulting from beaver activities.

After four months of learning about beaver natural history, beaver management techniques, considering the benefits and detriments of beavers, reviewing all their options, and selecting the most appropriate for the Walloon watershed, the Committee adopted a multifaceted approach to beaver management that included the following components:

1) Inventorying beaver dams and lodges in the watershed;

2) Monitoring water levels and wetland health above and below dams;

3) Providing education and information to residents in the watershed;

4) Protecting shoreline trees by individual property owners;

5) Managing beaver population through trapping;

6) Installing beaver foolers at appropriate locations; and

7) Dam removal under certain conditions.

In the years since, all elements of the management plan have been implemented, and two beaver foolers have been installed on two tributaries (one in partnership with the Charlevoix Road Commission). The beaver foolers, coupled with limited beaver removal, have maintained water levels behind the dams at appropriate levels and eliminated the need for dam removal (and the associated problems therein). Lakeshore residents still have the opportunity to observe beavers, and those who have taken the time to fence their trees have not suffered any damage from beavers. Through thoughtful research and involving interested parties, the Walloon Lake Association has accomplished their goal of "living with Walloon's beavers."

For more information about the Walloon Lake Association, contact:
P.O. Box 621
Petoskey, MI 49770
Phone: (231) 347-0100

Chapter 6 Citizen Involvement in Wetland Restoration

Michigan has lost approximately half of its original wetlands. Despite their numerous functions and values and the realization that they are ecologically vital, wetlands continue to be lost. Citizens can help reverse this trend by working to restore wetlands by advocating for wetland restoration, identifying restorable wetlands, and reviewing and commenting on proposed wetland restoration activities.

This chapter clarifies definitions, presents a process to help you identify potentially restorable wetlands and develop restoration plans, and provides some design considerations for a variety of wetland functions. It is important to note that most wetland restoration projects will require permits from the Michigan Department of Environmental Quality and authorization from local units of government and possibly the County Drain Commissioner. Some involved with wetland restoration feel that they are "doing a good thing" and should be exempt from

regulatory review. However, for the integrity of the permit process, all regulated activities (dredging, draining, filling, and constructing a use in a wetland) should go through the process. The permit review process helps to ensure that the project is indeed beneficial to the resource and that it does not inadvertently cause problems such as flooding neighboring property, reducing stream base flow, or damaging sensitive habitats. In addition, the permitting process provides an opportunity to receive input on design and management from MDEQ wetland specialists. Regardless of how beneficial your project may be, failure to get a permit may result in an enforcement action.

Historically, most wetlands were destroyed by draining for agricultural purposes. Land that has been effectively drained and successfully farmed in the past may be too wet in some years to produce a good crop. In these areas, the best use of that land may be to restore its original wetland hydrology and allow it to once again become a fully functioning wetland.

62

In Michigan, wetlands have formed in the landscape over thousands of years—since the last retreat of the glaciers. Given this, it is understandable that restoration or creation of a wetland that "totally duplicates" a naturally occurring wetland is practically impossible due to the complexity and variation in wetland ecosystems. However, some systems may be approximated and individual wetland functions may be restored or created. Flood storage, waterfowl habitat, and recreational open space are easiest to restore, but subtle ecological functions such as ground water discharge and recharge, food chain relationships, and certain water quality maintenance are more difficult.

At one time, it was thought that natural wetlands were good places to discharge wastewater because of their capacity for treating wastes. It is now apparent that the natural waste treatment function of a wetland can be over stressed by inputs of excessive pollutants. However, artificial wetlands are being successfully designed and constructed to treat wastewater. These systems are typically constructed in a way that allows for periodic removal of pollutants trapped by the created wetland. Nationwide, thousands of wetlands have been created for treatment of human sewage, agricultural and industrial waste, urban runoff, and acid mine drainage. Many wetlands have also been created to mitigate for losses due to permitted wetland degradation. From these efforts have come much of our present knowledge about techniques for wetland creation and restoration.

Citizen involvement in wetland restoration results in a range of benefits. With broad scale involvement in wetland restoration, the richness of Michigan's wetlands can be again realized. The community and surrounding watershed benefits from the functions that wetlands provide. But perhaps more importantly, the citizens themselves receive the personal satisfaction from being involved in a tangible act of healing a wounded ecosystem. Such involvement can be a source of pride and leave a wonderful living legacy for the next generation.

DEFINITIONS

Terms like wetland restoration, enhancement, and creation mean different things to different people. This guidebook uses the commonly accepted definitions noted below. Although we define each of these terms, the focus of this chapter is on citizen involvement in wetland restoration.

Wetland Restoration is a term used to describe activities that seek to return wetlands to a previously existing natural condition from a disturbed or totally altered state. It is not necessary to have complete knowledge of what the pre-existing conditions were. Rather, it is enough to know a wetland (of whatever type) was there and have as a goal the return to that same wetland type. The vast majority of wetlands were altered by ditching, tiling, stream channelization, or other hydrologic manipulation. Drained sites will retain hydric soils and likely retain a wetland vegetation seedbank for many decades. Wetland hydrology can often be restored by plugging drainage ditches, or by removing segments of drain tile. If the original wetland hydrology can be restored, then the site can again become a functioning wetland. It may, however, require planting or other ongoing care to bring it back to the original wetland type.

63

Wetland Enhancement is the improvement, maintenance, and management of existing wetlands for a particular function or value, possibly at the expense of others. Wetland enhancement activities can be divided into two categories: high impact and management. High impact enhancement involves dramatically changing the physical characteristic of the wetland from what it was historically. Examples of high impact enhancement activity include dredging to create a pond for waterfowl in a wetland that currently does not have open water or impounding water at a greater depth or duration than what occurred historically. High impact activities usually require permits and result in enhancing one wetland function at the expense of others. Management activities are those which do not involve changes in soils or hydrology of wetlands. Examples of management (or low impact enhancement) activities include installing nest boxes or platforms for waterfowl, controlling the spread of exotic species such as purple loosestrife, maintaining greenbelts around wetlands, and planting upland habitat with food cover. These and other management activities are addressed in Chapter Five.

Wetland Creation is the conversion of an area that was historically upland into a wetland. Wetlands are most commonly created by impounding water or excavating surface soils. This usually involves intensive, costly efforts, such as earth movement, dam construction, and vegetation planting. The most common successfully created wetlands have been shallow impoundments and shallow excavations in areas adjacent to existing wetlands and where the ground water table was already fairly close to the soil surface. In these situations, hydrology can often be easy to establish and revegetation by natural dispersal of seeds from the nearby wetland can occur quickly.

As a general rule, created wetlands do not function as well as restored wetlands. Furthermore, wetland creation is the most expensive of the three processes and has the greatest chance for failure.

IDENTIFYING POTENTIALLY RESTORABLE WETLANDS

One of the most useful activities that citizens can do to encourage wetland restoration is to help identify potentially restorable wetland areas. There are numerous agencies and organizations involved with wetland restoration, including the U.S. Fish and Wildlife Service, the Natural Resources Conservation Service, the Michigan Department of Natural Resources, county soil and water conservation districts, and private organizations such as Ducks Unlimited and the Michigan Wildlife Habitat Foundation. Citizen involvement is a valuable asset to all of these ongoing efforts. In addition, local involvement in identifying potentially restorable wetlands can serve as the catalyst to get these groups working in your community.

The steps below were employed to identify and prioritize potentially restorable wetlands in the Elk River-Chain of Lakes Watershed. They are offered here to help you develop your own citizen-based restoration effort and can easily dovetail into the efforts of ongoing agencies and organizations.

Step One - Set Goals and the Geographic Search Area

As with any endeavor, it is best to "start with the end in mind." Although each effort will be a bit different, here are some questions to ask that will help you and your group set its goals:

- What do you want to accomplish with this project?

- What wetland functions and values have been particularly impacted and are in need of restoration? (MNFI's map of pre-settlement wetlands and the companion MNFI report titled *Wetland Trends in Michigan Since 1800, a preliminary assessment* might be useful in answering this question.)

- Are there certain wetland functions and values that might be of more interest to potential partners in this endeavor?

- Are there other agencies or organizations that are doing similar things in the area? What are their goals? Is it possible to work together? What can you do to help their efforts?

- Do you want to focus on both public and private lands?

- What is the budget (in both time and dollars) for this project?

In addition to determining goals, it will help to focus your efforts if you can define the geographic area that you plan to inventory for potentially restorable wetland sites. Since numerous wetland functions are based on hydrologic connection and location in the watershed, selecting your geographic area on a watershed basis can make a lot of sense. The size of the area you select will depend on the nature of the area (i.e., extensive wetland impacts or minimal wetland impacts) and the time and dollars available for the project.

Your goals and selected geographic area should be such that they challenge you but also will be achievable. It is important to note that goal setting is an essential first step, but the results are not cast in stone. The goals you set are subject to change based on additional information uncovered as you proceed through the process.

Step Two - Find Out What's Already Been Done

Depending on where you are, some agency or organization may have already inventoried potentially restorable wetlands. Use the appendices to find phone numbers and addresses of those who have worked on wetland restoration and contact them to see if they've already done what you intend to do. If they haven't, inquire about their interest in your project and enlist their support. Cast as broad a net as possible in your research of what's already been done. In addition to the agencies and organizations listed

65

above in Step One, contact the MDEQ to see if there have been any wetland permits issued that required mitigation. Typically, as part of mitigation planning, the applicants provide information on potential wetland mitigation sites. In addition, contact your County Drain Commissioner, as some Drain Commissioners may be working to strategically restore wetlands to reduce flood damage.

Step Three - Gather Off-Site Resources

Assuming that no one has identified or inventoried potentially restorable wetlands in your watershed, the next step is to gather as much relevant off-site information as possible for your chosen geographic area. Essential information sources include USDA County Soil Surveys, Hydric Soils List, USGS topographic maps, NWI maps, MIRIS maps, and county plat maps. In addition, depending on your selected geographic area, there may be a wealth of additional information resources available. Two excellent sources of information for identification of potentially restorable wetland sites include the Natural Resource Conservation Service (NRCS) and the County Drain Commissioner. As part of their administrative responsibilities under the Farm Bill, the NRCS conducts aerial photography and mapping of prior converted wetlands and farmed wetlands, both of which are excellent candidates for wetland restoration activities. The County Drain Commissioners have maps of all legally established drains on a county-by-county basis. Such maps are sources of critical information and should include land elevations, depth of ditch,

the extent of drainage, watershed boundaries, and landowners in each drainage district. Although these information resources are widely available in hard copy, as state and federal agencies become more and more sophisticated, much of this information will be available in a GIS-compatible electronic form.

Step Four - Identify Potential Sites Based on Available Off-Site Data

Once all the information is gathered, the next task is to make sense of it. For those groups who have access to a computerized Geographic Information System (GIS), the task of analyzing the information can be simplified. In the absence of a GIS system, you will have to closely review each of the information sources to determine areas that were once wetlands. The NRCS maps of "prior converted" and "farmed wetlands" will be extremely helpful. Drainage district maps provided by the Drain Commissioner are the easiest and most reliable source of information on drained land. By comparing this information to a soil survey map or the NWI map, you may be able to identify areas that were clearly wetlands prior to drainage.

If you don't have access to drainage maps, perhaps the best place to start is with the county soil survey. Review the soils maps for your target area to identify soils mapped as hydric and those soils with hydric soil inclusions. Depending on the date the photos for your map were taken, and development in the area since that time, this first "cut" may identify numerous potential restoration opportunities. Once you've identified the hydric soils, the next step would be to use the other resources to identify those areas of hydric soil that are no longer wetlands. By going back and forth between the maps, and being cognizant of when each map was made, you can get a pretty good feel for areas that were formerly wetlands.

66

Step Five - Conduct a Windshield Review

Once the potential wetland restoration sites have been identified, it's time to do a windshield review. The windshield review gives you an opportunity to "get a feel" for the actual potential for wetland restoration. Drainage ditches, wet areas in fields, and subtle differences in vegetation color in a pasture (potentially indicating different hydrology or soil type in parts of the field) are some of the visual clues that will add to your offsite information. Your windshield review will also provide you with valuable information to help determine the practicality of a particular site for wetland restoration. If a housing development has been planted in former agriculture land that looked like drained wetland on the county soil survey, then you know the potential is very slight. Take copious notes and pictures of each potential site. For those that you can't get to by road, consider contacting the landowner at this stage to get on the site to do a preliminary review.

Step Six - Prioritize Potential Sites

Once you've gathered the information from your offsite identification and windshield review, it's time to prioritize your potential sites. Prioritization of your sites will help you to select those sites that will most likely contribute to accomplishing your goal and focus your energies for the next steps—contacting landowners and securing permission to conduct a thorough on-site review. To prioritize, first go back and look at your goals. Based on your goals, develop a set of criteria by which to prioritize each potential wetland restoration site. Individual criterion might include a minimum size, the potential to restore certain wetland types or functions, cost per acre, location in the watershed, etc. Once the criteria have been developed, apply them to your sites and select those that rank highest.

Step Seven - Contact Landowners and Conduct Site Visits

The number of landowners you contact and site visits you conduct will depend on the quantity of potential sites that meet your initial criteria and your available time and financial resources. At this stage, the cooperation of the private landowner or the manager responsible for public (either state or local) lands is essential. By focusing on the benefits to the individual and community of wetland restoration in your communications, most landowners will at least provide you access to conduct your site visit. When conducting the site visit, you want to gather as much information on the following questions as possible:

1) What method was used to convert the original wetland to upland?

2) What is the existing condition of the soils, hydrology, and vegetation on the site?

3 What methods will need to be employed to restore wetland conditions?

4) Are there nearby land uses that would threaten the success of wetland restoration at this location?

5) Is the area currently a wetland (and therefore requires a permit before restoration activities could commence)?

6) How interested is the landowner in participating in this project?

Refer to Chapters Three and Ten for useful tips on how to gather information to help answer these questions.

67

Step Eight - Select Sites That Best Meet Goals and Budget

When the site visits are completed, it's time to select the sites that best meet the goals and the available time and money resources. One of the most important factors in final site selection is support of the landowner (on private lands) or the entity charged with management responsibilities (on public). Assuming you have a willing landowner/manager and access to some dollars to put toward the project, it's time to plan and implement your project. At this point, if you haven't already been in touch with one of the organizations or agencies who focus on wetland restoration, it might be a good time to do so. If you want to "go it alone," the following section provides a recommended planning process to ensure that you adequately consider potential pitfalls.

PLANNING WETLAND RESTORATION PROJECTS

Although some general guidelines have been developed over the years, the science of wetland restoration and creation is still quite new, and the many opportunities are so diverse, that it is not possible (nor desirable) to develop simple "cookbook" guidance for wetland restoration, creation, or enhancement projects. Again, it is recommended that you contact one of the many conservation organizations, agencies, or consultants who are experienced in wetland restoration for project planning and implementation assistance. Below are some planning considerations that should help you successfully design and implement your project.

Some wetland restoration projects are quite simple and only involve the breakage or removal of drainage tiles, whereas others may involve excavation of sediment or dam construction. These considerations are designed to accommodate the range of wetland restoration, creation, and enhancement projects and assume that a suitable site for wetland restoration has already been selected.

Step One - Revisit Goals and Site Selection

Before you invest any more time or money, make sure that this project meets your needs and the landowner or land manager is fully on board.

Revisit Goals

What wetland functions and values are you trying to restore? The size and shape of the wetland will be largely determined by its purpose. For example, if the wetland is for waterfowl habitat, then an irregular shoreline with a mixture of islands, open water, and dense emergent vegetation will be best.

Evaluate the Site

Evaluate the site to make sure it will provide a real opportunity to meet the project's goals. The most important information includes soil type, watershed features (size, slope, water availability, water quality), existing vegetation cover types, adjacent land uses, property boundaries, and evaluation of fish and wildlife habitat (including threatened and endangered species).

Assess the Need for Permits

Based on project goals and the potential site, you should know at this stage of the process what permits may be needed. A permit will be needed when dredging, filling, draining, or construction occurs in regulated wetlands or legally established drains. Before commencing a project, check with the Michigan Department of Environmental Quality, U. S. Army Corps of Engineers, the County Drain Commissioner, and local governments to determine which permits will be required. The importance of considering and addressing permitting concerns early in the project planning phase cannot be over emphasized.

68

Step Two - Detailed Project Planning

Wetland projects can be designed with a variety of shapes, sizes, depths, degrees of wetness, and biogeochemical characteristics. Except in simple projects, a detailed planning and design stage is essential before beginning restoration activities. Wetland projects that involve the construction of berms or water level control structures should be designed and constructed according to civil engineering standards to provide reliability and safety at reasonable cost. Additional collection of detailed data will probably be necessary in this step in order to complete the project design. In general, the larger the project, the more information will be necessary to ensure that the project is adequately designed and implemented. The following basic information should be compiled when planning wetland restoration projects:

Topography

Include detailed topographic drawings showing existing and proposed contour intervals, property boundaries, prominent physical features, and the boundaries of existing wetlands and the proposed wetland.

Soils

Restoration is most successful in former hydric soils. However, depending on the activities that have taken place since the wetland was converted, the ability of the soils to fully support a wetland project may be compromised. For example, the site may have been subject to deposition of sediment and may contain a layer of mineral soils on top of the hydric soils. By boring, determine the types of different soils and their extent, and the depth to ground water.

Hydrology

For a wetland to function, it must have adequate amounts of water during appropriate times of the year. A detailed assessment should be made of the sources and losses of water, and water storage characteristics in the wetland. Sources of water include precipitation, surface runoff, stream flow, springs and seeps, and sub-surface ground water. Losses of water are due to evapotranspiration, soil infiltration, and outflow. If runoff will primarily supply the water, then the amount of surface runoff for the site must be calculated before determining wetland size. If ground water is to supply the water for the wetland, then the depth to ground water, range of water table fluctuation, and the yield of springs or seepages should be determined.

The hydrologic study should also look at potential maximum extent of flooding, the downstream impact of impounding or diverting water, and water chemistry. Water chemistry is important in determining the types of plants and animals which can live there. When analyzing the potential for flooding and the impacts of impounding or diverting water, it is very important to consider potential impacts to neighboring property owners.

Step Three - Develop Design and Secure Permits

Based on the results of your project planning, there are many design strategies available. Many of the design strategies, including dam construction, placing fill into existing drainage ways, or any construction of a structure in a wetland requires a permit. If you are unclear if your project requires a permit, contact the MDEQ to find out. The time spent finding out will surely be a lot less than the time

69

spent on a potential environmental enforcement action if you proceed without a permit. Some of the most common design and construction options for wetland projects are described below.

Design and Construction Options

Blocking Existing Drainage Systems

Because many drained areas were formerly wetlands, and the hydric soils are still present and hydrophytic seed bank is still viable, this is the single most cost-effective method of successfully restoring wetlands. In fact, this method is so inexpensive and effective that it is the only method that many agencies and organizations working on wetland restoration will pursue. Construction options to block existing drainage systems include breaking or removing field tiles or blocking (filling in) drainage ditches. If your project involves a designated drain, it may first be necessary to have the drain officially abandoned. The process for abandoning a drain is in Chapter 17 of the Drain Code, or contact your Drain Commission to inquire about the process.

Dams, Dikes, and Levees

Usually, these are embankments of earth constructed to contain water. They must be properly designed to prevent failure from overtopping, seepage, sloughing, or collapse. Design features include soil engineering properties, positioning, height, side slope, erosion control, and the use of special construction materials (like anti-seep collars on culverts).

Water Control Structures

These are often necessary to control flow in and out of the wetland. They include spillways, pipes with drop inlets, pumps, sub-surface drain tiles, and other structures.

70

Excavations

On suitable sites, excavated wetlands are simple to build, require minimal engineering, and are safer with respect to possible damage from flooding. However, they are usually restricted to relatively small areas of flat terrain. Typically, wetland restoration activities will not require excavation unless there has been significant sedimentation into the wetland.

Substrate Seals

Typically, wetland restoration will not require substrate seals. However, wetland creation projects are sometimes sited on soils that are too permeable, and excessive seepage losses may occur. This may be the result of an inadequate site investigation or a decision that the need for a wetland on a permeable site is more important than site restrictions. In this case, the bottom of the wetland needs to be sealed. Methods of sealing include soil compaction, importing clay soils, adding bentonite (a type of clay which swells when wet) to native soils, or the use of special waterproof linings of plastic or rubber.

Vegetation

A thriving, diverse vegetation community is an important component of a well functioning wetland. Vegetation can be established by two primary processes: natural colonization and planting. As long as wetland hydrology is present, some type of wetland vegetation will eventually become established. However, for natural colonization to occur in a timely manner, a source of propagules must be present in the soil or in adjacent wetland vegetation communities. Seedbanks of formerly drained areas usually provide excellent sources for wetland vegetation. Again, wetland restoration projects in these areas will have the highest levels of success.

Although rarely necessary, you can establish vegetation by planting seeds, bulbs, root stock, or transplanted sprigs. Depending on the type of vegetation you want to establish, transplanting is generally the most successful method (with trees and shrubs, for example, seeding is slower, has a lower survival rate, and is less predictable). Try to use locally grown plants, as they will be better adapted to local environmental conditions. Collecting wild local plants can be environmentally damaging (and may be illegal). There are many wetland nurseries which can provide plants, and several guidebooks which describe environmental requirements and general planting guidelines. Newly planted vegetation is subject to being wiped out by hungry populations of wildlife. To ensure that your investment in roots and bulbs does not go to fattening up the local goose or deer population, freshly planted wetland vegetation may need to be protected in some way (e.g., enclosing them in fencing). After a planted vegetation community is established, it will likely change over time due to the dynamic nature of natural communities.

Accessory Structures
Depending on the goals of your project, you may want to include accessory structures in your plan. These include boardwalks and observation platforms to enhance education and interpretation, nesting or loafing structures for wildlife, fencing, fishing piers, access roads, etc.

Securing Appropriate Permits

As a citizen advocate interested in protecting wetlands, it is important that your project proceed with proper authorization. In addition to ensuring that you won't be tangled up in a violation of local, state, or federal regulations, your participation in the permit process can serve as a positive example to local developers and landowners. The regulatory chapters in this book should provide you with adequate information to complete wetland permit applications. Consult local officials regarding local permit requirements not addressed in this book.

As mentioned above, it is advisable to seek the expertise of professionals when planning and designing wetland restoration projects. Not only will these individuals provide valuable insight into site assessment and design, but they can also help to secure necessary permits. A permit will be needed when dredging, filling, or other construction or soil disturbance occurs in regulated wetlands or legally established drains. Before commencing a project, check with the Michigan Department of Environmental Quality, U. S. Army Corps of Engineers, the County Drain Commissioner, and local governments to determine which permits will be required.

Step Four - Implement the Project

During implementation of the project, design modifications necessary to achieve success may become apparent. Closely inspect the work of contractors to be sure that the design is being followed. Correcting oversights once the land is flooded can be difficult. Special equipment, such as vehicles equipped to work in soft ground or water, may be necessary. Scheduling construction for the driest times of the year or during winter when the ground is frozen may be wise.

71

Step Five - Monitoring and Routine Maintenance

Monitoring is recommended to measure the success of the project. Most wetlands which have been restored or created are not assessed adequately to determine whether they have been successful. Monitoring and assessment of these areas should include: water levels throughout the year, establishment of wetland vegetation, use by animal species, development of wetland soil profiles, and patterns of plant succession. If the area has a surface water component, basic parameters of surface water quality should be monitored, including pH, temperature, turbidity, phosphorus, nitrogen, and chloride. If monitoring indicates that the goals for the project are not being met, then corrective action should be taken.

Minimal maintenance activities are often required to ensure success. Typical maintenance activities include maintaining buffer zones, preventing soil erosion and sedimentation, inspecting and nurturing plantings, and controlling exotic species. In some cases, ongoing operational management is necessary. For instance, seasonal manipulation of the water level in waterfowl floodings can help to provide maximum food production and nesting habitat.

FUNCTION-BASED PLANNING CONSIDERATIONS

The citizen's role in wetland restoration and management can go beyond identifying potentially restorable wetlands or helping to plan restoration projects. Your role as reviewer and commentor on projects that seek to restore and create wetlands is also important. With most wetland permit applications that involve permanent wetland conversion, a mitigation plan is proposed. As wetland mitigation banking is utilized more and more by developers as a way to offset wetland loss, more wetland restoration and creation projects will need to be scrutinized by the public.

72

Below are some common planning and design considerations for a variety of wetland functions. They are intended to provide you with information to serve as background in your own project planning efforts and to help you review the projects proposed by others. It is important to note that some management goals may contradict each other. As both a planner and a reviewer, it is important for you to be able to point out contradictions and recommend modifications to ensure success.

Wildlife Habitat

Wetlands provide breeding, nesting, feeding, and safety cover for amphibians, reptiles, birds, and mammals. Wetland restoration and projects should be designed to provide water at depths, time, and duration to promote desired vegetation, make it accessible, and provide other habitat elements required for the targeted species of wildlife. Habitat requirements for water, food, cover (for protection from adverse weather and predators), and reproduction (pairing and mating, nesting, and brooding) for the target wildlife species should be considered. The location of the wetland project site in relation to migration corridors as well as proximity to other wetland habitats should also be considered. Species requirements and habitat design elements are detailed in NRCS field office guides, plant and animal reference sheets, and numerous other references.

Fish Habitat

Wetlands provide valuable spawning and nursery areas for fish. They also provide habitat for aquatic invertebrates which are essential food for fish. If restoring or creating fish habitat is a goal, then the design must incorporate an area of permanent water. Depending on the desired fish species, it is recommended that some part of the pond be at least eight feet deep to protect fish from winterkill. The bottom topography should be undulating. Parts of the pond designed for breeding and nursery habitat and food production should be less than three feet deep and provide free access to the associated deep water habitats. Water quality, especially summer and winter oxygen levels, is the key to survival and production of fish and other aquatic organisms. Conservation practices are often needed to control watershed erosion and stormwater inputs to ensure that the area functions properly.

Water Supply and Ground Water Recharge

Wetlands are a source of ground and surface water. Wetlands store precipitation and runoff for direct or indirect use by humans, livestock, and fish and wildlife. While serving these functions, a wetland can provide habitat for fish, wildlife, and endangered species, and provide recreation and other opportunities. Hydrology is the most critical element of a successful wetland restoration or creation. Proper design requires a thorough knowledge of the hydrologic inputs and outputs of the system, including loss to ground water. If you plan on using the wetland to provide a water supply or to ensure year-round deep water for fish populations, impermeable (or nearly impermeable) substrates are needed. On the other hand, if ground water recharge is a goal, then a permeable substrate is necessary.

73

Habitat for Threatened and Endangered Species

Wetlands provide critical habitat for many federal and state listed threatened and endangered species. Many rare species and species of special concern that may be candidates for listing are also dependent on wetlands. Because their population levels are so low, endangered species require special consideration when it comes to wetland restoration design and management. Management for threatened or endangered species of plants or animals can often exclude or limit management of wetlands for other uses, even other wildlife resources. On the other hand, management for other functions, such as waterfowl hunting, water storage, and flood control, may be compatible with the needs of endangered species. With regard to planning and design, specific requirements of targeted species of animals or plants must be considered. Recovery Plans developed by the U.S. Fish and Wildlife Service and other information on the species must be referred to for habitat needs and design requirements.

Recreation

Wetlands are used for hunting, trapping, fishing, bird-watching, photography, painting, canoeing, hiking, and for general enjoyment of the beauty of a natural environment. Recreational activities may need to be restricted during periods where some species of wildlife are especially sensitive to human disturbance, such as breeding and nesting seasons. Specific requirements for desired activities must be considered in the design phase, as must the type of materials, construction methods, and the compatibility with other wetland resources. Recreation design includes providing access and special features, such as walkways, paths, and observation platforms to facilitate enjoyment of the wetland without adversely effecting the natural functions and values. Keep in mind, however, that permits are needed for construction of boardwalks in regulated wetlands.

74

Water Quality Maintenance

Natural physical, chemical, and biological processes at work in wetlands help to maintain water quality. It is important to keep two basic considerations in mind when designing wetlands to serve this function: wetlands can easily be over stressed by the input of too many pollutants, and wetlands that are used as a treatment area for polluted water can serve as an "attractive nuisance" for wildlife. Accordingly, design of wetlands for water quality purposes must be based on the concentration of the contaminants in the influent, treatment objectives, and the compatibility with other potential functions. If the primary function of the wetland is to improve water quality, then some sort of pre-treatment basin that can be physically cleaned out may be desirable to extend the life of the wetland and allow other functions to operate. Design considerations include detention time, vegetation type(s), soils, and allowances for removal of vegetation and accumulated pollutants. The effectiveness of the wetland in removing the contaminants is increased by spreading the influent evenly over the wetland, having a diversity of vegetation communities, eliminating stagnant areas, and increasing the detention time.

Sediment Control

Sediments are trapped in wetlands due to the generally flat topography and the physical structures of plants which together slow the velocity of water flowing through. Use of wetlands for sediment entrapment can benefit many downstream uses through improved water quality. However, like with excess contaminants, excess sediment load into a wetland can impair its ability to serve other wetland functions. Design of wetlands for sediment control must consider the quantity and characteristics of the sediment anticipated over the life of the project. If the expected sediment load is so great that it would require periodic removal and proper disposal of sediment, then construction of a sediment basin may be a more appropriate solution to the problem. However, the best way to deal with sedimentation is to take corrective actions at its source. There are many resources available to help landowners control erosion that may be impacting wetlands or other water resources.

Erosion Control

Wetland vegetation along the Great Lakes, inland lakes, rivers, and streams helps to control shoreline and streambank erosion in two ways: plant roots stabilize soil at the land/water interface, and the stems and leaves slow current speed and dampen wave energy. Stabilization of stream, lake, and reservoir banks and shorelines with wetland vegetation can benefit many other uses, primarily through reduction of sediment and improved water quality. In addition, wetland vegetation installed for erosion control provides habitat for wildlife, improves aesthetic and recreational values, and protects adjoining uplands from erosion. Because wetland restoration projects to control erosion are usually located in areas that are prone to erosion, they often require careful and vigilant maintenance during establishment.

Flood Storage

Wetlands trap and store water during heavy rainfall and slowly release it to downstream areas, lowering flood peaks and maintaining stream flows during dry periods. Numerous smaller wetlands in a watershed can cumulatively have a significant effect on flood water storage. Flood waters stored in wetlands with more permeable substrates can also benefit ground water recharge. When designing for flood storage, the primary factors to keep in mind are the location of your project in the watershed and the hydrology of the lake or stream system, including average and expected flood elevation and duration. Design of wetlands for flood storage can be very diverse and incorporate many other wetland functions.

75

Timber Production

With proper management, forest products can be harvested in a way that is compatible with other wetland functions and values. The habitat needs of forest species (such as the endangered Indiana Bat) should be carefully considered in planning any harvest or timber management activities. It is important to plant or assure the natural revegetation of several key indigenous cover and food-producing species that will encourage and provide habitat diversity. The effect of timber harvesting practices on other forest and wetland functions must be carefully considered. In wetlands, intensive timber harvest can impact hydrology and nutrient cycling, expose remaining trees to wind-throw, and be difficult to re-vegetate. Private consultants, forest activist organizations, and state forestry and wildlife agencies can help provide feedback on proposed timber harvest activities and development of timber management plans.

Education and Research

Wetlands are unique ecosystems that provide great outdoor classrooms to teach practically all principles of ecology and serve as important laboratories for scientific research. Education and research activities are generally compatible with other functions, although human activity may at times impair use by wildlife, particularly for sensitive species during critical times of the year. Specific design criteria may only be needed where special landscape features

must be restored or constructed to accommodate educational objectives (e.g., inclusion of deep water habitat for "pond life" exercises). Depending on the intended use of the wetland, the design may also need to consider issues related to accessibility for school groups, disabled persons, and other special circumstances.

Open Space and Aesthetic Quality

Wetlands can be areas of great diversity and beauty and provide open space for recreational and visual enjoyment. The natural beauty of wetland ecosystems can be readily designed into restored and created wetlands. Although beauty is in the eye of the beholder, designing for aesthetics generally includes the establishment of a diversity of vegetation communities, planting native flowering herbs or shrubs in highly visible areas, and allowing for a combination of near and far vistas when possible. Care must be taken to assure that any boardwalks or observation platforms blend in with the surroundings.

WETLAND RESTORATION ASSISTANCE

Although the information in this chapter may seem daunting, take heart—there is a substantial amount of assistance to help promote wetland restoration in Michigan. Thanks to the realization of the importance of wetland functions and values, and the realization of the need to restore wetlands across the landscape, there are numerous public agencies and private organizations involved with wetland restoration. The projects described below are results-oriented and focus on working with the private landowner. These programs can provide assistance to citizens, and conversely, these programs offer valuable opportunities for citizens to get involved and contribute their time and talents (and dollars!) to wetland restoration activities. Contact information is provided in the appendices.

76

Wetlands Reserve Program
Natural Resources Conservation Service

The Wetlands Reserve Program (WRP) is an important conservation component of the Farm Bill and was authorized by the Food, Agriculture, Conservation, and Trade Act of 1990. WRP is a voluntary program offering landowners a chance to receive payments for restoring wetlands. Under WRP, landowners are provided cost-share funds to restore wetlands in return for a conservation easement. Areas under easement can also include existing natural wetlands and adjacent uplands deemed necessary to protect the wetlands.

Owners of eligible lands apply for enrollment at their local NRCS or USDA Farm Services Office by declaring their intent to participate. Ducks Unlimited will assist in covering the landowner's portion of the cost-share agreement. The NRCS and the U.S. Fish and Wildlife Service (FWS) then determine the eligibility of the acres offered. Sites are ranked using a variety of priority factors, including: 1) habitat for migratory birds and other wildlife; 2) wetland functions; 3) location significance; 4) wetland management requirements; and 5) physical conditions of the site.

A Wetland Reserve Plan of Operations (WRPO) is developed for each of the high priority areas. The NRCS, with the assistance of FWS, will help landowners develop the plans. Each plan will describe intentions and objectives of restoration practices needed to accomplish the project, landowner requirements for maintaining the restored wetland values, and other details. The acceptable uses of the land after the easement is filed will also be spelled out in detail in the WRPO. No activities may degrade or diminish the wetland functions and values of the land under easement.

After completion and approval of the plan by the agencies and the landowner, the landowner may accept the amount offered by NRCS for the easement. The government's offer will be based on the appraised agricultural value of the land. Between 75-100% cost-share will be paid for restoring the wetlands and adjacent lands. Ducks Unlimited has stepped in to pay for the landowner's portion of the restoration cost. All legal costs associated with recording the easement are paid by the government.

The landowners will maintain full control over public access to and use of the WRP easement lands. The WRP easement does not open the areas to public hunting, fishing, or other forms of recreation unless the landowner desires to do so. The landowner will be responsible for maintaining the area and for paying property taxes. As with other conservation easements, the reduction in development potential should reduce the property tax burden. Landowners must request the post-easement tax assessment from their local tax assessor. When lands are sold the easement will follow the sale and the new owner assumes the easement obligations.

In Michigan, WRP is statewide. Eligible lands require an agricultural history with hydric soil types that were drained for farming practices.

Partners for Wildlife
U.S. Fish & Wildlife Service

The Partners for Wildlife program offers technical and financial assistance to landowners who wish to restore degraded wetlands, riparian corridors, streams, and other critical habitats. The program focuses primarily on reestablishment of original natural communities. Special consideration is given to projects that contribute to the objectives of the North American Waterfowl Management Plan or the National Wildlife Refuge System, or that contribute to the survival of endangered, threatened, or candidate species, or migratory birds of management concern.

Assistance may take the form of informal advice on the design and location of potential restoration projects, or it may consist of designing and funding restoration projects under a Wildlife Management Agreement with the landowner. Restoration efforts may include, but are not limited to, plugging drainage ditches, installing water control structures, constructing low dikes, fencing riparian corridors, and re-establishing grassland vegetation for nesting cover.

Before funds are spent for project construction, landowners are required to sign a Wildlife Management Agreement through which they agree to leave the habitat restoration project in place for a minimum of 10 years. Longer agreements are desirable, and may be required depending on the cost of the project. Landowners and other partners are encouraged to provide cost-share funds or in-kind services for projects. Citizen advocacy efforts to encourage restoration can support this effort, and Fish and Wildlife Service staff involved with this program can serve as excellent resources of wetland restoration expertise.

Matching Aid to Restore States Habitat (MARSH)
Ducks Unlimited

The MARSH program was instituted in 1985 to address the need to develop and protect waterfowl habitat in the United States. The MARSH program is coordinated by Ducks Unlimited, Inc. (DU) operating under principle partnerships with MDNR, U.S. Forest Service, U.S. Fish and Wildlife Service, USDA, and other private conservation groups. These funds are used to provide cost-share assistance on wetland restoration projects. This reimbursement program provides matching funds for wetland acquisition and habitat restoration and enhancement in each state based on Ducks Unlimited's income within that state.

Projects submitted for MARSH funding must significantly benefit waterfowl. Normally, all projects must be on lands under the control of a public agency or private cooperator with which DU has an approved memorandum of understanding. Control must be through ownership, lease, easement, or management agreement. Control must be adequate for protection, maintenance, and use of the project throughout its projected life.

The amount of money available to fund MARSH projects in each state is currently based on 7.5% of the sum of DU's income within that state, plus any unused money from the previous year. Accordingly, the MARSH allocation will fluctuate as DU's income fluctuates in each state. DU's goal is to match MARSH funds at least dollar for dollar by private, state, or federal sources.

78

DU will consider proposals from any public or private conservation agency or group that is 1) able to execute long-term habitat agreements, 2) capable of delivering and managing the projects proposed, and 3) willing to assume all liability associated with the project. In Michigan, the MARSH program is coordinated through the MDNR Wildlife Division. MARSH funds are also used by the U.S. Fish and Wildlife Service Field Office to cost-share wetland restoration projects on private lands (see Partners for Wildlife).

Michigan Wildlife Habitat Foundation's Private Wetlands Project

The Michigan Wildlife Habitat Foundation has an innovative wetland restoration program that involves the use of trained volunteers as well as professional staff. Trained volunteers identify potential wildlife restoration areas and help implement wetland restoration projects designed by professionals. The majority of the work involves blocking small open ditches and removing parts of underground drainage tiles to restore wetland hydrology to drained basins.

This program is conducted on private lands only. Landowners must sign an agreement that they will not reverse activities for 10 years. Although the project is focused in the southern half of Michigan's lower peninsula, it is available throughout the state. Michigan Wildlife Habitat Foundation pays for the cost of wetland restoration activity, but requires a $200 cost-share contribution from the landowner. Funds are expended on a first-come, first-served basis.

If you would like to volunteer to assist in this effort, or attend one of the Michigan Wildlife Habitat Foundation wetland restoration training sessions, contact the Foundation (see Appendix A).

Wetland Protection Spotlight

Michigan Wildlife Habitat Foundation
Dennis Fijalkowski

If you travel on Route 27, eight miles north of St. Johns where the highway crosses the Maple River, to the west you will see Mileander Marsh, which consists of over 400 acres of wetland. Here bald eagles nest and ospreys hunt, great blue herons roost, and over 200 cormorants summer. But before 1984, none of these birds were there.

In 1984, the still-young Michigan Wildlife Habitat Foundation transformed an old agricultural field into the bastion of biological diversity that it is today. This was, in fact, the largest private-sector restoration project ever done in the State of Michigan. Dennis Fijalkowski, co-founder of the group, points to this project as testimony to the incredible potential for wildlife habitat restoration. "This is something we are very proud of. And it's indicative of what can be done. These animals are just waiting for places. Just give them the water and they'll be back."

The Michigan Wildlife Habitat Foundation is a membership organization founded in 1982, during the economic recession and the beginning of the Reagan era when agency budgets were being slashed. Seeing a need to ensure that wildlife habitat be restored, regardless of the whims of agency funding, they organized with the mission to "restore and enhance living space for wild creatures."

79

The group is small—only two full-time staff and several part-time and seasonal workers. But they've been able to achieve a lot with very little, restoring over 5,600 acres of wetlands since their founding. The group has, indeed, discovered the demand for their services has far out-weighed what they have been able to supply.

In addition to private landowners, the group has also been working with nature centers, schools, zoos, and a national wildlife refuge. Dennis is particularly excited about the school project, which seeks to bring nature closer to the city. Not surprising, considering that Dennis grew up in the city himself. "I've always been interested in wildlife," he recalls. "I grew up in the inner city, but it was always in me. I had some connection with the land that was inexplicable, even growing up in the city.... I was always catching snakes and frogs. I flushed my first pheasant along a railroad track in Detroit." The group has created and improved habitat at over 100 school sites, most of them in large cities. "We're trying to take wildlife opportunities to kids where they are....The feedback has just been phenomenal."

The group has been hard at work on the Bengal Wildlife Center in Bath, Michigan. This center serves as a training facility and demonstration site for the Foundation to teach others how to restore habitat. Trainings are geared toward a very wide range of people—landowners, architects, developers, engineers, foresters, farmers, and citizen groups. The Foundation holds classes, and also provides the hands-on experience crucial for this work. "If they have questions about a project, we can go get a backhoe from the barn, dig it up, and show them how to put it in," Dennis says.

The Foundation hopes that this center will allow them to expand their efforts without becoming a big, bureaucratic organization. They also hope that the center will give the people that are altering the landscape the tools to minimize their impact, and to be able to recognize potential restoration sites.

While a certain amount of knowledge is required for successful restoration work, Dennis is quick to not discourage people from learning these skills and getting involved in restoration. "It's not rocket science, that's for sure," he notes. "But there is some level of experience you need. It's more than just reading. There's a learning curve involved…But I don't want to discourage anyone from doing this."

The Bengal Wildlife Center, he hopes, will help interested people get this training. In addition, he hopes that citizen advocates will help to encourage developers and others to attend the Center's trainings.

For more information about the Michigan Wildlife Habitat Foundation or the Bengel Wildlife Center, contact:
6380 Drumheller Road
P.O. Box 393
Bath, MI 48808
Phone: (517) 641-7677
Fax: (517) 641-7877
e-mail: wildlife@mwhf.org
website: www.mwhf.org

80

Chapter 7 Education and Outreach

Wetlands are some of Michigan's most valuable landforms. However, the functions and values that wetlands provide are poorly understood by the vast majority of Michigan residents. Education is an integral part of any successful wetland protection program. Informed citizens will serve to raise the overall awareness about wetland values and functions and generate public support for wetland protection efforts. Wetland protection advocates are critical in providing information regarding wetland functions, values, and regulations to the other members of their communities. Citizens can focus in the following topic areas to help protect wetlands through education and awareness raising:

1) The functions and values that wetlands provide;

2) Wetland policies, including legislation and regulatory guidelines;

3) Opportunities for involvement in the process of planning, regulation, and management of wetland resources;

4) Opportunities for involvement in incentive options to achieve wetlands conservation; and

5) Effective restoration, protection, and management techniques for wetland resources.

In order to develop an effective educational campaign, wetland protection advocates must consider the most appropriate educational mechanisms for each of the target audiences they are seeking to educate.

MECHANISMS AND MATERIALS

There are many educational materials and mechanisms available to the citizen wetland protection advocate. The list below provides an overview of the types of educational mechanisms and materials that are currently available.

1) **Newsletters:** Newsletters can be effective in sharing information between people or groups regarding wetlands. Newsletters such as *Great Lakes Aquatic Habitat News* carry stories about how wetlands have been protected across the Great Lakes basin. *The National Wetlands Newsletter* is a great source for current science and policy. Most environmental organizations in Michigan involved with wetland protection publish periodic newsletters that often contain information relevant to wetland protection.

2) **Publications:** Many government and nongovernment agencies publish informational booklets and brochures regarding wetlands and wetland protection. These publications serve as excellent resource documents.

82

3) **News Media:** Newspapers, and radio and television news play a very important role in informing the public about various issues and forming public opinion. Although the quest to get a "good scoop" on behalf of news media can tend to result in biased reporting on an issue, wetland advocates can utilize the media to focus attention on wetland protection. Citizens can provide the media with press releases about recent newsworthy wetland events, provide pertinent "human interest" pieces on wetland values and functions, and encourage editorials in support of wetlands protection. In situations where a particular paper presents wetland issues in a biased manner, citizens can respond with letters to the editor or guest editorials. Conversely, citizens should also take the time to compliment thorough and balanced coverage of wetland issues. Citizens involved in wetland protection should develop a good working relationship with the local media, which will help to ensure that wetland stories are reported in a fair manner.

4) **Radio and Television Public Service Announcements:** As part of their licensing requirements, radio and television stations must devote a certain portion of their broadcast time to public service announcements. Wetland protection advocates can use this mechanism to educate the general public regarding wetland values and protection. Radio stations will usually read a written public service announcement on the air. Community access cable stations may provide free training and use of video production equipment. Professional video public service announcements can be produced commercially. Corporate sponsors can be obtained to help cover production costs and air them during prime time viewing hours.

5) **Television and Video:** Video is a very powerful public education tool. There are several wetland videos available that can be aired on community access television or viewed by various groups throughout the state. In addition, wetland protection advocates can encourage local commercial broadcast stations to provide quality programming regarding wetland functions and values. There are many opportunities for cooperation between the private sector, nonprofit organizations, and government on the production of educational wetland videos. Given the quality of "consumer" equipment, decent videos can be produced at relatively low cost.

6) **Curricula Programs:** Programs that provide complete educational materials and clear implementation strategies have been well received by teachers and school systems. Classroom materials on wetland values and functions are widely available. Educational curricula that provides students with an opportunity to solve problems related to wetland protection or read about how other people have solved wetland protection problems can help students develop skills that can be used to protect wetlands in the future. An Internet search using keywords "wetlands" and "education" will provide dozens of potential classroom materials.

83

7) **Workshops:** Citizen organizations can coordinate and present workshops to educate the public, local officials, developers, or wetlands activists about programs to protect wetlands. Interactive workshops provide an opportunity for participants to ask questions and engage themselves in the material. Workshops that are cooperatively sponsored by different entities (e.g., environmental organizations and regulatory agencies) can have wide appeal to different target groups and help to build wetland protection coalitions. For a workshop to be successful, the information presented must be relevant and tailored to the audience. There are several professional wetlands training firms in the United States that provide technical wetlands courses. In addition, professional conferences provide the opportunity to present programs or attend workshops.

8) **Demonstration Projects:** Practically any ongoing wetland protection and management activity can be turned into a demonstration project. Successful restoration projects can be used to demonstrate techniques to other landowners who are considering wetland restoration. To be most effective, the projects should be presented through either on-site workshops or detailed publications. They should be done in such a manner that the critical practices are clear, including ways in which those practices can be replicated in other situations.

9) **Wetland Manuals for Decision Makers:** Many officials, elected or appointed, are often unaware of laws, policies, regulations, plans, programs, authorities, references, or incentives covering wetlands use and management. The Tip of the Mitt Watershed Council has developed educational manuals for citizens, landowners, and for local officials. Similarly, several national organizations, including the Izaak Walton League, the Environmental Law Institute, and the National Wildlife Federation have developed wetland protection manuals.

10) **"Adopt a Wetland" Programs:** Several organizations in Michigan have initiated waterbody adoption programs. Although the exact nature and focus of these programs vary, they all provide the opportunities for local citizens or youth groups to "adopt" an aquatic resource and act as environmental stewards. By extending these programs to wetlands, citizens will learn more about a particular resource, and be more motivated to protect it. The second half of this chapter describes some potential activities for "adopting a wetland."

11) **Field Trips:** The ecology, functions, and values of wetlands can be best appreciated when experienced first hand. Field trips to local wetlands can provide excellent opportunities to learn about all aspects of wetlands in a manner that encourages individuals to appreciate their unique qualities.

12) **Phone Hotline:** The EPA has set up a toll-free phone number (1-800-832-7828) that citizens, developers, and/or local government officials can call for information about wetland values, existing policy, incentive programs, and the status of wetlands policy and legislation. On the local or statewide level, such a Hotline could be developed and used to provide information specific to wetlands regulations in Michigan, status of individual project applications, or to report wetland violations.

13) **Billboards:** Public service messages to protect, wisely manage, and value wetlands could be placed on billboards, at transit stops, or on rapid transit lines in both urban and rural areas. Pithy, memorable quotes could convey messages to promote wetland protection. Some examples include: "Wetlands – They're Too Precious to Waste," "Environmentally Safe (Wildlife) Housing in Your Community," "Wetlands – Lifestyles for the Wet and Famous," or "Wetlands are Not Wastelands." Although this mechanism can be expensive, and may be at odds with citizen organizations seeking to preserve scenic vistas by removing billboard blight, some advertising agencies may offer a reduced cost for public service messages.

14) **Bumper Stickers** (or buttons, iron-on T-shirt decals, sun shields for cars, etc.): These could convey similar pithy, quickly read, memorable ideas about wetlands conservation, to sensitize a broad spectrum of the public to issues, concerns, and remedies.

TARGET AUDIENCES

Each community's wetland educational needs will vary. For example, in a community where there have been several unpermitted wetland fills, efforts to educate the contractors engaging in the unauthorized activities would be appropriate. In a township that is about to engage in developing a local wetland protection ordinance, it is essential that the planning commission, township board, and other township officials are well versed regarding wetland protection options and the elements of a sound wetland protection ordinance. To ensure that the next generation is aware of wetlands and supportive of their protection, educational efforts that are directed toward school-aged children are important. Although each situation is different, several ideas regarding educational strategies for critical target audiences are provided below.

1) **Private Landowners:** Since wetland owners are ultimately responsible for activities that degrade wetlands, they are possibly the single most important individuals to reach with wetlands education materials. Landowners are being asked to move beyond awareness to personal action, and to accept individual responsibility for preserving wetlands. All landowners should be aware of the standards that regulate activities in Michigan's wetlands. Landowners who are being asked to participate in voluntary protection programs need to be informed about wetland values and the ecological importance of protecting wetlands. In addition, information regarding the financial incentives that can result from permanent wetland protection must be made clear.

2) **Developers and Contractors:** Developers and contractors provide a critical link in the wetland protection process. Although the individual landowners are ultimately responsible, it is usually a developer or contractor who is actually engaging in activities that degrade wetlands. Programs for this target group should focus on regulatory standards and best management practices. Since the relationship between wetland advocates and developers is

85

often adversarial, educational programs or workshops that are jointly sponsored by environmental organizations and members of the development community, or by regulatory staff, tend to be more effective than those sponsored by an environmental group alone.

3) **Realtors:** Realtors can also be a critical link in the wetland protection process. Realtors can be instrumental in informing land purchasers regarding the functions, values, and regulatory constraints related to wetland property. Local boards of Realtors meetings provide valuable opportunities to present workshops or programs regarding wetland identification, values, and regulations.

4) **Local Governments:** Local government officials are important target audiences for wetland protection. In situations where municipalities are considering local wetland protection programs or regulations, they will need solid information regarding all aspects of wetland regulation, including functions and values, wetland definitions and delineation methods, and state and federal regulatory standards. Even in those communities that are not considering local wetlands regulation, local government officials play an important role in wetlands protection. Not only are local governments given the opportunity to comment on dredge and fill applications, but their local planning and zoning decisions can have severe impacts on locally significant wetland resources. Efforts to educate local government officials should focus on the wetland values that benefit the local residents (e.g., the cost savings of using intact wetlands for flood prevention). It is also important to remember that there is an extremely high "turnover" rate on local government boards and commissions. As a result, educating this target group is an ongoing process.

5) **Regulators:** It is unrealistic for the citizen activist to expect that those charged with implementing wetlands regulations have expertise in all aspects of wetlands ecology and management. Regulatory staff are seldom granted the opportunity to attend workshops and seminars to enhance their knowledge and skills. Corps and MDEQ officials benefit from information provided by wetland advocates regarding local regulations that impact wetland protection, recent scientific advances, and policy changes at all levels. Citizens will benefit by cultivating positive information sharing relationships with the regulatory staff who serve their area.

6) **School-Aged Children:** Although school-aged children don't normally participate in the protection activities described in this guidebook, they are nevertheless essential target audiences. Educating today's children on wetland values and functions will ensure that tomorrow's voters and professionals make informed decisions regarding wetland protection and management. In addition, not all benefits that come from educating school-aged children are realized after a child is grown. It has been shown that a child's awareness of environmental issues also serves to raise the awareness of the adults with whom he or she interacts.

The biological productivity and diversity that wetlands represent provide excellent outdoor classrooms to teach practically all key concepts of ecology and biology. Educational programs for school-aged children should provide the opportunity to experience wetlands first hand. To help build important decision-making and action-taking skills, educational programs should provide students with the opportunity to engage in wetland protection activities or provide examples of how other individuals have successfully worked to protect wetlands.

7) **Conservation and Environmental Organizations:** There are many conservation and environmental organizations that are not currently involved in wetland protection. Efforts should be made to provide them with the necessary informational tools to empower them to play a positive role in protecting wetlands. It is critical that even individuals and organizations who are working to protect wetlands continue to raise their level of awareness and understanding of wetland ecology, regulation, nonregulatory protection mechanisms, and successful protection strategies. Each year, numerous professional workshops, courses, and conferences on wetland topics provide valuable education opportunities. As wetland protection advocates gain more expertise, their level of effectiveness and credibility will increase.

8) **The General Citizenry:** Although all the individuals in the target audiences listed above are citizens, there are millions of Michigan residents who don't fall into any of the above categories. Efforts should be made to inform these individuals regarding the values that wetlands provide and the importance of protecting

87

them. This overall awareness raising will provide an informed citizenry that will support regulatory and non-regulatory wetland protection efforts. Mechanisms that have broad public outreach and appeal such as television or print media should be utilized as much as possible.

Whether it is through the reduced risk of flooding, clean water for drinking or swimming, a successful duck hunt, or a peaceful sunset over a marsh, every Michigan resident and visitor benefits from the functions that wetlands provide. Efforts to increase the awareness of wetlands will serve to deepen the appreciation, respect, and protection that wetlands are provided. Citizen wetland protection advocates can initiate these projects on their own, through the work of a local wetlands protection team, or through existing environmental organizations.

ADOPTING-A-WETLAND

88

Perhaps the best way to deepen your knowledge of wetlands, and to share that knowledge with others, is to get to know a particular wetland intimately. As your knowledge grows, so too will your appreciation. Many organizations in Michigan, such as the Huron River Watershed Council, have successful "Adopt-A-Stream" programs. These programs provide valuable opportunities for local citizens or youth groups to "adopt" a stream and become environmental stewards of it. By learning about a particular resource, they are more motivated to protect it. Likewise, wetlands on public or private land, with permission of the landowner, government agency, or resource manager, can be "adopted." The activities below are offered in an effort to encourage the development of "Adopt-A-Wetland" programs and to help you learn more about the wetlands you are working to protect.

It is important, however, to remind ourselves that trampling or over-use of an area can reduce its ecological functions. You surely don't want to "love your wetland to death." For example, intense human use of an area may adversely impact use of the area by wildlife. By using caution and being sensitive to disturbing vegetation and wildlife, you will increase your overall enjoyment of the area.

OBSERVE WILDLIFE

Providing wildlife habitat is one of the most important wetland functions. The diversity of habitat types found within wetlands makes them attractive to more species of wildlife than any other ecosystem type. Wetland adopters can be blessed with sights and sounds that most people do not have the opportunity to experience: a mallard duck herding her ducklings into the cattails, the chorus of spring peepers ushering in an April twilight, or the snake-like movements of a hunting mink.

Frog and Toad Surveys

If you are interested in exploring the frogs and toads that use your wetland, the Michigan Department of Natural Resources (MDNR) Natural Heritage Program is coordinating a state-wide Frog and Toad Survey program. This innovative program was initiated in response to a growing awareness and concern about globally declining amphibian populations. The objective is to monitor state-wide the long-term population trends of native species of frogs and toads.

Those who participate in the program are provided with a tape recording that identifies the calls of native frog and toad species. A survey route consisting of 10 sites in wetlands is established and is monitored three times during the amphibian's breeding season, which is generally between April and early to mid-July (exact times vary from year to year, and depend on the location within the state). Participants record weather conditions, water temperatures, and after listening at each site for 3-5 minutes, a call index for each species heard. The call index provides a measurement of the abundance of each identified species.

If you are interested in participating in the state-wide Frog and Toad Survey as part of learning more about your wetland, contact:

**Wildlife Division
Michigan Department
of Natural Resources
Natural Heritage Program**

P.O. Box 30180
Lansing, MI 48909
(517) 373-9418

Observing wildlife and making a list of species that you see or hear is a great way to start exploring your adopted wetland. All you'll need is a pencil and note pad; clothes appropriate for weather, wetness conditions, and biting insects (not all wetland animals are cute and cuddly!); a pair of binoculars; a few field guides; and some time. Perhaps the most important item on this list is time. Like hunting, successful wildlife observation requires us to take enough time to become part of the landscape. When we quietly fade into the background of the wetland, the wildlife suddenly emerge and we are given front-row seats to experience the drama of nature.

Your list of wildlife species should include the date and time of day the animal was seen and the number of individuals observed. Although the hour before sunset and the hour after sunrise are considered "magic hours" for wildlife observation, you might find it interesting to observe wildlife at different times of the day. Ideally, you will be able to observe your wetland throughout the year. This way you'll be able to discover what different animals use the wetland during different seasons. In addition to the names of animals, you can include notes on what the animals are doing. Are they building nests, foraging for food, or interacting with other animals? Don't forget to include frogs, butterflies, and other smaller creatures on your wildlife list. Often we overlook these animals for more charismatic fauna, but they too can be very interesting and entertaining to observe with our eyes and ears.

Your list doesn't need to be limited to animals that you actually see or hear. Keep lists of signs of wildlife as well. Animal tracks, bird nests, feathers or hair, and scat (droppings) also should be included in the list since it may be difficult to view many of the wildlife species that use your wetland. You may consider putting in a viewing blind where you can sit quietly and wait for wildlife to appear. Your blind should be made in a way that it blends into its surroundings. Volunteer wetland monitoring programs such as the

89

MDNR's Frog and Toad Survey and the Marsh Monitoring Program developed at the Long Point Observatory in Ontario employ a "route" that is consistently walked at specific times to observe wildlife. This is a good way to get consistent observations of wildlife in your wetland in a way that allows you to objectively compare observation visits. To set up your own route, try to make sure that you cover each different habitat type in your wetland and locate the route so that important habitat or sensitive vegetation communities do not become trampled.

Because you can use your ears to "see" them, birds can be especially interesting to observe. Find a spot to sit comfortably and quietly, close your eyes, and listen. As the echoes of the farm machinery, office, or job site fade from your ears, how many different bird sounds do you hear? Can you see the birds making the calls? Can you identify the different birds by only their song? Do not be discouraged if you cannot identify all the bird calls. There are many bird call training tapes available from mail order catalogs, wild bird specialty shops, and organizations such as the National Audubon Society. When you learn bird calls, you will be amazed at how much more you hear when you are in your wetland. If you find that birding really appeals to you, you might want to participate in the annual breeding bird survey. For information, contact your local Audubon Society chapter.

If you have permanent open water in your adopted wetland, or your wetland is adjacent to a lake or stream, then fish may be an important component of the wildlife that you can observe. Most fish

90

in Michigan utilize wetlands for some portion of their life cycle and they are a very important part of the food chain for other animals. Your ability to observe fish will depend on a variety of factors, including time of year, clarity of water, accessibility, species of fish using the wetland, and glare from sunlight off the water. Perhaps the most exciting time of the year to observe fish in wetlands is during the spring spawning season. Large fish such as northern pike, largemouth bass, long-nosed gar, and carp spawn in or near wetlands. During daylight hours, observation can be enhanced by wearing polarized lenses. Since many large fish are most active during the night, a spotlight and a rowboat can be a very effective combination for seeing fish spawning and feeding in wetlands.

INVESTIGATE VEGETATION

The types of plants that grow in a wetland greatly influence the habitat for wildlife and play a critical role in such important wetland functions as flood storage and water quality protection by nutrient and sediment retention. There are several different ways to explore and assess wetland vegetation.

Species Diversity

One reason why wetlands provide excellent wildlife habitat is because many different plants grow there. Making a plant list is probably the simplest way to explore the plant diversity of your adopted wetland. Like the wildlife list, keep track of the plants you see as you visit your wetland.

91

Get Involved in Statewide Bird Surveys!

Michigan Audubon Society (MAS), the state's oldest conservation organization, annually seeks new and continuing volunteers to participate in two ongoing bird surveys:

MAS Winter Bird Feeder Survey
Each winter, hundreds of Michigan naturalists count the various species of birds visiting their feeders. Participants in the survey count the maximum number of species they observe at their feeder location at any one time—on one day during the months of November through April.

MAS Seasonal Bird Survey
This annual survey is a tradition spanning more than 70 years. It allows individuals to participate to the level and degree that they choose. You can cover as much area or as little as you like. Survey birds regularly or infrequently. Count all species observed or just those that interest you.

The goal of both surveys is to determine and document changes in the seasonal distribution and abundance of Michigan's bird populations and to monitor their long-term population fluctuations.

If you would like to participate, contact:

MAS Winter Bird Feeder Survey
Kalamazoo Nature Center
7000 N. Westnedge Ave.
Kalamazoo, MI 49004
(616) 381-1574

MAS Seasonal Bird Survey
6011 W. St. Joseph Hwy.,
Suite 403
P.O. Box 80527
Lansing, MI 48908-0527
(517) 886-9144

If you can't identify a specific plant, make a sketch of it and note some of its characteristics so you can include it in the list and identify it later. Some identifying characteristics include flower type and color, height, leaf shape, and whether it is woody. There are many very useful plant identification guides that will help you to identify Michigan's plants. Some of them have step-wise keys that lead you through a process to help you identify a particular plant. If you've never used a plant key before, it's helpful to practice by using it to "identify" plants that you already know.

In scientific terms, diversity is a single measure with two different components: the number of species (termed richness); and the distribution of individuals among species (termed evenness). In simple terms, a truly diverse vegetation community has a lot of different species and the individual populations of each species are fairly even. So, in addition to simply listing the species, it is often helpful to quantify how many of each species there are in a given area. There are many ways to do this, ranging from counting individual plants to estimating percent aerial cover. When you determine the relative abundance of each of the plant species present, you can then determine the dominant plant species. Dominant species are those which, when ranked in descending order of their abundance and cumulatively totaled, exceed 50 percent of the total, plus any species comprising 20 percent or more of the total. Knowing the dominant plant species is helpful when characterizing a wetland. For example, a swamp is typically identified by its dominant plant species (e.g., a red-maple swamp or a lowland conifer swamp where cedar and balsam fir are dominant).

It might be interesting to compare the diversity of plant life in a wetland to other ecosystems. One way to do this is to count herbaceous plant stems in randomly located equal-sized plots. The simplest way to do this is to build a wooden frame or hoop of plastic tubing (of a manageable size—for example, a small "hula-hoop" would be fine) to

be placed on the ground in different habitats. Randomly place the frame or hoop anywhere in your wetland, and count the numbers of different plants you find there. It is not necessary to identify the plants, just note the number of different species and how many of each there are. Do this in several locations throughout the wetland. Take the same frame and do the same tests in other surroundings (e.g., upland forest, old field, etc). Although there are some types of wetlands where this sort of analysis will not work very well (e.g., a monotypical cattail stand or the understory of a densely shaded swamp where not much grows on the ground), most of the time you should find there is much more variety in the wetland—proof again of the diversity of these ecosystems.

Vegetation Communities

As you investigate the vegetation in your adopted wetland, you will notice that certain species of plants are located in discrete locations and are usually found in association with certain other plant species. These associations of plants are referred to as communities. Plant communities reflect a variety of factors: soils, water table depth, water quality, characteristics of adjacent water bodies, slope, aspect, and adjacent land use. Sometimes these vegetation communities are distinct (such as a shrub-scrub swamp alongside a sedge meadow). Other times they are harder to identify (such as a hardwood swamp that has been logged in the recent past adjacent to a shrub-scrub swamp). As you become more familiar with the types of vegetation in your wetland, you will start to understand the underlying reasons for each of the communities. For example, you may note that the tag alders and willows only grow in soil that is saturated to the surface all year, whereas the cedars grow on somewhat higher and dryer sites.

To visualize the "big picture" of the vegetation in your wetland, it is helpful to map the various vegetation communities. This can be done by making a simple sketch of your wetland which indicates where the vegetation changes occur. A more detailed map can be developed by walking transects and indicating the precise distances from a baseline where each vegetation community change occurs. The distances are then translated onto a scaled map. No matter how you make your vegetation community map, the key to a good one is that it provides a reasonable representation of the vegetation communities in your wetland. A map of the vegetation communities provides useful information regarding the diversity of wildlife habitat that your wetland provides. In addition, plant community diversity (also called interspersion) can be important with respect to water quality and flood storage. Different plant communities slow water and uptake nutrients in different ways. Areas with high interspersion are able to take advantage of the differences in how each plant community functions. As a result, the entire wetland provides flood storage and water quality maintenance functions in a more comprehensive manner.

As noted in Chapter 2, Michigan's wetlands provide habitat for more than half of Michigan's rare, threatened, or endangered plant species. As with threatened and endangered animal species, if your adopted wetland is home to threatened or endangered plants, you have a unique opportunity to be steward of a very rare resource. If you think you may have found threatened or endangered plants, contact the Michigan Natural Heritage Program, Wildlife Division, Michigan Department of Natural Resources or the U.S. Fish and Wildlife Service Field Office in East Lansing. Agency staff can provide information and help develop management plans to protect these valuable species.

DEFINE YOUR WATERSHED

A watershed (also called a drainage basin) is the geographic area that drains to a single water body. A large watershed, such as that for Saginaw Bay, is made up of many smaller watersheds (e.g., Shiawassee River, Tittabawassee River, etc.). How your adopted wetland is situated in the watershed influences its function. The United States EPA maintains a database on their website of thousands of watersheds across the country. Point your browser to www.epa.gov/surf to see what information is available on your watershed.

Determining what lands drain to your adopted wetland is a fairly simple process. A good 7.5 minute topographic map (1:25,000 scale) and your own knowledge of the watershed are all it takes.

Once you have the topographic map(s) for your area, find the location of your wetland on the map. In most cases the wetland will be at a low elevation and the surrounding land will rise (the numbers on the lines of the topographic map will increase as you go away from your wetland). Because topographic maps only have general wetland boundaries identified, you might need to consult some of the other resources listed in Chapter 3 (e.g., NWI Map) to better determine the size and shape of your wetland. Now, draw a line on the map that encompasses all the lands that "shed" water to your wetland. One way to do this involves starting at the north end of your wetland and, moving northerly, follow the rising topography lines until you reach the spot where the land elevation is the greatest. The highest elevation point marks the edge of the wetland's watershed in this direction. The water that falls on land north of this spot will flow away from your wetland; that which falls south of it will flow toward your wetland. Use this same exercise to mark the southern, eastern, and western boundaries of the watershed. Keep repeating this procedure in different directions from your wetland until the dots on the topographic map start to reveal the watershed. Then connect the dots with a line that follows the land's high points. This is the boundary of your watershed. (It should be noted that given the scale of even the best topo maps, this process might not work for very small wetlands, as the actual watershed boundary may not be revealed in the map's resolution.)To check your watershed mapping, tour your wetland's watershed and compare your boundary with identifiable landscape features such as roads, hilltops, lakes, streams, etc. Remember to ask permission before entering private properties.

Once you have determined what land drains to your adopted wetland, it will be easier to determine what or who may be affecting the wetland. You may want to continue working with your map, labeling or marking where different activities are occurring, and thinking about the likely effects. Essentially, what you are doing is mapping land use and cover type. To do this, consider where current activities that benefit or may harm your wetland are occurring. Where is the intact forest cover? Is there a new subdivision or a plan for one in the watershed? How about shopping malls and their associated runoff? What fields are irrigated nearby? Are there animals pastured close to streams or lakes? Are there abandoned fields? Where is manure being spread or fertilizers and pesticides being sprayed? Where have you seen dredging activities in nearby wetlands or water bodies?

93

When you've identified the lands and activities that affect your adopted wetland, then you can take an active stewardship role and work with others to cooperatively manage and protect the wetland and the larger ecosystem. An alternative to creating your own maps of the land use and cover type in your watershed may be to acquire a copy of the MIRIS map for your area. Although MIRIS maps are somewhat outdated, they do provide a good snapshot of land use and cover type. However, keep in mind that MIRIS maps were not developed on a watershed basis.

Now, looking beyond the area that directly drains your adopted wetland, use the topographic map to determine how your wetland is situated in the larger watershed. Depending on the watershed size, you may need to look at several topographic maps. First, determine the streams, rivers, and lakes to which your wetland is connected. Then, using the same procedure used to map the watershed boundary of your wetland, map the watershed boundary of the water bodies to which your wetland is connected. Once this is complete, you can see how your wetland fits into the larger watershed. Alternatively, contact the MDEQ and request a copy of their map of the major watersheds and subwatersheds in Michigan.

Coupled with a knowledge of surrounding land use, location in the watershed is important when assessing wetland functions such as flood storage, fish and wildlife habitat, and water quality protection. For example, wetlands in the upper reaches of a watershed are generally considered to be more important to flood storage, whereas wetlands directly adjacent to lakes and streams in more developed areas lower in the watershed are generally considered more important to water quality.

You may find that your wetland is not connected to any other surface water body. In this case, you may have a bog or other type of isolated wetland. Isolated wetlands provide many important functions, including habitat for rare, threatened, and endangered species, oases for wildlife in developed areas, critical water storage, and ground water recharge in some cases. Because many of these functions are dependent upon adjacent land use and proximity to other wetlands and water bodies, it still may be informative to map land use and cover type in the area.

94

GET YOUR HANDS DIRTY!

By exploring the soils in your adopted wetland, you get a glimpse into the past and can start to understand how the three indicators of wetlands (hydrophytic vegetation, wetland hydrology, and hydric soils) are connected. Soil type is one of the most useful "clues" used to determine whether an area is a wetland. This is because the soils that form under saturated or wet conditions are distinctly different from other soils. A primary difference is the rate at which organic matter (dead plants, leaves, etc.) is decomposed. Both aerobic (requires presence of free oxygen) and anaerobic (does not require free oxygen) bacteria decompose organic matter (mostly carbon compounds). However, decomposition in aerobic conditions happens much more quickly. In upland soils, the spaces between the soil particles are filled with air (which contains plenty of oxygen). Therefore, decomposition is relatively rapid. In saturated soils water replaces the air in the spaces, leaving little or no oxygen available to soil bacteria. As a result, the organic matter decomposes very slowly and accumulates as mucks or peats.

You can observe this by digging a soil pit in your wetland. The soil pit should be large enough to allow you to see several feet down into your wetland. Most wetland soils have an upper layer made up of peat or muck. Muck and peat are composed of the same thing—partially decomposed vegetation. However, the organic matter in mucks have undergone more decomposition than peats. Mucky soils are very dark—sometimes almost black—and feel greasy when rubbed between your fingers. Peats are not as decomposed and usually appear brown in color. When you rub peat between your fingers, you can feel fibers from long-dead vegetation and may be able to make out bits and pieces of grass, wood, and other organic material.

As mentioned in Chapter 3, the soil in your wetland may have a strong odor similar to rotten eggs. In wetland soils that have a mineral component (a layer of clay or sand often located under the layer of peat or muck), you might observe soil color features known as mottling or gleying. Gleyed soils are identified by dull bluish, greenish, or grayish colors. Gleyed soils form when soils are saturated almost all of the time. Mottled soils are identified by a combination of brightly colored splotches of soil in a dull soil matrix. Mottles form due to the movement of ions in the soil column when soils are alternatively saturated and unsaturated during the growing season. Compare these soil characteristics to a soil pit you dig on dry upland ground. Note differences in color, depth of organic material, texture, smell, and wetness. Depending on the amount of iron in your upland soils, it may appear to be a bright reddish-gold color. Because the upland soil, unlike wetland soils, has plenty of oxygen, the iron is oxidized (or rusted). It is for this reason that many wetland consultants tell their clients to "go for the gold" when determining where to locate houses, roads, and other developments.

95

EXPLORE HYDROLOGY

Water is the driving force in wetland ecosystems. The presence and duration of water in the soil column and on the surface of the ground influences the soils that form there and the plants that grow there. However, unlike plants that are rooted and relatively easy to identify, and unlike soils that form over thousands of years and can be investigated at any time, wetland hydrology is constantly in flux and difficult to assess.

Ground Water

One way to begin to understand what's happening in regard to your adopted wetland's hydrology is to monitor the water table. You may have already encountered your water table when digging your soil pit. Did you notice any of the indicators of wetland hydrology mentioned in Chapter 3?

Wetland hydrology fluctuates from season to season under the influence of a variety of factors, including rainfall, evapotranspiration from vegetation, temperature, and land use activities in the watershed.

Water Table Well

Screw Cap Top

2″ PVC Pipe

Band Saw Slits

36″

Cap Bottom

The simplest way to measure this fluctuation is to install a water table well. A water table well is simply a tube with many small holes or slits in it that is vertically sunk into the ground. Because the slits in the tube let water in, the ground water level in the tube is representative of the ground water level in the soil. On a periodic basis (once every week or so), the water table level is measured, by placing a yard stick into the tube, with the measurements being referenced to the surface of the ground. The measurements are then placed on a graph that has the measurements on the vertical axis and the date on the horizontal axis. The resulting line shows the fluctuation in water table depth throughout the year. From this information, you can determine just how long the ground water is influencing the root zone of the wetland.

Surface Water

If your adopted wetland has areas of open water or a stream running through it, a similar procedure can be utilized to measure the fluctuations in the level of the surface water. Instead of a water table well, you can install what is called a staff gauge. A staff gauge is simply a device to measure surface water fluctuation from a fixed point. A useful staff gauge could simply be a metal rod that is hammered securely into the bottom of the wetland to serve as a reference point (measurements of water levels are made with a separate ruler and based on plus or minus the reference point), or a metal ruler that is attached to a secure post or other immovable object in the water. The location and structure of any staff gauge (if it is intended to be used from year to year) should be selected to withstand projected water flows and the ice that comes with Michigan's winters. As with the water table well, the staff gauge data can be graphed to show the seasonal fluctuations. In addition, it is also interesting to compare this information with local rainfall data to get an idea of how the water in your wetland is influenced by precipitation and how it may serve as a flood water retention area.

In addition to water levels, if you have a stream entering or leaving your wetland, you may be able to take stream flow (or discharge) measurements to estimate the amount of water coming in and out of your wetland via the stream. The first step in taking stream flow measurements is to measure the stream's velocity. To measure the velocity, you'll need a tape measure or a 50-foot rope length, a highly-visible object that will float freely (an orange works fine), and a stopwatch. Pick a section of stream that is not backed up by a dam or debris. Measure 50 feet along the stream bank, drop the orange into the middle of the stream, and record the time it takes for the orange to travel the 50 feet. Do this three times and calculate the average time it takes the orange to travel the distance.

Divide the distance (50 feet) by the average time and you will know the approximate speed the water is moving in feet per second. If your stream is moving very slowly, or if you can't find a uniform 50-foot stretch, you might need to reduce the distance. Any timed distance will work adequately. This procedure gives you the surface velocity. The average velocity for the entire column of water is usually a bit slower—approximately 80 percent of the surface velocity.

The next step is to determine how much water is moving at that velocity. To do this, you must first measure the cross-sectional area of the stream. Pick a spot on the stream that is representative of the area where you took the speed measurement. Going across this point perpendicular to the stream flow, measure the total stream width.

Next, use a yardstick to measure the depth of the stream at consistent intervals across the stream (one-foot intervals work fine). Average these measurements to give you an average stream depth. The average depth multiplied by the width gives a rough estimate of the cross-sectional area of the stream (in square feet). This value, when multiplied by the speed the stream is flowing (in feet per second) gives you the volume of water that is flowing past that spot (referred to as the stream's discharge) in cubic feet per second (cfs).

If you have a stream flowing through your wetland, try to determine stream flow both upstream and downstream and compare the difference. If you have many different streams coming into your wetland and only one leaving, you'll have to calculate all incoming streams and add them together before you can compare the quantity of incoming flow to outgoing flow. If the difference is very large, you can assume your wetland is either storing water or releasing water. Try this during different times of the year to see whether

there are changes with wet or dry conditions. Some wetlands store water during some parts of the year and release water at others. For many larger streams in Michigan, the United States Geological Survey has recorded stream levels and discharge data. Contact your local government to see if recorded data exists for your stream.

It should be noted that the above activity is not recommended in streams that have mucky bottoms. The reasons for this are two-fold: 1) wading in muck in the middle of the stream will stir up sediments, and 2) mucky stream bottoms do not provide sure footing.

CAPTURE IT IN PHOTOS

With all the wonderful wildlife and plant species available, wetlands are a great place to practice nature photography. Photographs also can be used to document the changes that take place in your adopted wetland as the seasons pass. For teachers who plan on having successive classes adopt the same wetland, annual pictures can help students see changes over time. Select a few different spots within your wetland that represent different habitat types and take pictures at each spot. Return to these same spots through the year and take pictures again. In this way you will have documented the seasonal progression of your wetland.

How serious you are about photographing your wetlands depends on your time, interest, and equipment. A 35mm camera is a minimum requirement. There are many different lenses from which to choose—practically one for every shot. A macro lens is great for photographing flowers and insects. A telephoto lens can allow you to capture wildlife "up-close and personal." A wide-angle lens is useful for scenic landscape shots. Your choice of film should be geared to your available light (considering shade, time of day, time of year, cloud conditions, etc.), potential use of the photos (e.g., snapshots for the family album or color slides for a civic club presentation), and most importantly personal preference. Wildlife and nature photography is a challenging art. If you aspire to learn more about this art form, consider taking a course at your community college or arts center. A wetland naturally changes in character as the years go by. If you make a point to take pictures from the same spot over a period of time—say every five years—you may eventually be able to see the subtle changes that are occurring in your wetland as it ages. Change should occur gradually over a long period of time. A noticeable difference from year to year in vegetation communities, ground water levels, or newly eroded banks may indicate that the integrity of the wetland is being adversely affected, and suggests the need for land use management and protection efforts.

Wetland Protection Spotlight

Project Cattail
Sally DeRoo

Ten years ago, Sally DeRoo was on a bus in Louisiana with a group of teachers. They were passing some road construction, which was destroying wetlands. Disturbed by this destruction, Sally and the other teachers on the bus began a discussion about what they, as educators, could do to make a difference. They realized that by working together, they could get a lot done, and Project Cattail was born.

Sally carried this project idea back to her home in Dexter, Michigan, about ten miles from Ann Arbor. Project Cattail is a network of teachers, mostly in the Great Lakes Basin, but including educators throughout the country. The program provides materials and trainings for teachers, who then take their new knowledge back to their classrooms.

This project is unique in that it not only serves to educate students about ecology and biology, but also involves the students in their communities. When a community issue involving wetlands comes up, the students will begin a project that crosses curriculum lines. By developing petitions, talking to newspapers, writing reports and doing research, the students hone their writing, reading, speaking, and research skills. In addition, by monitoring areas and performing studies, the students learn technical skills and about the biology, ecology, and chemistry of the area. All this while learning how to be responsible citizens, voters, and consumers.

"Kids have to experience it," says Sally. "It's beyond the books. They go out there and they sit and listen and hear, and they make a positive difference." Indeed, children that Sally and other teachers have taught through Project Cattail, and another group that Sally helped form in her school district, Students Helping a Polluted Environment (SHAPE), who are now adults, have come back to their old schools to help develop nature areas, do stream clean ups, and teach a new generation of children.

Sally coordinates a week-long summer class each year, with graduate and undergraduate teachers. She involves naturalists who take the teachers and teachers-to-be out in the field to learn plant and animal identifications, wetland ecology, and the uniqueness of these ecosystems. She has found that she can find places to do these types of trainings anywhere. She's used county parks, state parks, metroparks, and sometimes just roadside ditches and little wetlands that she finds on the school grounds.

Sally began SHAPE while she was a teacher at Plymouth-Salem High School. This group was initiated by the students, who would meet after school to develop ways to improve the environment on the school grounds, and to educate the community about the need to protect their environment. Every year students choose a project

99

100

within their district in which they can make a positive impact "I'm really proud of projects like SHAPE," she says. "It really made a difference."

More than anything, Sally stresses the need to get children and teachers out into the field. "So many people have read the books, seen the pictures, seen the videos, but they've never held a little tree frog in their hand and identified that this is a living critter that needs a home. That's the thrust of this—interaction with living things."

Sally, who was a teacher for more than 35 years, now teaches at Wayne State-Oakland University. "I still do go out a lot to work with kids," she says. "But now my focus is on the teachers. I've done it with the kids, and now my interest is in teaching the educators how to do it."

For more information on Project Cattail or other wetland education projects, contact:
Sally DeRoo
5819 Merkel
Dexter, MI 48130
Phone: (734) 426-8895
Fax: (734) 426-7033
e-mail: sderoo3360@aol.com

Chapter 8

State and Federal Wetland Regulations

Wetlands provide many important functions that benefit not only the landowner, but others as well. The value of these wetland benefits to society is typically referred to as the public interest. The purpose of all wetland regulations is to explicitly acknowledge the public interest in wetland protection and provide guidelines for activities in wetlands that protect the public interest. Given the similarities between state and federal regulations, and the fact that Michigan has assumed administration of the Federal wetland program over much of the state, this chapter provides a primer on state and federal wetland regulations. Chapter Nine discusses citizen involvement in local wetland regulatory programs.

Understanding that landowners have certain rights that run with the title of a piece of property, wetland laws attempt to navigate the sometimes rocky waters of determining where an individual's property rights end and where the public's interest in resource protection begins. An analogy that is sometimes helpful is the example of the fist and the nose: my individual "right" to swing my fist is restricted by my responsibility to respect your nose. In the terms of wetland regulation, the property owner's right to alter his or her wetland (dredge, fill, drain, etc.) is limited by their responsibility to act in a way that does not impact neighbors nor society at large. At no time in the history of the United States have individual landowners had the unrestrained right to use their land in a way that harms others. Knowing that wetlands provide valuable functions that go beyond property boundaries, it follows that individual actions which degrade wetland functions will have impacts beyond the property boundaries that result in harm to the public. It is precisely these impacts that wetland regulations seek to avoid and minimize. As you will see in the next chapter, precisely because wetland regulations seek to protect the public interest, citizens have an important role to play in the regulatory process.

MICHIGAN'S WETLAND REGULATORY PROGRAM

At the heart of Michigan's wetland regulatory program is Part 303, Wetland Protection, of the Natural Resources and Environmental Protection Act (Act 451 of 1995), formerly referred to as the Goemaere-Anderson Wetlands Protection Act, P.A. 203 of 1979 (see appendices for full text). The MDEQ administers the permit program. As part of this program the MDEQ has assumed the administration of Section 404 of the Clean Water Act (see discussion later in this chapter).

Part 303 has several components. First, it establishes a state policy to protect the public against the loss of wetlands and makes explicit findings as to the benefits wetlands provide. Second, it establishes a permit program regulating most activities that alter wetlands. Third, the Wetland Protection Act provides enforcement language and sets maximum penalties for violations. Fourth, it explicitly authorizes regulation of wetlands by local governments.

102

Wetlands below the ordinary high water mark of a lake or stream are considered part of the lake or stream and are also regulated by the same Parts that regulate activities in lakes and streams. While a separate permit under Part 303 is not required, Part 303 criteria still apply to any permits that may be issued. Part 301, Inland Waters (formerly the Inland Lakes and Streams Act, P.A. 346 of 1972), regulates dredge, fill, or construction activities in inland lakes and streams and associated wetlands below the ordinary high water mark. Part 325 (formerly the Great Lakes Submerged Lands Act, P.A. 247 of 1955) applies to the Great Lakes and Lake St. Clair, including adjacent wetlands.

The basis for regulation is clear: wetlands provide public benefits and no one has the unrestricted right to alter the natural character of wetlands, as alterations may pollute the water, increase flood risks, lower lake or well water levels, destroy fish and wildlife habitat, or cause other public nuisance or harm.

Activities Regulated

Under Michigan's Wetland Protection Act, a permit is required for the following activities:
1) Deposit or permit the placing of fill material in a wetland;
2) Dredge, remove, or permit removal of soil or minerals from a wetland;
3) Construct, operate, or maintain any use or development in a wetland; or
4) Drain surface water from a wetland.

It is important to note that these activities are regulated regardless of the intention of the dredging, filling, construction, or draining activities. For example, if a landowner plans to fill wetland to construct a dike for the purpose of a waterfowl flooding, this activity still requires a permit even though the landowner may feel that the project will benefit the environment.

Furthermore, these requirements apply only to wetlands and activities that meet the following criteria: 1) wetlands as defined in Part 303; and 2) activities which are not specifically exempted in section 30305 (2) of Part 303. Each of these requires some elaboration.

Activities in wetlands requiring Part 325 or Part 301 permits are not subject to an additional Part 303 permit, although Part 303 regulatory standards apply. In situations where two or more resource management acts apply, MDEQ reviews one permit application under the criteria of all the applicable acts. This permit consolidation prevents unnecessary duplication of permits and review processes.

Jurisdictional Wetland Definition

The activities that are regulated by the Wetland Protection Act only apply to wetlands as defined in the Act. The definition of wetlands in the Act has two components. First, the Act defines wetland as "land characterized by the presence of water at a frequency and duration sufficient to support, and that under normal circumstances does support, wetland vegetation or aquatic life, and is commonly referred to as a bog, swamp, or marsh." Chapter Three provides detail on how this definition is actually implemented to make wetland determinations and delineate wetland boundaries.

Second, jurisdiction over wetlands depends on the size of the wetland and whether it is contiguous to a water body. Contiguous wetlands are those found in close proximity to a lake, stream, pond, Great Lake, etc., and/or have a direct hydrological relationship with it. According to the administrative rules promulgated for the Act (see appendices), wetlands within 500 feet of an inland lake, stream, or pond and within 1,000 feet of a Great Lake generally are considered contiguous. Non-contiguous wetlands are isolated from lakes and streams hydrologically and, generally, geographically. (See Rule 1(b) for definitions of "contiguous.")

103

Activities in contiguous wetlands are regulated without regard to the size of the wetland because of their close relationship to lakes and streams. Non-contiguous wetlands, however, are regulated only if they are greater than five acres in size. In counties of less than 100,000 people, non-contiguous wetlands are not regulated at all until a wetland inventory is complete. However, as authorized by section 30301(d)(iii), the MDEQ can regulate non-contiguous wetlands of any size anywhere in the state if the wetland is determined to be essential to the preservation of natural resources of the state and the landowner is notified of this determination.

Exemptions

During the legislative process when the Wetlands Protection Act was originally passed in 1979, a variety of activities were exempted from the need for a wetlands permit due to the state of wetland science and intense lobbying pressure. Unfortunately, many of the exemptions that were deemed appropriate at the time the Act was passed are not fully supported by current wetland science.

Specific exemptions are listed in Section 30305 of the Act (see appendices) but are still subject to other laws of the state (such as the Michigan Environmental Protection Act (MEPA)). In summary, the exempted activities include:

1) Recreation activities such as fishing, trapping, hunting, boating, hiking, and swimming;

2) Cutting of vegetation, including harvesting of commercial forest products (mechanized land clearing is not exempt);

3) Agricultural activities including grazing of animals, plowing, cultivating, irrigation ditching, minor drainage as defined by the Act, and construction or maintenance of farm or stock ponds for the production of food, fiber, and forest products. Wetlands altered for farming purposes cannot be used for non-farm purposes (e.g., housing development) without a wetland permit. (Some agricultural exemptions do not apply to contiguous wetlands or those non-contiguous wetlands determined to be necessary for preservation);

4) Some minor road improvements if adverse effects are minimized;

5) Distribution power line and small gas or oil pipeline construction and maintenance if effects are minimized;

6) Maintenance or operation of serviceable structures, including dikes and levees, in existence on October 1, 1980;

7) Straightening, widening, or deepening of private agricultural drains and drains constructed or improved (not just designated) pursuant to the Drain Code of 1956, as amended, but only if necessary for agricultural production, and subject to limitations imposed by Part 301; and

8) Construction of farm roads, forestry roads, or temporary roads for moving mining or forestry equipment if effects are minimized.

There are 18 exemptions in all. Unfortunately, other than those addressing recreation (e.g., hunting, fishing, trapping, swimming, hiking, and boating), many of the exemptions have resulted in significant wetland degradation.

General Permits

The MDEQ may issue general permits on a state or county basis for a category of activities that are similar in nature and have only a minimal adverse individual or cumulative effect on the environment. In the current program, applications under a general permit still undergo a full review, including a site inspection or the presentation of site specific information, and must meet all regulatory standards. However, the general permit process allows the Department to reach a decision without public notice. This allows the MDEQ to process minor applications more quickly. The Department has the authority to issue a public notice on an application that would otherwise qualify under a general permit category if they determine that the project warrants public review and comment. General permits can be revoked if adverse effects warrant the use of individual permits.

Permit Standards

Section 30311 of the Wetland Protection Act details the specific standards that must be met before a permit is issued. Wetland advocates should become familiar with these permit standards, particularly when reviewing permit applications. The permit standards essentially involve the application of three "tests" to each application: public interest, acceptable disruption to aquatic resources, and wetland dependency/alternatives analysis.

Public Interest Test

The rationale behind wetland regulation is that the public interest in the functions that wetlands provide needs to be protected. Accordingly, the regulatory criteria requires the regulatory agency to determine the impact of the project on the public interest. In determining whether the proposed activity is in the public interest, the reasonably foreseeable benefits of the project are weighed against the reasonably foreseeable detriments. Since wetland dredging, filling, and draining typically benefit the applicant, whereas the detriments are typically felt by the public at large, the public interest test usually boils down to a private gain versus public loss question that is difficult to determine. However, some activities that require a wetland permit, such as certain wetland restoration activities, clearly benefit both the applicant and the public. To determine whether a project is in the public interest, Part 30311(2) of the Act provides the following list of issues to consider:

1) The relative extent of the public and private need for the proposed activity;

2) The availability of feasible and prudent alternative locations and methods to accomplish the expected benefits from the activity;

3) The extent and permanence of the beneficial or detrimental effects which the proposed activity may have on the uses to which the site is suited, including the benefits the wetland provides;

4) The probable impact of each proposal in relation to the cumulative effect created by other existing and anticipated activities in the watershed;

5) The probable impact on recognized historic, cultural, scenic, ecological, or recreational values and on the public health, fish or wildlife;

6) The size of the wetland being considered;

7) The amount of the remaining wetland in the general area;

8) Proximity to any waterway; and

9) Economic value, both public and private, of the proposed land change to the general area.

105

Unacceptable Disruption to Aquatic Resources Test

According to Section 30311(4) of the Act, "a permit shall not be issued unless it is shown that an unacceptable disruption will not result to the aquatic resource." In applying this test, the law instructs agency staff to consider the issues raised when considering the public interest test and all the functions and values that wetlands provide (as listed in section 30302 of the Act), including flood storage, fish and wildlife habitat, erosion control, and the range of water quality protection functions. Furthermore, in considering a permit application, according to Section 30311(3), the MDEQ shall give serious consideration to findings of necessity for the proposed activity which have been made by other state agencies.

Wetland Dependency/Alternatives Analysis Test

Section 30311(4) also states that "a permit shall not be issued" unless the applicant also shows either that the proposed activity is "primarily dependent upon being located in the wetland" or that "a feasible and prudent alternative does not exist." The rationale behind this test is simple: if there is a way to accomplish the goals of the project in a way that does less damage to the wetland, then it should be utilized. These two tests are linked because the result of the first part (wetland dependency) impacts the rigor of the alternatives analysis. If a project is determined to be wetland dependent (e.g., peat mining, since peat only forms in wetlands), then the non-wetland alternatives to accomplish the goals of the project are quite limited. However, if the project is not wetland dependent (e.g., constructing a home), then less damaging upland alternatives are presumed to exist.

106

Although the "burden of proof" lies squarely on the shoulders of the applicant to counter this presumption, citizens can provide a valuable service by identifying less damaging alternatives and presenting them to the regulatory agencies. In most cases, the application of this statutory "test" results in the modification of the application to minimize impacts to wetlands. Remember, the overall goal of this test is to first avoid impacts to wetlands, then to minimize those that are not avoidable. Mitigation is usually required to offset unavoidable impacts. In 2000, the administrative rules to the Wetland Protection Act were revised to clarify wetland dependency. See the appendices for the rules as approved in 2000, or check the MDEQ's website for the most recent version.

These three tests serve as the justification for permit denial or approval. The next chapter will help you respond to permit applications in a way that ensures your comments are as effective as possible in addressing the statutory requirements.

Mitigation and Mitigation Banking

If the agency staff determine that a project meets the criteria described above and issue a permit authorizing wetland impacts that are determined to be unavoidable, Michigan's Wetland Protection Act authorizes the MDEQ to require the applicant to take actions to mitigate the loss of wetland area and function. The mitigation guidelines listed in the Act's administrative rules require a no net loss of wetlands; encourage mitigation projects that will replace the lost wetland functions on or near the same site as the impacted wetland (if that is determined to not be possible or beneficial to the resource, then a high priority is placed on requiring mitigation within the same watershed); and give consideration to replacement of predominant functional values lost within the impacted wetland.

In 1997, the MDEQ formalized guidelines for the establishment of wetland mitigation banks in Michigan. These administrative rules can be found in the appendices and on the MDEQ's website. A wetland mitigation bank is a site where wetlands are restored, created, or in exceptional circumstances, preserved expressly for the purpose of providing an off-site alternative to compensate for authorized wetland losses. As part of their approved mitigation plan, those impacting wetlands can purchase credits in the bank to offset permitted wetland impacts. Wetland mitigation banking does not mean that those wishing to dredge, fill, or drain wetlands simply "pay the bank" to get their permit. The MDEQ may authorize the use of credits from an established mitigation bank only to offset the unavoidable loss of wetlands as approved in accordance with state wetland laws. Before approving the use of a mitigation bank, the MDEQ shall determine that the applicant has taken all feasible and prudent steps to avoid the loss of wetland resources and has used all practical means to minimize impact to wetlands. The purchase of credits from a mitigation bank does not eliminate the need to comply with wetland permit review criteria.

It is also important to note that the MDEQ now requires a conservation easement over mitigation sites, and occasionally, over undisturbed wetlands on the site of a permitted activity. If local groups are aware of these easements, they might be able to report violations of the easement (e.g., clearing of vegetation or construction in an area protected by a conservation easement). However, because the MDEQ now obtains the easement prior to construction of a mitigation site, there will initially be some construction activity at the location where an easement has beed placed over a new wetland restoration or creation site.

107

Another opportunity for citizen input into decisions regarding mitigation occurs when preservation of existing rare and threatened wetland habitat is used as a form of mitigation for permitted impacts. Wetland advocates can comment on the most appropriate location for mitigation within a watershed, ideally based on existing watershed or resource management plans.

Enforcement

Failure to obtain a necessary permit, or a violation of a condition in a permit issued under the Act, is subject to civil and criminal penalties. Actions may be brought by either local prosecutors or by Michigan's Attorney General, and if found to be in violation, financial penalties, restoration, and/or jail sentences may be imposed by court verdict or order. The court may order restoration or may impose a civil fine of $10,000 per day of violation of the Act or violation of a court order.

Criminal penalties are slightly different. A person who violates the Act is punishable by a fine of up to $2,500. Willful or reckless violations of permit conditions by a person or corporate officer can result in a fine of not less than $2,500 nor more than $25,000 per day of violation, and/or imprisonment for not more than one year. A second such violation constitutes a felony, punishable by a fine of up to $50,000 per day of violation, and/or up to two years of imprisonment. In addition to these penalties, the court may order a person who violates this act to restore the affected wetland as nearly as possible to its original state.

The MDEQ investigates reports of possible violations and initiates enforcement actions. Federal agencies, or local governments with wetlands ordinances, may also choose to pursue enforcement action independent of any state action. Few violations result in effective enforcement actions by the MDEQ for a variety of reasons. Among them the lack of interest on behalf of some County Prosecutors to pursue violations, staffing constraints, and the Attorney General's workload. To increase the effectiveness of permitting programs and deter violations, wetland advocates must support proper enforcement of the Act as much as possible.

OTHER STATE LAWS AFFECTING WETLANDS

The role of state government in protecting Michigan's natural resources is mandated by the Michigan Constitution. Article 4, Section 53 of the constitution provides that:

> The conservation and development of the natural resources of the state are hereby declared to be of paramount public concern in the interest of the health, safety, and general welfare of the people. The legislature shall provide for the protection of the air, water, and other natural resources of the state from pollution, impairment, and destruction.

108

Consistent with this mandate, there are many state regulations that affect wetlands in Michigan. A brief synopsis of these laws appears below.

Soil Erosion and Sedimentation Control (Part 91 of Act 451 of 1994, formerly P.A. 347 of 1972) is designed to protect the waters of the state from sedimentation caused by soil erosion. Although the law stipulates that all individuals and entities are responsible for controlling erosion and offsite sedimentation, not all activities require a permit. Permits are required for earth changes which disturb one or more acres of land or which are within 500 feet of a lake or stream, excluding plowing, tilling, mining, and logging activities. Before a permit is issued, the applicant must prepare a soil erosion and sedimentation control plan. Permits are issued by counties or local agencies through programs approved by the MDEQ. Local units of government may adopt soil erosion and sedimentation control ordinances that have higher standards than the state act. If local agencies are failing to administer their soil erosion regulations appropriately, citizens can request a program review by the MDEQ.

Land Division Act (P.A. 591 of 1997, formerly the Subdivision Control Act–P.A. 288 of 1968) requires the approval of the Michigan Department of Environmental Quality for the preliminary plat of any subdivision containing lots within or affected by a floodplain, and any subdivision involving land abutting a lake or stream where public rights may be affected. In many cases, wetlands are involved and are brought to the attention of the developer and appropriate agencies during the review process.

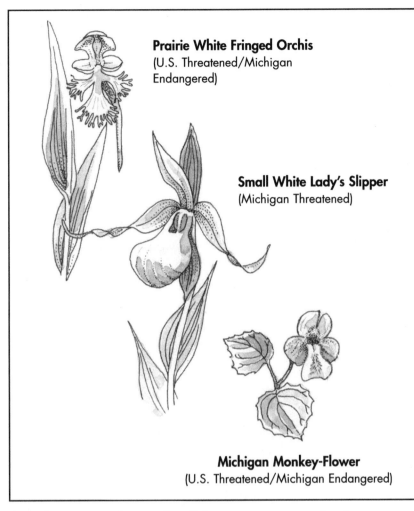

Prairie White Fringed Orchis
(U.S. Threatened/Michigan
Endangered)

Small White Lady's Slipper
(Michigan Threatened)

Michigan Monkey-Flower
(U.S. Threatened/Michigan Endangered)

109

Michigan Environmental Protection Act (MEPA) (Part 17 of Act 451 of 1994, formerly P.A. 127 of 1970) places a duty on all individuals and organizations, whether private or public, to prevent or minimize environmental degradation which is caused or likely to be caused by their activities. Its requirements are in addition to those provided by any other law. MEPA prohibits any conduct which is likely to pollute, impair, or destroy a lake, stream, wetland, or other natural resource of the state unless the entity proposing or authorizing the activity can show: 1) there are no less harmful feasible and prudent alternatives; and 2) the "conduct is consistent with the promotion of the public health, safety and welfare in light of the state's paramount concern for the protection of its natural resources from pollution, impairment, or destruction." Any person, organization, or governmental body can go to court to enforce MEPA against any other person, organization, or governmental body.

Michigan Endangered Species Act (Part 365 of Act 451 of 1994, formerly P.A. 203 of 1974) requires a permit for activities that could adversely impact threatened and endangered plant and animal species or their habitat. Since a large percentage of Michigan's endangered or threatened species reside in wetland areas, this Act can be useful in providing another layer of review to protect critical habitats.

Water Resources Protection (Part 31 of Act 451 of 1994, formerly P.A. 167 of 1968) assesses the location and extent of floodplains, streambeds, stream discharge, and stage characteristics for the state's watercourses to minimize flood damage. A permit is required for any dredging, grading, or construction of a building within the 100-year floodplain of any river, stream, or lake.

Inland Waters (Part 301 of Act 451 of 1994, formerly P.A. 346 of 1972) regulates lakes and streams and associated wetlands, excluding the Great Lakes and Lake St. Clair. The Act applies to artificial or natural lakes, rivers, streams, and creeks as defined by having definite banks, a bed, and visible evidence of a continued flow or continued occurrence of water. This includes intermittent or seasonal streams. Permits are required to dredge, fill, or construct or place structures below the ordinary high water mark and connect any waterway to an inland lake or stream.

Shorelands Protection and Management (Part 323 of Act 451 of 1994, formerly P.A. 245 of 1970) protects parts of the Great Lakes shoreline that are specifically designated by the Natural Resources Commission as high risk erosion, flood risk, and environmental areas. To be designated, environmental areas must be deemed necessary for the preservation and maintenance of fish and wildlife along Great Lakes shorelines and areas influenced by Great Lakes water level fluctuations.

Great Lakes Submerged Lands (Part 325 of Act 451 of 1994) is responsible for regulating construction activities along 3,165 miles of Great Lakes shoreline and over 38,000 square miles of Great Lakes bottomlands, including coastal marshes. The program regulates the recovery and use of submerged cultural resources (shipwrecks and associated artifacts) located in the Great Lakes, administers the underwater preserve program, and as of July 21, 2000, is responsible for regulating the recovery of submerged logs from Great Lakes bottomlands under Part 326, Great Lakes Submerged Logs Recovery. The State of Michigan is trustee of the bottomlands and waters of the Great Lakes and has a perpetual duty to manage these resources for the benefit of its citizens.

Sand Dunes Protection and Management (Part 353 of Act 451 of 1994, formerly P.A. 146 and P.A. 147 of 1989) provides protection for designated critical dune areas in Michigan, many of which contain interdunal wetland swales. The Act prohibits construction activities, vegetation removal, and other uses involving contour change that may increase erosion and decrease stability.

Michigan Drain Code (P.A. 40 of 1956) authorizes the establishment of an agency in each county responsible for the movement and management of water resources from a local perspective. Using existing riparian laws in the early 1800s, and later codifying those laws into the Michigan Drain Code, the pioneer residents of Michigan used the Drain Code to prepare land for agriculture and facilitate commercial and residential development. The Drain Code is administered by elected Drain Commissioners. The Drain Commissioner is authorized to assess property owners in a watershed to pay for water management activities.

COMMON LAW

It is possible that an alteration of a watercourse or wetland may alter streamflow, water quality, or runoff patterns so that certain common law doctrines may be relevant. Riparian, surface water, nuisance and trespass law may all apply. For instance, if a landowner drains a wetland or alters surface water flows so as to discharge an increased amount of water onto the property of another, the latter may sue for damage and an injunction preventing further discharge in excess of natural conditions.

THE FEDERAL WETLAND REGULATORY PROGRAM

The federal government's power to regulate discharges into the waters of the United States arises from authority conferred on Congress by the "Commerce Clause" contained in the U.S. Constitution. The phrase "waters of the United States" is broadly defined to include rivers, lakes, streams, ponds, and wetlands that are, or could be used in interstate or foreign commerce.

The Federal Water Pollution Control Act of 1972 (referred to as the Clean Water Act, as amended) serves as the regulatory framework for the federal government's regulation of activities that impact waters of the United States. There are three sections of the Clean Water Act that are specifically involved with regulating activities that impact wetlands: Section 401, Section 402, and Section 404.

In Michigan, the MDEQ and the U.S. Army Corps of Engineers (Corps) share the responsibility of administering and enforcing the federal wetlands regulatory program. The wetland regulatory authority and responsibilities of the Corps are based on Section 10 of the Rivers and Harbors Act of 1899 (33 U.S.C. 403) and Section 404 of the Clean Water Act of 1977 (33 U.S.C. 1344). The Corps has the authority to bring enforcement actions, including criminal or civil actions, against violators of these laws. However, in its day-to-day administration of the federal wetlands program, both the Corps and the MDEQ are subject to oversight by the U.S. Environmental Protection Agency, which is ultimately responsible for the administration of the Clean Water Act.

Section 10 of the Rivers and Harbors Act of 1899

Section 10 of the Rivers and Harbors Act of 1899 (33 U.S.C. 403) regulates virtually all work in, over, and under waters listed as "navigable waters of the United States." Some typical examples of projects requiring Section 10 permits include beach nourishment, boat ramps, breakwaters, bulkheads, dredging, filling or discharging material (such as sand, gravel, or stone), groins and jetties, mooring buoys, piers (seasonal or permanent), placement of rock rip-rap for wave protection or streambank stabilization, boat hoists, pilings, and construction of marina facilities. Section 10 waters include the Great Lakes, connecting waters, and those inland waters that have been designated federally navigable (e.g., Lake Charlevoix, parts of the St. Joseph River, etc.)

Section 404 of The Clean Water Act

The Section 404 program—the primary federal program governing activities in wetlands—regulates the discharge of dredged or fill material into the waters of the United States (the definition of which includes wetlands) and is intended to minimize adverse impacts by preventing the unnecessary loss of wetlands and other sensitive aquatic areas. Filling and grading work, mechanized land clearing, sidecasting of material during ditching or other excavation activity, material stockpiles, backfilling around structures or into excavation areas, certain pile supported structures, and fill associated with property protection devices such as seawalls and bulkheads all constitute discharges of dredged and/or fill material under the Corps' regulatory authority. Section 404 regulates a larger area than Section 10. The 404 program is intended to minimize adverse impacts by preventing the unnecessary loss of wetlands and other sensitive aquatic areas. Both the Corps and the EPA have the authority to bring enforcement actions, including criminal or civil actions, against violators of these laws.

In the permit review process, the Corps analyzes the impacts of the proposed activity under a simultaneous review process demanded by three different sets of regulations: Regulatory Programs of the Corps (33 CFR Part 320-330), Corps Regulations for Implementing the National Environmental Policy Act (33 CFR Part 23), and, in 404 discharges, the Section 404(b)(1) Guidelines for the Specification of Disposal Sites for Dredged or Fill Material (40 CFR Part 230).

Like Michigan's Wetland Protection Act, the federal wetlands permitting program requires application of a "public interest test." In determining the impacts on the public interest, the Corps considers all factors of the proposed activity, including conservation, economics, aesthetics, general environmental concerns, historic values, fish and wildlife values, flood damage prevention, land use, navigation, recreation, water supply and water quality, energy needs, safety, food production, and the needs and welfare of the public.

111

For activities involving 404 discharges, a permit will be denied if the discharge that would be authorized by such a permit would not comply with the U.S. Environmental Protection Agency's 404(b)(1) Guidelines (see sidebar). The Corps must prepare an environmental impact assessment and make a finding of whether an environmental impact statement should be prepared. The guidelines require that practicable alternatives to degrading a wetland be considered before a permit is approved.

If the basic activity to be carried out on the proposed fill area does not require being located in a wetland or other special aquatic site in order to take place, it is presumed that less damaging practicable alternatives to the discharge are available.

The guidelines also state that no permit should be issued if it would:

1) Cause violations of state water quality standards;

2) Violate toxic effluent standards;

3) Jeopardize federally listed endangered or threatened species;

4) Cause significant adverse effects on human health and welfare, municipal water supplies, plankton, fish, shellfish, wildlife, or special aquatic sites (including wetlands);

5) Cause significant adverse effects on the capacity of a wetland to assimilate nutrients, purify water, or reduce wave energy;

6) Significantly reduce recreational, aesthetic, and economic values; or

7) Violate federal protection requirements for designated marine sanctuaries.

Mitigation is an important element of both the Section 404(b)(1) Guidelines and the public interest review. The term mitigation is defined as the lessening of adverse impacts through avoidance, minimization, and finally, compensation. After strict applications of the permitting standards, a permit may be issued for a project that will have adverse wetland impacts, provided that appropriate and practicable steps are taken to minimize adverse impacts to the aquatic ecosystem. In such a situation, the lost wetland functions and values should be replaced.

Compensatory mitigation is sometimes inappropriately used to try to convince wetland managers to issue a wetland dredge and fill permit that would otherwise have an unacceptable adverse impact on the aquatic resource. The Corps does not issue permits based on compensatory mitigation plans, but rather considers the total impact of the proposal without the possible compensation. However, the Corps does approve permits that include compensatory mitigation for losses they are convinced are unavoidable and have been minimized.

The 404 (b)(1) Guidelines and the specific public interest review factors should be referred to when commenting on a Corps Section 404 permit application.

EPA's Section 404(b)(1) Guidelines

No permit to fill wetlands or other waters of the United States can be approved unless the project meets the 404(b)(1) Guidelines. These regulations require the applicant to comply with four main requirements to ensure the proposed project does not have a significant or avoidable effect on the environment. The applicant has the burden of proof to demonstrate compliance with the 404(b)(1) Guidelines.

1) Alternatives: Prohibits issuance of a permit for projects where feasible, less environmentally damaging alternatives are available. For projects which would fill wetlands but do not depend upon wetlands in order to fulfill their basic purpose (are not water dependent), the regulations presume the availability of less environmentally damaging alternatives.

2) Adverse Impacts: Prohibits issuance of a permit for projects which would cause or contribute to significant adverse impacts to the aquatic environment.

3) Water Quality: Prohibits issuance of a permit for projects which would violate any applicable state water quality standard.

4) Mitigation: Requires project proponents to eliminate avoidable impacts and to minimize and compensate for unavoidable impacts to the extent appropriate and practicable.

A unique aspect of the Section 404(b)(1) Guidelines is its "advance identification" (ADID) authority. Under Section 230.80 of the guidelines, agencies have the ability to identify and provide public notice of areas unsuitable for dredge or fill discharges. The Clinton River Watershed Council and the Huron River Watershed Council have initiated ADID projects in their watersheds. This component of the federal wetland program provides a potential tool to guide development activity away from critical wetland areas. Citizens and local governments can initiate consideration of important wetlands for potential ADID designation.

THE ROLE OF OTHER FEDERAL AGENCIES AND REGULATIONS

As mentioned above, the U.S. Environmental Protection Agency has ultimate authority over the Section 404 program. The EPA has primary responsibility for approval of 404 regulations, provides comments on water quality issues, ensures compliance with 404(b)(1) Guidelines, and has the power to veto some categories of Corps and MDEQ permit decisions. The U.S. Fish and Wildlife Service (FWS) is charged with reviewing permit applications to assure that impacts on wildlife and endangered species are acceptable according to the Fish and Wildlife Act of 1956 (16 U.S.C. 742a, et seq.), the Migratory Marine Game-Fish Act (16 U.S.C. 760c-760g), the Fish and Wildlife Coordination Act (16 U.S.C. 661-666c) and the Endangered Species Act (16 U.S.C. 1531 et seq.). The National Environmental Policy Act of 1969 (NEPA) (42 U.S.C. 4321-4347) declares the national policy to encourage a productive and enjoyable harmony between people and their environment. Although these federal agencies are routinely notified regarding permit applications, in several instances across Michigan, review of Corps permitting activities by other federal agencies has been initiated by citizen action.

113

Section 401 of the Clean Water Act–Water Quality Certification

Section 401 of the Clean Water Act provides Michigan and other states with a powerful tool to protect wetlands. Under Section 401 of the Clean Water Act, no federal permit to discharge pollutants into waters of the United States is valid unless the state where the discharge occurs grants certification, or waives its right to certify, that the permit will not violate state water quality standards. This authority is typically used by states to address the physical, chemical, and biological impacts of conventional and non-conventional pollutants, toxic pollutants, and to develop new regulatory performance standards. Each Corps' Section 404 individual permit application and all proposed federal general permits are subject to Section 401 review by the state. However, for a state to take advantage of this oversight power, the state's water quality standards must have criteria specific to wetlands. The MDEQ has recommended wetland water quality standards which have not yet been approved. Michigan is one of the only two states in the Great Lakes that has not yet adopted wetland water quality standards.

Section 402 of the Clean Water Act—National Pollution Discharge Elimination System

The National Pollution Discharge Elimination System (NPDES) is the key to enforcing the effluent limitations and water quality standards of the Clean Water Act. Every point source discharger must obtain a permit from either the EPA or an authorized state agency. Unless in compliance with a permit, all dischargers are considered unlawful and are subject to the civil and criminal penalties in Sections 301 and 309 of the Clean Water Act. Many NPDES discharges may impact wetlands. Peat mining operations involve substantial drainage activities, the effluent from which are typically acidic and contain nutrients, heavy metals, sediments, and other pollutants that are released to receiving waters, thus requiring a NPDES permit.

114

The Federal Endangered Species Act

Recognizing that threatened and endangered species of fish, wildlife, and plants are of esthetic, ecological, educational, historical, recreational, and scientific value to the nation and its people, the Federal Endangered Species Act (ESA) was passed in 1973 to provide a means to conserve the ecosystems upon which endangered and threatened species depend. An endangered species is one in danger of extinction throughout all or a significant part of its range. A threatened species is one likely to become endangered if it is not protected. The U.S. Fish and Wildlife Service is responsible for administration of the ESA. Sections of the ESA provide for determination of threatened and endangered species, cooperation with state wildlife and regulatory agencies, and interagency consultation for federal authorizations (such as wetland permits) or actions that might impact threatened and endangered species (Section 7 Consultation). Given the occurrence of threatened and endangered species in wetlands, many wetland permit applications will require ESA consultations.

STATE ASSUMPTION OF THE SECTION 404 PROGRAM

Michigan is unique in that it is the only state in the Great Lakes to formally assume the responsibility of administering Section 404 of the Clean Water Act. The MDEQ (formerly the MDNR) assumed administration of the Section 404 wetlands program on inland waters of the state in 1984. The Corps has retained jurisdiction in Michigan on the Great Lakes, connecting channels, and rivers to the federally-determined head of navigation. In these "joint jurisdictional" waters, permits to impact wetlands are needed from both the Corps and the MDEQ. For example, in Emmet and Cheboygan Counties along the Inland Water Route, or in the Detroit River, those wishing to alter wetlands must have two permits, one from the MDEQ under Part 303 and one from the Corps under Section 404 and/or Section 10. On most inland lakes and streams, only a MDEQ permit is required. Contact the Corps for a list of federally navigable waters in Michigan.

Authority to assume the federal wetland regulatory program was granted due to the similarities between Section 404 and the activities regulated by state regulations, and because MDEQ had demonstrated its ability to administer the regulations as effectively as federal agencies. Primary responsibility for a state-assumed permit program rests with the EPA. EPA's oversight authority allows it to review all Section 404 permit applications submitted to the state. However, the EPA has waived review of all applications except the following:

   1) Authorizations of general permits;

   2) Major discharges (as defined below); and

   3) Discharges into critical areas established by state or federal law, including sanctuaries and refuges, national and historic monuments, wilderness areas, parks, components of the National Wild and Scenic Rivers system, designated critical habitat of threatened and endangered species, sites identified or proposed under the Historic Preservation Act, and sites identified by the EPA in advance under provisions of the Section 404(b)(1) Guidelines.

"Major discharges" are defined as:

   1) Discharges that contain toxic materials;

   2) Discharges into areas identified by the EPA, in consultation with the Corps and the FWS, which could impact waters that are unique for a particular region, significantly reduce the commercial or recreational values of a significant area of waters of the United States, or affect a federally-listed or proposed threatened or endangered species;

   3) Discharges involving more than 10,000 cubic yards of fill;

   4) New construction of breakwaters or seawalls that exceed 1,000 feet in total length; or

   5) Culvert enclosures of more than 100 feet with more than 200 cubic yards of fill or channelization of more than 500 feet of a river or a stream.

115

In the case of "major discharge" applications, the EPA coordinates review of the application by the Corps and FWS through the public notice process and coordinates with the FWS as necessary pursuant to Section 7 of the Endangered Species Act to protect federally listed threatened and endangered species. As most peat mining operations involve activities that qualify as major discharges, most peat mining applications in Michigan would be reviewed by federal agencies. Although the state still has jurisdiction, the MDEQ cannot issue a Section 404 permit over an objection from the EPA. If the state and the EPA disagree, and EPA's objections cannot be resolved, then 404 jurisdiction *for that particular application* reverts to the Corps. This is the only situation under which the Corps would actually regain jurisdiction for administration of the Clean Water Act on inland waters of the state.

For those applying for permits to alter wetlands in joint jurisdictional areas, the MDEQ and the Corps have coordinated efforts to avoid permit duplication. The Corps and the MDEQ have jointly developed a single application form to be completed by the applicant. This one form is sent to the Permit Consolidation Unit of the MDEQ. If the activity requires Corps review, a copy is made and forwarded to the Corps. From this point on, the applications undergo similar, but separate processes. In some cases, an MDEQ permit will be issued, but a Corps permit will be denied, or vice versa. Again, activities in joint jurisdictional water must have both permits to be authorized. In areas that are not under joint jurisdiction, the federal agencies review MDEQ Public Notices for major discharges, but do not issue a separate 404 permit.

Both state and federal wetland regulatory programs provide opportunities for the public to become involved in the permitting process. Please see the next chapter for more information regarding citizen involvement.

Chapter 9

Citizen Involvement in State and Federal Wetland Regulations

Both state and federal regulations provide opportunities for citizens to participate in the wetland regulatory process. In addition to providing comment on public notices for local, state, and federal applications to alter wetlands as provided by law, citizens can effectively promote wetland protection in many other ways. Given that many wetland violations go unaddressed by regulatory staff, informed citizens can play a key role in reporting wetland violations and encouraging regulatory response. In addition, informed citizens can raise the overall level of appreciation for wetland resources and support for wetland protection.

The success of any regulation largely depends upon public support. This is particularly true in the case of Michigan's Wetland Protection Act, the enforcement of which almost always relies upon the efforts of citizens reporting violations and locally elected prosecutors accepting cases. As citizens are informed and motivated to participate in local wetland protection efforts, their activities will necessarily influence local, state, and federal initiatives in a positive manner. Thus, local action is instrumental in providing a political force to promote wetland protection at all levels. This chapter focuses on citizen involvement in state and federal wetland permit processes and reporting violations. Citizen action as it relates to promoting local wetland ordinances and grassroots organizing are topics of subsequent chapters.

PARTICIPATING IN THE PERMIT PROCESS
Obtaining Public Notices

The first step of actually participating in the permit process is to obtain information regarding permit applications. Applications that are public noticed are typically sent to the appropriate lake association, adjacent landowners, watershed councils, and local units of governments (townships, municipalities, and Soil and Water Conservation Districts). Although this sounds like broad distribution, most public notices go virtually unnoticed by the general public. Fortunately, the MDEQ and Corps operate notification programs that provide the opportunity for citizens to be aware of wetlands permit applications in their area.

MDEQ Notification Process

As mentioned in Chapter Five, the MDEQ administers the Michigan Wetland Protection Act and other state regulations impacting wetlands. You may obtain information from the MDEQ about permit applications on file by either visiting the MDEQ website or subscribing to a list that is mailed bi-weekly.

118

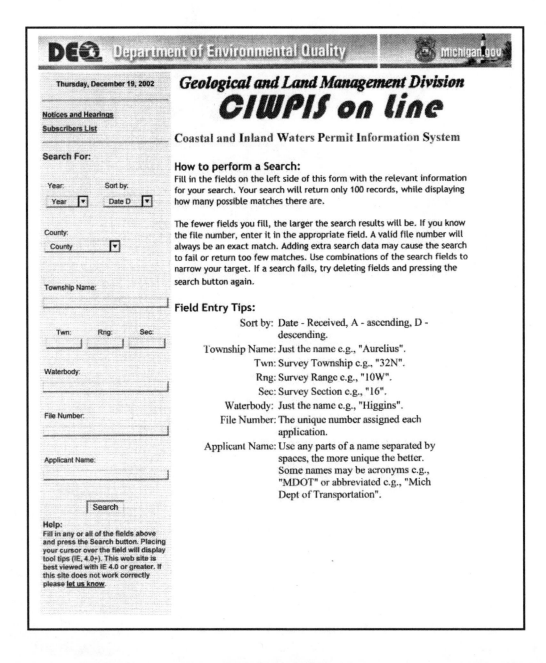

The MDEQ has developed an on-line permit tracking system called the Coastal and Inland Waters Permit Information System or CIWPIS. It allows you to search for permit applications using criteria such as year, county, township, waterbody, file number, and applicant name. You may also check their "subscribers list" which will display a statewide list of applications posted over the previous two weeks or other recent intervals of time. To access the CIWPIS site, visit www.deq.state.mi.us/ciwpis.

For a $25.00 annual fee, anyone may receive by mail a weekly listing (distributed bi-weekly) of all permit applications the MDEQ receives. To receive the weekly listing, send a $25.00 check payable to the State Of Michigan with a written request for the list to:

> Michigan Department of Environmental Quality
> Geological and Land Management Division
> P.O. Box 30204
> Lansing, MI 48909

It is important to note that both lists are simply an accounting of all applications that the MDEQ receives and only serve as a first line of notification for the wetland advocate. Both lists can be used to identify proposed projects in a particular area. If using CIWPIS, this can be done easily by searching on a county, township, or waterbody. On the mailed list, applications appear in order according to their application or file number. The first two digits represents the year, the second two represent the MDEQ District Office. First look for the applications submitted in your MDEQ District, then the project location can be pinpointed by county, waterbody, and township section.

Both lists indicate which is the controlling statute. On the CIWPIS site this is listed with "activities" and on the mailed list it appears under the "application number" column. If Part 303 of Act 451 is noted, then the project involves a wetland. If it is Part 301 or 325, the project may or may not be in a wetland. A separate Part 303 permit is not required if a 301 or 325 permit is also required. Therefore, the MDEQ reviews the project under Part 301 or 325 but must also consider Part 303 requirements. In these cases, you must review the application to determine if wetland activity is proposed. An application listed for your area does not necessarily mean that it will be public noticed and that public comment will be solicited. Often, the permit application will be processed as a general permit, and therefore not subject to public notice, or the applicant will withdraw the application.

The opportunity for public comment is provided for a dredge and fill application if the MDEQ issues a formal public notice. The MDEQ issues a public notice for most individual applications. The public has 20 days to submit written comments on the proposed activity, whereas local governments have 45 days to file comments. Since a copy of the full application is not always posted with the public notice (e.g., the alternatives analysis may be missing), a special request may need to be made to the MDEQ for further information. Also, since the MDEQ does not routinely send public notices to individuals, a special request must be made to receive notices for a specific area.

The MDEQ may choose to issue a public notice and call for comments even if an activity is otherwise covered by a general permit, but they do not normally do so. The purpose of the general permit is to avoid delays in permit decisions for minor activities. Although watershed councils receive copies of general permit applications, public notice and comment are eliminated. Current general permits include: open pile boardwalks; exploratory pad locations and access roads for mineral drilling activities; and others.

Corps Notification Process

As explained in the previous chapter, the Corps has authority to issue permits for activities regulated under Section 10 of the Rivers and Harbors Act and on selected waters under Section 404 of the Clean Water Act.

In some cases, the Corps jurisdiction overlaps the MDEQ's, and a "joint public notice" is issued by the Corps. Comments are received by both agencies when a joint public notice is issued. Included with the joint notice is a description of the proposal and sketches of the proposed activity. As with the MDEQ notice, individuals have 20 days to file comments.

To receive Army Corps notices, write to:

> District Engineer
> Detroit District
> U.S. Army Corps of Engineers
> P.O. Box 1027
> Detroit, MI 48231-1027

120

The Corps also has the authority to issue general permits which may not be public noticed. However, general permit standards differ between the state and federal regulatory programs. As a result, a permit application that is not public noticed by one agency might be by the other.

Evaluating and Commenting on Permit Applications
The Role of the MDEQ and Corps

The Corps and MDEQ coordinate application processing to some degree. Applications to authorize activities in wetlands are submitted to the Michigan Department of Environmental Quality in Lansing. The application is first reviewed by the Permit Consolidation Unit (PCU) and listed on the weekly listing of applications received by the Department. If the application materials are incomplete, PCU staff contacts the applicant for more information. If an applicant doesn't respond to a request for further information within 30 days, the application may be considered withdrawn.

When the information is considered administratively complete, PCU staff determines if the permit will be reviewed under the general permit process and if the permit is subject to Corps regulation. In areas of joint jurisdiction, a copy of the permit application is forwarded to the Corps' Detroit District Office. Although the process is similar, MDEQ and Corps application reviews are conducted separately and independently.

Dredge and Fill Permit Review Process

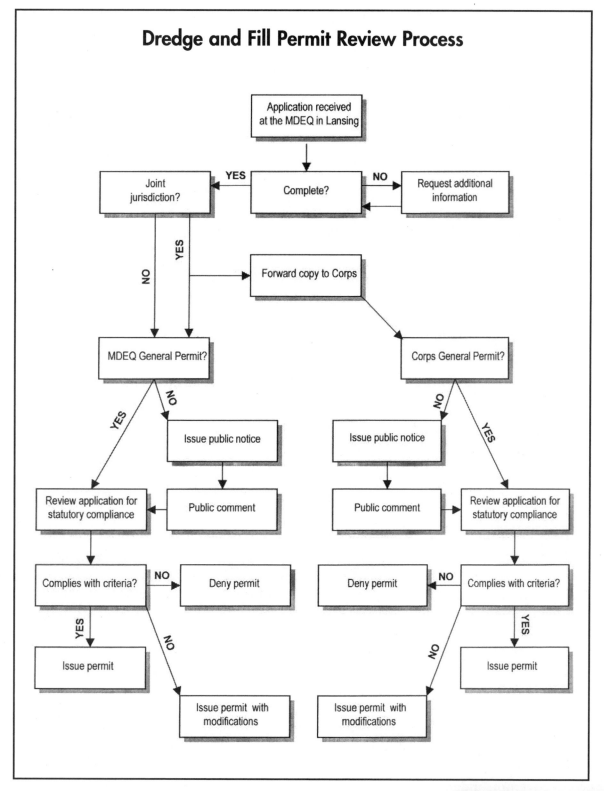

121

Sometimes, the activities for which a permit is being sought have already begun. In these cases, the application is referred to as an "after-the-fact" application. The MDEQ is not required to accept an after-the-fact application if it is apparent that the site should be restored. In these instances, the case will be processed as a violation. If the activity is potentially permittable, staff evaluate the project using the same criteria as if the project had not commenced. The permit application fee is doubled. If the final decision is a permit denial or a modification of the work done, the applicant may be required to restore the wetland completely or modify the existing project to minimize impacts.

MDEQ 2001 PERMITTING ACTIVITIES

	Public Notices (Parts 301 and 303)	Minor Permits (Part 301)	General Permits (Part 303)	TOTAL ACTIONS
Issued	822 (57%)	2282 (74%)	299 (62%)	3403 (68%)
Issued modified	383 (26%)	533 (17%)	108 (22%)	1024 (21%)
Issued after-the-fact	72 (5%)	116 (4%)	33 (7%)	221 (4%)
Denied	100 (7%)	54 (2%)	12 (3%)	166 (3%)
Closed	66 (5%)	92 (3%)	28 (6%)	186 (4%)
TOTALS	1443 (100%)	3077 (100%)	480 (100%)	5000 (100%)

In most cases, permit applications reviewed by the MDEQ field offices and under the Corps individual permit process receive a site visit by agency staff. The field review of the subject parcel enables the agency staff person to make site-specific determinations about the proposed project. Agency staff must review the proposed project in light of the regulatory standards and criteria stipulated by law (see previous chapter). In addition, agency staff must also consider public input, the comments of local units of government, and the findings of other state and federal agencies. In the case of the MDEQ, if a public hearing is requested on a wetland dredge and fill application, then one must be held. The Corps staff have discretion regarding holding public hearings (see the discussion on public hearings later in this chapter).

Although the Corps has no statutory time limit, the MDEQ has 90 days to make a decision after receiving a complete application. The time is extended if a hearing is held.

If the local government denies a permit application under its ordinance, the MDEQ may refuse to issue a Part 303 permit except where statewide or regional benefits are involved. A local decision to issue a permit, however, is not binding on the MDEQ if Part 303 standards would be violated. Violations of local ordinances have their own remedies.

When the agency staff has reviewed public comments, other agency comments, and applied the regulatory standards, a decision is made. There are basically three options:

1) Denial of the permit application;

2) Issuance of the permit with modifications; or

3) Issuance of the permit as it was originally proposed.

Although the MDEQ and Corps' wetland protection programs are sometimes seen as a major impediment to development by developers and politicians, the majority of permit applications are issued.

When the decision is made to issue the permit with modifications, a "draft" permit is sent to the applicant for his or her signature. When the draft permit is signed and returned to the Department, it is then issued and the applicant must comply with its terms and conditions. For unmodified permits, the permit is issued directly from the MDEQ. The permit may be valid for a period extending until the end of the following calendar year, or in some cases for a longer period. Up to two 12-month extensions may be granted if there is no change in the activity for which the permit was originally issued.

Any person aggrieved by an MDEQ decision on a permit application may request a formal contested case hearing from the MDEQ to review the decision. See discussion of contested case hearings later in this chapter. If appeals to the MDEQ are exhausted, then an aggrieved person may go to court. The Corps has a separate administrative appeals process. Unfortunately, access to the Corps appeals process is limited to the applicant who is seeking to appeal a Corps permit denial. The only avenue for citizens to appeal a Corps permit issuance is through the federal court system.

123

The Citizens' Role

The citizens' role in evaluating permit applications is very important to the wetlands protection process. Not only do citizens provide valuable information, but they also serve as a reminder to agency staff that the purpose of the wetland regulations is to protect the public's interest in maintaining the functions and values that wetlands provide. In this sense, public participation helps to ensure that regulatory staff are accountable to the public interest. The process described below presents a simple procedure to help citizens analyze public notices and determine the best course of action.

Step One: Understand the permit application.
Assuming you have taken the steps to receive a public notice, there are important pieces of information contained in the public notice of which you need to be aware. These pieces of information include:

1) The date the public notice was issued (the agencies will receive public comment for 20 calendar days from the issue date);

2) The application file number (this number should be included in any correspondence);

3) The project location (this is helpful when you are trying to investigate the site);

State of Michigan
Department of Environmental Quality

Land and Water Management Division
2100 West M-32
Gaylord MI, 49735
989-731-4920

File No. 02-40-0016-P

Date: August 16, 2002

PUBLIC NOTICE

Carol Dubuc, 12618 – 10 Mile Road, South Lyon, Michigan 48178, has applied to this office for a permit under authority of Part 303, Wetlands Protection, of the Natural Resources and Environmental Protection Act, 1994 PA 451, as amended. The applicant proposes to construct a new home, pond and driveway within wetlands for the purpose of providing a single family home. The home foundation will be a full basement or a crawl space depending on the soil type found during excavation. Approximately 1,178 cubic yards of soil will be excavated if a basement is possible, if not 589 cubic yards of soil will be excavated for a crawl space and 282 cubic yards will be used as backfill around the home foundation. Approximately 106 cubic yards will be excavated for the garage and 262 cubic yards will be used as backfill around the garage. Approximately 711 cubic yards will be excavated for the pond of which 148 cubic yards will be used as a berm around the pond. Approximately 266 cubic yards of fill will be used in the septic system, and 266 cubic yards of fill will be used for the driveway. The total area of wetland impacted on this site is 20,676 square feet or .47 acres with a total of 1,024 cubic yards of fill. The entire lot is within regulated wetlands and no mitigation is proposed. The project is located in T28N, R8W, Section 30, Clearwater Township, Kalkaska County, Michigan, in accordance with plans attached to this notice.

THIS NOTICE IS NOT A PERMIT

When an application is received for a permit to authorize work in wetlands of the State of Michigan, pursuant to PART 303, WETLANDS PROTECTION, OF THE NATURAL RESOURCES AND ENVIRONMENTAL PROTECTION ACT, 1994 PA 451, AS AMENDED, provides that the department shall submit copies for review to the director of public health, the city, village or township, and the county where the project is to be located, the local soil conservation district, the local watershed council organized under Part 311, if any, the local port commission, if any. Additionally, notification is provided to certain persons as provided by statute or determined by the department.

A city, village, township or county wishing to make comments on the proposed project shall furnish this office with their comments in writing no later than 45 days from the date of this notice. All other persons wishing to make comments shall furnish their comments to this office within 20 days after date of this notice. Unless a written request for a public hearing on this project is filed with the department within 20 days after submission of this notice, the department may approve or disapprove the permit application without a public hearing. The determination as to whether a permit will be issued or a public hearing held will be based on an evaluation of all relevant factors as defined in Section 30311 of the part, including the effect of the proposed work on the public trust or interest. Written comments on these factors will be made part of the file and will be considered in determining if it is in the public interest to grant a permit. Objections must be factual and specific and fully describe the reasons upon which any objection is founded.

cc: DNR, Wildlife – Natural Heritage   DNR, Fisheries - Cadillac
      DNR, Wildlife - Cadillac   Kalkaska Co. Health Dept.
      Kalkaska Co. Clerk   Clearwater Township Clerk
      Kalkaska Co. Drain Comm.   Kalkaska Soil Conservation Dist.
      MUCC   History Division
      Carol Dubuc, applicant   Tip of Mitt Watershed Council
      Dan Bramlage   Paul Dore
      Elk-Skegemog Lake Assoc.   Kalkaska Co. CEA

124

4) Adjacent landowners (these individuals are often very helpful in providing information about the site);

5) The type and extent of the activity (this is critical when assessing project impacts);

6) The wetland boundaries (keep in mind that the boundaries as drawn on the application materials may be those of the applicant and subject to agency verification); and

7) The purpose of the proposed activity (this is critical when determining if the proposed project is dependent on being located in a wetland and if there are available alternatives).

Step Two: Gather information.
Now that you have the permit application in your hand, it is time to apply your knowledge regarding wetland definitions, functions and values, and the appropriate wetland regulatory standards. To be most effective, any individual or group commenting on an application should have first-hand knowledge of the wetland values and functions of each site in order to determine the potential project impacts. Fish and wildlife values, shoreline stabilization values, hydrologic values, endangered or threatened plants and animals, nutrient and sediment retention capabilities, recreational uses, and any other benefits should be identified.

Information can be sought from a variety of sources. Although not always granted, permission to visit the site should be requested from the landowner. If permission is not granted, then the site should be investigated from adjacent private or public land. The informational resources mentioned in Chapter Three should be reviewed for pertinent information regarding the wetlands on site. The MDEQ staff person who is responsible for reviewing the application can be an excellent resource to help you understand the project as proposed. Other agencies such as the Michigan Natural Features Inventory, the U.S. Fish and Wildlife Service, and college and university faculty may provide valuable information. It is very helpful in the evaluation of a project if people with knowledge of the site provide information regarding the functions that the wetlands provide. For instance, in regards to habitat values, reliable information regarding animals, birds, or fish, etc., that use the wetland should be collected.

Step Three: Apply the regulatory standards.
The effectiveness of your comments will depend upon how relevant they are to the regulatory standards that the agency staff must apply. The requirements for Part 303 and the Section 404(b)(1) Guidelines are presented in Chapter Eight. In reviewing both the Corps and MDEQ public notices, there are three main questions that the wetland protection advocate should always consider. These questions effectively summarize the regulatory standards.

1) Do feasible and prudent (or "practicable" in Corps' permits) alternatives exist? If the project is not dependent upon being placed in a wetland, then less damaging alternatives are presumed to exist. Although by law the applicant has the burden of proving that no alternatives exist, often the alternatives analysis provided by the applicant is very superficial. Common alternatives that

125

minimize impacts on the wetland resource include the use of upland building sites, alternate methods of construction to minimize fill, or bridges over wetlands instead of culverts and fill. Remember, alternatives can also include practicable alternate locations not presently under the applicant's control but reasonably available. Local knowledge regarding alternatives can be very important. Because local citizens are familiar with the area in question, they may know about alternatives (such as available land or other access sites) that are not apparent to the regulatory staff.

2) Is the project in the public interest? The degradation of wetlands harms the public by effectively depriving the functions and values that those wetlands provide. When determining if a project is in the public interest, consider the following questions: Is there a demonstrable need in the community for the project? Will the benefits of the project to the community outweigh the negative harm to the public?

3) Will an unacceptable disruption to the aquatic resources result? When trying to assess the disruption to the aquatic resources, consider the following questions: What individual and cumulative impacts will the proposed project have on public and private uses of the wetland and the wetland's natural functions? Is the wetland habitat for endangered, threatened, rare, or special concern plants and animals? Have the impacts been minimized to the greatest extent possible? Will negative impacts be appropriately mitigated by the applicant?

Step Four: Take action.

After answering the questions above, the wetland advocate must determine whether or not to take action. If the project has no alternatives, is in the public interest, and will have an acceptable disruption on the aquatic resources, then there is no need for further involvement. However, this is seldom the case. In practically all cases, citizens can provide comment valuable to the permitting process. The most effective ways to provide comment are through letters and public hearings.

Most concerns can be adequately expressed by letter. Written comments should always indicate the application or process number and be addressed to the contact person in the written notice, as this ensures that the comments will be considered for the appropriate application. Written comments to the MDEQ or Corps should be straightforward and factual. Opposition to issuance of a permit or suggestions for modifications should be stated clearly. Comments should include information on environmental impact and statutory compliance, including local ordinances. If a project violates a local code, the MDEQ may deny the permit. If you plan to engage in follow-up activities, request that you be notified regarding the agency's final decision.

The Corps will send a copy of every written comment to the applicant. The applicant is given the opportunity to respond and encouraged to contact those who have commented. Some applicants directly contact those who file comments to discuss their concerns. In many cases, this provides a good forum to discuss alternatives that minimize or avoid wetland impacts.

When submitting your written comments, you may choose to request a public hearing. The wetland advocate must be strategic when determining when to call for a public hearing. Although the Corps is given some discretion when a public hearing is requested, the MDEQ is required to hold one. The regulatory agencies have limited resources. Public hearings that are called for reasons extraneous to wetland protection will do nothing to protect wetland resources. Staff time spent on superfluous public hearings takes time away from duties such as enforcement or investigating potential violations. Unnecessary hearings can work against the wetland advocate by providing the opportunity for the applicant to make his or her case stronger.

Public hearings should be requested when greater public involvement would be effective or when written comments may not be adequate. Public hearings can be useful for providing additional comment on applications where large projects are proposed that would impact many individuals, involve wetlands important for maintaining the water quality of a lake or stream, have valuable fish and wildlife habitat, serve important hydrological functions, or are rare or representative examples of particular wetland types. In addition, public hearings often serve to educate the local community about wetland values and the wetland regulatory process, while giving the public a chance to have their voices heard.

A written statement should be prepared in advance of the hearing, and the major points of the statement should be presented at the hearing. The written statement should be left with the hearing officer for the official record. Any opposition to the project should be explained and justified, factually and succinctly. Additional comments may be submitted after the hearing if necessary.

It is important to understand that public hearings have their shortcomings. These shortcomings arise from the disparity between agency staff obligations and citizen expectations. The technical purpose of a public hearing is for the agencies to gather public comment on only those issues that are pertinent to the specific statute being implemented. Citizens often request a public hearing because they desire a public forum to discuss all aspects of a proposed project. They are frustrated when the Corps or MDEQ hearings officer does not answer their question or consider relevant those comments that are not germane to the statute.

127

An alternative to this is to call for, and in many cases coordinate, a public meeting. This provides the opportunity for the citizens to discuss all issues related to the project in addition to wetlands impacts. Although public meetings are sometimes called by MDEQ staff to discuss the project, they are often coordinated by a local government, local citizens, or the applicant themselves. For a public meeting to be effective, all stakeholders in the project should be invited and the meeting should be run by an experienced facilitator to ensure a productive discussion.

Step Five: Follow-up on agency decisions.

In most cases, after a letter is sent or a public hearing is held, the citizen and the agency staff person never have another interaction. Follow-up on agency actions is important to the wetland advocate. A request for notification of the final permit decision will usually be granted. However, if for some reason it is not, the permit decision can be requested in writing under the Freedom of Information Act (FOIA).

If the final decision is to deny the permit, be aware that the applicant can always reapply. More importantly however, be aware of what wetland activists call "post-denial negotiations." This occurs when the applicant agrees to modify the proposed project in a way the MDEQ can accept after the permit is denied. Unfortunately, this post-denial negotiation is not conducted with any public input or oversight. Many a wetland advocate has been very frustrated to see the bulldozers on the site of a project for which the application had been denied, only to

find that the applicant and the MDEQ had struck a compromise after the denial letter. The only way to keep from being blindsided is to communicate with your MDEQ field staff frequently (either through informal communications or formal FOIA requests) to find out if post-denial negotiations are taking place.

If the permit is issued, make sure you understand the permit conditions, if any. Noncompliance with the conditions of a permit constitutes a violation of the wetland protection statutes. Agency enforcement of the provisions may depend on citizen notification of the violation. In addition, follow up on agency decisions can provide useful background when assessing cumulative impacts in a watershed, and provides helpful direction for future wetland protection efforts.

ENSURING ENFORCEMENT

Many wetlands are degraded due to ignorance of permit standards or before necessary permits are obtained. Both the MDEQ and the Corps are responsible for enforcing their respective wetland protection programs against unauthorized and unpermitted activities. Violators of both state and federal acts can be made to restore the wetland to its natural state and/or be subject to fines and jail sentences (see previous chapter).

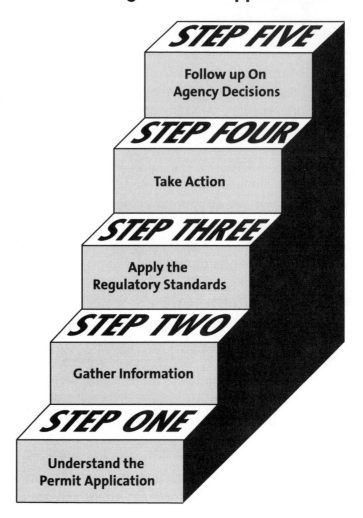

Steps To Reviewing Dredge and Fill Applications

STEP FIVE
Follow up On Agency Decisions

STEP FOUR
Take Action

STEP THREE
Apply the Regulatory Standards

STEP TWO
Gather Information

STEP ONE
Understand the Permit Application

Reporting Violations

Citizen complaints frequently trigger enforcement actions. As agency staff resource limitations provide for minimal enforcement, citizens can serve as the "eyes and ears" to ensure that wetlands are not being illegally degraded. However, to participate in enforcement actions effectively, the appropriate types of information must be reported to the regulatory agencies. Nobody benefits from inaccurate violation reports, as they waste valuable regulatory staff time and result in overall fewer enforcement actions. To make sure that your role in enforcing wetland regulations is as effective as possible, the following process is recommended:

Step One: Assess the wetland.
Citizens reporting violations should be able to provide information regarding the following:

128

1) The exact location of the wetland, including Township, Range, and Section numbers (include detailed maps when possible);

2) Evidence showing that the area is indeed a wetland (see Chapter Three); and

3) Circumstances to show that the wetland is likely to be jurisdictional under state and federal law.

Step Two: Assess the activities.
Do the activities indeed constitute violations of state and federal wetland regulations? The exact activities that are taking place in the wetland must be assessed and the dates these activities took place must be included. Keep in mind that there are many exempted activities in both state and federal wetland regulations (e.g., cutting trees in a wetland). Complaints to the regulatory agencies regarding exempted activities will not be addressed by agency staff.

Step Three: Assess the ownership, agents, contractors, or controlling interests.
Any agency enforcement action must be addressed to the appropriate responsible parties. Information regarding the property owners and the individuals or contractors who are engaged in the wetland activity saves agency staff valuable time. If you are unsure of the property ownership, a call to the county equalization office will provide the appropriate information quickly.

Step Four: Determine if permits have been issued.
Many complaints that are reported to the MDEQ or Corps involve activities that have been permitted. Unless there is a gross violation of permit standards, the agency staff will not investigate activities in wetlands that have received a permit. However, remember that in areas of joint jurisdiction, a permit is needed from both the MDEQ and the Corps. In these areas, activities done in compliance with a permit from one agency may constitute a violation of the other's wetland protection statute. Determining if a permit has been issued can sometimes be difficult. Usually, an issued permit will be posted at the site. If this is not the case, the landowner or agent should be able to provide a copy of the permit. The appropriate agency can also be contacted to provide information on permit issuance.

129

Step Five: Report to the appropriate agencies.
Getting your violation report to the appropriate agency staff person is very important. If you are in areas of joint jurisdiction, both the MDEQ District Field Office and Corps should be notified by letter and phone. In areas of sole MDEQ jurisdiction, the MDEQ District Field Office should be notified. In addition, in several circumstances, Conservation Officers have been effective in initiating enforcement actions. Violations should also be communicated to these individuals. If a local ordinance is in place, contact the appropriate local officials also. A municipality may be able to issue a stop work order in a more timely manner than Corps or MDEQ staff.

When reporting violations, you should both call the appropriate agency and write a letter or send an e-mail. The phone call may initiate the enforcement action, and it is harder for agency staff to ignore a letter in the file. In addition, you may want the written documentation of your report when following-up and encouraging enforcement action. In addition, violations in which several calls or letters are received tend to get more attention. For this reason, other wetland protection advocates should also be encouraged to report particular violations.

To be most effective, letters and phone calls should include all the information listed above in a clear manner. In addition, as the agency staff may want additional information, your phone number and address should also be included. The identity of those reporting violations will be kept confidential to the greatest extent possible. However, the citizen wetland protection advocate should be aware that the violator can request information regarding who reported the violation through the Freedom of Information Act. Although this is unlikely, you may want to file an anonymous complaint. Be aware that MDEQ and Corps staff are less likely to respond to anonymous complaints.

Step Six: Follow up on your violation report.

Due to a variety of constraints, enforcement action is not always a high priority for the MDEQ and the Corps. As a result, it is very important to follow up on enforcement activities with the appropriate agency staff person. Not only can citizens provide additional information, but they can also provide motivation to agency staff.

OTHER OPTIONS

130

The wetland protection advocate may find that the Corps and MDEQ fail to take enforcement action against a violator. In that situation, other avenues are available to ensure that the law is enforced. Options such as the Contested Case process or filing legal suits for injunctive relief provide mechanisms for citizens to further protect wetlands when the activities of MDEQ or the Corps are inadequate. Although these options do provide opportunities, they are not without cost.

Contested Case Hearings

Under Michigan's Administrative Procedures Act (P.A. 306 of 1969) all citizens are provided the opportunity to file for an administrative hearing to contest any action or inaction of a state agency. The contested case hearing process is commonly used by applicants to contest permit denials, but can also be used by wetland protection advocates to contest permit issuances or other regulatory activities (often called "third party contested cases"). The MDEQ has a packet of materials explaining the contested case process available to the public.

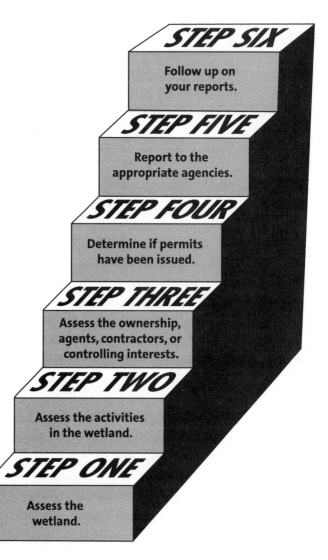

Steps To Follow When Reporting Violations

STEP SIX
Follow up on your reports.

STEP FIVE
Report to the appropriate agencies.

STEP FOUR
Determine if permits have been issued.

STEP THREE
Assess the ownership, agents, contractors, or controlling interests.

STEP TWO
Assess the activities in the wetland.

STEP ONE
Assess the wetland.

The contested case process has limited utility for the wetland protection advocate. There are two major drawbacks: 1) it does not provide injunctive relief, and 2) there is currently a two year wait for a contested case hearing. As a result, third party contested cases can be filed, but wetland dredge and fill activities done in compliance with an issued permit can still continue. Theoretically, by the time the contested case hearing is held, the work could be completed. For this reason, lawsuits requesting injunctive relief are usually filed along with the contested case hearing request.

131

Judicial Remedies

Unlike the citizen suit provisions in the Clean Water Act, Michigan's wetland statute does not specifically authorize citizens to file suit to ensure that the law is not violated. However, there are other legal avenues. The Michigan Environmental Protection Act (MEPA) (Part 17 of Act 451 of 1994) authorizes any person, organization, or governmental body to file suit against any other person, organization, or governmental body to prevent or minimize environmental degradation. On the federal level, Section 505 of the Clean Water Act allows citizens to bring suit to enforce the guidelines in Section 404. In addition, since the destruction or impairment of the values that wetlands provide may adversely impact adjacent landowners, common law doctrines, including riparian rights, nuisance, and trespass law may be applicable.

Although these options exist, they are seldom utilized. This may be due to the fact that substantial resources (time and money) are usually required to pursue these options. In legal challenges to wetland activities, it is critical to have specific and credible scientific information. Expert witnesses will be brought in to support both sides of the conflict; without credible experts legal challenges to enforce wetland protection regulations will be unsuccessful. In addition to biological information, engineering and economic information may also be necessary. In all cases where the wetland advocate considers pursuing legal means, an attorney skilled in environmental law should be consulted. The Michigan Environmental Law Center is a non-profit organization specializing in representing citizens in environmental litigation, research, and referrals (see Appendix A for contact information).

ADVOCACY GUIDELINES

Citizen involvement is critical to protecting Michigan's wetlands. It is important that citizens take this role seriously and participate with integrity. Even though wetland advocates may feel like the "deck is stacked against us," following certain guidelines will ensure that public participation is given the respect that it deserves. Although each of us go about protecting wetlands in our own way, these general guidelines help ensure that public participation is taken seriously:

1) Base your position on solid technical information and sound policy analysis;

2) Gather information in legal ways;

3) Respect the legal rights of others, including the potential violator;

4) Don't use wetlands protection as a "red herring" to further other goals that have nothing to do with wetlands; and

5) Continually work to improve and expand your knowledge of wetland definitions, values, functions, and the regulations that protect these valuable landforms.

More information about increasing your ability to be an effective advocate can be found in Chapter Fourteen.

132

Wetland Protection Spotlight

Cross Village "Harbor of Refuge"
Jenny Feldmann

When newspapers in the small community of Cross Village announced that the Michigan Department of Natural Resources (MDNR) had dusted off an old plan to develop the Cross Village public beach into a "harbor of refuge," most residents thought it sounded like a good idea. The plan, as local citizens soon found out, went far beyond just a safe refuge. At stake was a unique beach, dune, and interdunal wetland swale complex, and three species of threatened and endangered plants, the last public beach access site in Cross Village, and a small beach-nesting bird, the endangered Piping Plover. "This was not just a safe refuge project, this was a major commercial marina," recalls Jenny Feldmann, one of the Cross Village residents who worked to save the beach and wetland complex.

133

The area where the marina was to be built includes a small community bathing beach, where parents take their children to swim, a small boat ramp, and a very small parking lot. "On any given day, you might drive past and see maybe five cars parked there," Jenny notes. The MDNR had big plans for this little beach. The project plans called for two separate breakwaters totaling over 1900 feet, two connecting dikes totaling over 900 feet, 150 boat slips, two boat launches, and a parking lot for eighty cars, which would completely alter this fragile and unique ecosystem.

After hearing about the project, Jenny became very concerned about the possible effects. "I became alarmed at [the MDNR's] lack of consideration for the environment, the community, and the economic base. What they were proposing would have dramatically changed the environment and community of Cross Village." And so Jenny and other concerned citizens formed a loose coalition to protect the area and began to try to get community support to halt the project as proposed. This group was simple and unstructured—just a group of neighbors who would meet occasionally. This arrangement, while loose, proved to be very effective.

The group began to voice their concerns, and the lines were soon drawn. "It was a very divided community for a long time. There were some people who wanted economic development at any cost," Jenny recalls. "It wasn't even that we were opposed to the project altogether. It was just the shear scale at which it was proposed." Despite the difficulty of getting people visibly involved, due to the smallness of the community, Jenny and many others began a letter-writing campaign. They wrote hundreds of letters, and made many, many phone calls.

They first tried to work with the agency to scale back the project, but their concerns went unaddressed. "We were dealing with people who have a lot of power in terms of the decision-making process. There was just no talking to them. There was no reasoning involved....That's when you have to get loud and start making noise." And they did. They did get some response from the Army Corps of Engineers, particularly when they learned that the endangered Piping Plover, a dune-dwelling shorebird, was present in the area, and suspected to be nesting. The MDNR, however, would not consider the citizens' concerns about the plover unless the site was used for nesting. At the eleventh hour, a nest was found in the area of the proposed project. "Timing was critical. All of a sudden a nest was discovered. It got to the point where people who wanted the development were accusing the rest of us of planting the nest," Jenny laughs.

It was a long fight, but finally, the project, which was flawed from the outset, was stopped. Today, Piping Plovers are still nesting on the beach, kids can still swim at the bathing beach, and there is no asphalt covering the rare dune ecosystem or conveying polluted runoff into the shoreline wetlands.

Jenny's sudden immersion into grassroots organizing taught her a lot. "One thing I would advise people is to know what's going on in your community. Pay attention. Read the paper. That was one of the ways we became aware of the project. It's not as if they send out letters to everyone saying, 'We want to do this in your backyard.' You need to pay attention to what's going on around you at a really local level."

Chapter 10

Citizen Involvement in Local Wetland Protection

I n Michigan, local government has traditionally shouldered the primary responsibility for land use control through zoning. Local wetlands protection in addition to MDEQ regulation is consistent with this home rule tradition. Michigan's wetland protection statute authorizes municipalities to regulate wetlands using the same definition, regulatory standards, and application procedures established in state law. This authority is supplemental to the existing authority of a municipality to enact zoning ordinances in the public interest under the County, Township, and City and Village Zoning Enabling Acts. Given the importance of the functions and values that wetlands provide, some municipalities in Michigan have adopted local wetland zoning ordinances.

Many local governments have enacted stand-alone wetland regulatory ordinances or integrated wetland protection into their local zoning. Although the type and level of protection provided by these local ordinances varies greatly, all of them ensure that local citizens can play a role in the process. The Michigan municipalities that have enacted wetland protection ordinances are listed in the appendices. If you live in one of these municipalities, you should contact the appropriate local agency to see how you can participate in the process.

Indirectly, county sanitary codes and local ordinances which regulate the placement of septic systems may be used to protect wetlands. If a sanitary code prohibits septic systems in areas with high water tables, then those areas are not likely to be used as building sites requiring dredging and filling. These high water table areas may also be wetlands. Thus, in some cases, enforcement of sanitary code provisions may prevent wetland destruction that might result from housing development. However, engineered "mound" septic fields are often permitted in wetlands and provide a loophole around the sanitary code standards.

At a minimum, review of state and federal wetland dredge and fill applications should include an analysis of the local zoning ordinance to assure compliance with any local provisions that might be used to protect the wetland. If the project violates the local ordinance, the MDEQ and Corps should be notified during the public comment process. In addition, the local zoning administrator or reviewing body should be made aware of the proposed activity to ensure appropriate local review. Keep in mind that local governments have 45 days to review the application and provide comments – where the citizens only have 20 days.

Local wetland regulation often generates much controversy. Although local municipalities seek to enact wetlands ordinances in an effort to provide for the health, safety, and general welfare of local residents, opponents often see these efforts as "over-regulation." Regardless, from the perspective of the resource, the individual wishing to alter the resource, and the general public, many benefits result from the local regulation of wetlands in addition to the state and federal programs.

136

Benefits of Local Wetlands Regulations

Benefits to the resource:

- Local wetlands ordinances can protect important wetlands not covered by state or federal law.

- Local zoning regulations can require ecological buffers to protect the ecological integrity of a wetland system.

- Local involvement in wetland regulation can provide the opportunity to integrate wetland protection into development plans early in the process.

Benefits to the applicant:

- Local wetland ordinances can provide the early identification of lands subject to wetland permits, thus reducing costs and time delays.

- Local units have the authority to provide incentives for wetland protection that state and federal governments cannot, including conservation design options, density bonuses, zoning variances, and tax incentives.

- Local involvement in wetland regulation helps ensure complete applications and thus expedite and clarify state and federal permit processes.

Benefits to the general public:

- Local wetlands ordinances foster better land-use decisions, thus ensuring the long-term integrity of a community.

- Insofar as wetlands will be better protected, their presence will contribute to community well-being with improved water quality, reduced flood damages, wildlife habitat, and valuable recreation and open space.

- Local ordinances avoid public and private expenditures to replace the functions that wetlands provide naturally, such as flood and erosion control.

- By protecting wetlands, local regulations save individual homeowners money by avoiding the costs of settling foundations, driveways breaking up prematurely, leaking basements, and other adverse results of wetland development.

Perhaps the greatest advantage of local wetlands regulations is the ability to achieve quick response to violations. Local government inspectors make frequent visits to construction sites. The presence of easily accessible and responsive local enforcement personnel can ensure compliance and address violations in a timely manner. Conversely, state and federal enforcement actions may proceed very slowly through the court system.

PROMOTING ADOPTION OF LOCAL WETLAND PROTECTION PROGRAMS

Communities that do not currently have wetland provisions in their zoning codes should be urged to enact them. Citizen wetland protection advocates can play an integral role in initiating regulatory and nonregulatory wetland protection activities at the local level. There are many local wetlands protection options available and each community is different. Successful wetland protection zoning provisions or ordinances must be individually tailored to meet a community's needs. Many communities typically combine two or more options to fit the communities' needs and established regulatory framework and procedures. Although the process that leads to the enactment of successful wetland protection at the local level is different in each case, the following steps serve as a general guide to follow when initiating local wetlands protection efforts.

Step One: Identify community leaders supportive of wetland protection.
Enacting any ordinance is a political process. To be successful, community opinion leaders must be educated on wetland values and enlisted to support wetland protection. It is also important that the wetland protection advocate involve leaders from the regulated community (developers, contractors, Realtors, etc.) in supporting the efforts. If these individuals are not involved in the process at the beginning, they may block the process later on.

Step Two: Encourage your local government to investigate their options.
Citizen wetland protection advocates should provide information to the local government officials regarding the benefits of wetlands protection at the local level, the range of regulatory and nonregulatory options, what has worked in other communities, the critical issues that must be addressed, and innovative ways to fund local wetland protection programs. In addition to the local initiatives that focus solely on regulation of wetlands, local governments can also initiate natural features ordinances, stormwater management guidelines, and other resource management options that will benefit wetlands.

Step Three: Educate the local community and media.
To be successful, local wetlands protection efforts must have a broad base of support. An informed citizenry is critical to ensuring this support. Since local television stations and newspapers play a very important role in forming attitudes, wetland protection advocates should make extra efforts to ensure media sources are well informed.

Step Four: Participate in the process.
If the local unit of government is serious about protecting wetlands and there is adequate public support, they will begin to engage in developing a wetland protection program. In most cases, this will involve drafting zoning provisions or ordinance language by the planning commission, planning staff, or the establishment of a committee. In each of these situations, the wetland advocate will have the opportunity to participate either through public hearings or serving on an advisory committee.

The ordinance should be tailored to the local government's available resources. Clear, detailed, and reasonable standards and requirements are the key to successful wetland zoning. To ensure success, the ordinance should be in accordance with prior planning efforts and be based on a thorough knowledge of the local wetland resource. Since existing state and federal programs will impact the local efforts, the appropriate agencies should be consulted prior to enactment.

Step Five: Ensure enforcement.
Once a good ordinance is in place, proper administration and enforcement become crucial. Funding is essential for good enforcement, as well as community support for the ordinance. Citizen wetland protection advocates must continue to be involved in raising awareness of wetlands protection in the community, participating in the local wetlands review, and reporting violations.

LOCAL WETLAND PROTECTION OPPORTUNITIES

Local wetland protection can take many forms. Some communities integrate wetland protection provisions into their zoning ordinances, while others have comprehensive stand-alone ordinances with regulatory standards, procedures for permits, and enforcement provisions. The type of wetland protection program enacted in a municipality is based on many aspects, the local political climate, available funding or funding mechanism, staff expertise, etc. Accordingly, every local ordinance will be different. Although each local wetland protection program is unique, it is important to note that all local regulatory programs must be consistent with the provisions in the state regulatory program.

Because local government is "closer to the people," there are great opportunities for citizens to help local officials develop sound wetland protection programs. A dozen potential options are included below. In addition to these, there are many opportunities for local governments to join with local conservancies and watershed councils to initiate creative public/private partnerships to protect wetlands. Local citizens are often the most effective catalyst for passing local wetland ordinances.

Local Wetland Protection Option #1
Linking Local Approval to State and Federal Permits

The most basic approach to local wetland protection is to tie local approval for a proposed development to the acquisition of the necessary state and federal wetland permits required for project completion. This regulatory technique links approval for all local permits to the receipt of state and federal wetland permits (or alternatively, a letter from the agency stating that no permit is necessary). The advantages of this local/state/federal regulatory networking approach include:

- It facilitates communication between local government and federal and state regulatory agencies;

- It ensures that wetland issues are considered (at least according to state and federal laws and priorities);

- It provides information on water resources to the local government with little additional cost; and

- It can help local governments better understand the environmental aspects of project design.

If local governments pursue this easy but effective option, some local wetland conflicts can be avoided altogether. The shortcoming of this approach is that it leaves some significant land use decisions regarding wetlands entirely up to state and federal officials, often limiting local government involvement in the water resource decision–making process.

Local Wetland Protection Option #2
Local Stand-Alone Wetland Protection Ordinances

In Michigan, local governments have been delegated the primary responsibility of making land use decisions. Given the importance of the functions and values that wetlands provide communities, and the demands for wetland protection that more and more Michigan residents are making, many Michigan municipalities have adopted local wetland protection ordinances. The following is a discussion on some of the most important considerations regarding the implementation of a local wetland protection ordinance.

Benefits to Communities That Protect Wetlands

The MDEQ and the Corps regulate certain activities which impact wetland resources in Michigan. While the state has jurisdiction over many wetland areas, protection of many isolated wetlands is absent. Municipalities often get involved in local wetland protection because many of Michigan's isolated wetlands are not protected by state or federal law, yet members of their community demand this protection. This absence of protection is not because these wetlands are not highly valuable for flood control, pollution uptake, or wildlife habitat, indeed many of these isolated wetlands have more value on a per acre basis than regulated wetlands. The lack of protection of small wetlands arose out of political compromise when the wetland laws were originally drafted.

Community Considerations When Developing a Wetland Protection Ordinance

139

Land use regulations vary considerably among communities, just as landscapes and local concerns vary from community to community. Part 303 of the Natural Resources and Environmental Protection Act (Act 451 of 1994) authorizes municipalities to regulate wetlands as long as they use the same wetland definition, regulatory standards (local governments can regulate wetlands smaller than five acres), and application process as the state. If you are interested in pursing the adoption of a wetland protection ordinance in your community the following strategic points will help ensure success.

Mapping Wetland Areas

If a local government is going to regulate wetlands they must produce a wetland map to accompany the ordinance. Although the state wetland protection statute does not require any specific data layers to be included in a local wetland inventory, the National Wetlands Inventory (NWI), Michigan Resource Inventory System (MIRIS), soil surveys, and current aerial photos, with some field verification are often used. This map will serve as a guide for the community, not as a detailed site specific jurisdictional map. In fact, it is clearly stated in the statute that wetland inventories and maps are non-jurisdictional. Property owners must still conduct a wetland delineation on their land if activities are proposed in or near a wetland.

Communities have found it helpful to produce a wetland map as early as possible in the ordinance development process. Producing and disseminating a wetland map early clarifies the potential locations of wetlands for the public and allows property owners who may be affected by the regulations to understand how they may be impacted.

Networking and Coordination with MDEQ

Communities that have developed a wetland protection ordinance are required by Michigan's wetland statute to notify the Michigan Department of Environmental Quality. Communities should coordinate with MDEQ to improve the efficiency of the permitting process. A local unit of government that adopts an ordinance regulating wetlands must use an application form supplied by the MDEQ. If the municipality requires additional information for its own ordinance, they may attach a supplemental form.

Determining the Size of Wetland to Regulate

Communities choose to protect wetlands because many of Michigan's isolated wetlands are not protected by state or federal law, despite the fact that these wetlands provide vital water quality, wildlife, and flood control functions.

Some communities have a minimum regulatory size limit. For example, Meridian Township in Ingham County regulates wetlands as small as a quarter of an acre. Other communities, such as Superior Township in Washtenaw County, have avoided setting a lower limit and regulate all wetland areas regardless of size. The advantage of including wetlands of any size in a local ordinance is that the decision whether to allow alteration of a wetland can be made based on the wetlands value to the community, rather than an arbitrary size minimum.

Providing Community Education

No protection effort will stand if the community is not supportive. Early community outreach and proper public notification of ordinance development are essential components of the adoption/implementation process. Yet there will always be naysayers. Producing and distributing the wetland map early in the process gives community residents adequate time to learn if wetlands might be on their land and how this may affect them. Perhaps the most important part of community education is raising awareness about the function and values that wetlands provide.

Legal Review

Care must be given to integrating new standards in a way that minimizes legal risks associated with any challenge to the regulations. Local wetland regulatory programs must be consistent with the standards put forth in Part 303 of P.A. 451 of 1994. It is important to ensure that the municipal attorney is involved throughout the ordinance development process.

Consistently Apply Regulations

Consistent application of the adopted wetland regulations is essential to protecting a local wetland ordinance from challenge. The first time a zoning administrator or planning commission fails to consistently apply a regulation, it will sow the seeds for invalidation and strengthen the conviction of opponents. It is important that all administrators and planning commissioners understand how the ordinance is to be applied and that staff are well trained in wetland ecology or that the local government retains competent consultants to provide technical assistance.

Set Examples

An important nonregulatory first step at implementation is to solicit the support of one or more landowners who are already voluntarily abiding by the new regulations (or better yet -- exceeding them). This will stimulate similar efforts and will greatly ease the burden of the administrative staff. It will also reduce the likelihood of legal challenges. Formal support of the business community (such as the Chamber of Commerce) is invaluable.

Wetland Mitigation

In consideration of all development proposals, the first priority is to avoid wetlands. If wetlands cannot be avoided, then impacts should be minimized and mitigation (creation of new wetlands as replacement for lost wetlands) required for the loss. Due to the widely accepted fact that created wetlands are generally less effective at providing wetland functions than natural wetlands, the replacement ratio for wetland mitigation should exceed a 1:1 ratio. The MDEQ's current mitigation rules call for ratios that range from 1.5:1 to 5:1 for creation or restoration; 10:1 for preservation; automatically doubled ratios for after-the-fact permits; and increased ratios for out-of-kind mitigation.

Summary

Communities which adopt wetland protection ordinances will see tremendous benefits from their labor. Highly valued open space will be preserved, developments will be designed with a greater sensitivity to the natural landscape, and the valuable functions that wetlands provide will be preserved for the benefit of all residents. It takes time, commitment, and a certain level of economic capacity to successfully implement a wetland protection ordinance, but the short- and long-term benefits will be obvious.

Local Wetland Protection Option #3
Floodplain Management at the Local Level

Protecting floodplains from development is an urgent public health and safety matter for officials in many Michigan communities. Floodplains are the natural low areas adjacent to surface water bodies that hold floodwaters. It is estimated that 80% of the nation's wetlands are found within the 100 year floodplain. The 100 year floodplain is the area with a one percent chance of flooding in any given year. Since it is common to find extensive wetlands in the floodplains of rivers, lakes, and streams, floodplain management generally involves wetland protection.

When floodplains are altered by development, filling, sedimentation, and/or vegetation destruction, their ability to handle floodwaters are greatly reduced, aggravating flooding and subsequent flood damages, especially downstream. Communities throughout the state have developed specific regulations to control development in floodplains. Local floodplain regulations generally promote the following goals:

- Control the alteration of natural floodplains, stream channels, and natural protective barriers (e.g., floodplain slopes) which help accommodate flood waters;

- Control filling, grading, and dredging which may increase flooding;

- Prevent construction of flood barriers which will unnaturally divert flood waters or may increase flood hazards in other areas;

- Prevent encroachment on stream and river channels;

- Prevent or limit the removal of vegetation in the floodplain;

- Slow the stormwater loading (runoff) rate to prevent "flash" floods that generate excessive sediment and channel damage;

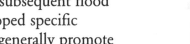

- Keep sediment from reaching stream and river channels;

- Promote intergovernmental cooperation (state, federal, and local coordination) through consistent application of regulations–so one unit of government does not transport flooding problems to another because of poor floodplain management; and

- Require that new structures are constructed above the 100 year flood elevation to reduce damage.

The MDEQ has jurisdiction over many floodplain areas, yet local governments can regulate development in floodplains through a separate floodplain ordinance or through special provisions in the zoning ordinance or building code. Coordinating state and local floodplain regulations is essential for appropriate management of floodplains.

Defining and Mapping Floodplains

One of the first steps for local governments interested in protecting floodplains is to delineate the floodplain area on an official map. This map becomes the basis for local regulations. (Using floodplain regulations may not protect isolated wetlands, or wetlands not found within the designated floodplain.) Many Michigan communities already have official floodplain maps, developed by the Federal Emergency Management Act (FEMA).

If a flood hazard map does not exist for a community, then the expertise of a wetland scientist or hydrologist may be required for the preparation of a map. The use of the National Wetlands Inventory (NWI) Map, Michigan Resource Inventory System (MIRIS) maps, soil surveys, current aerial photos, USGS topographic maps, and field verification will be necessary. This map will serve as a guide, not as a detailed site specific map. To inquire about the availability of flood hazard maps in your area contact the State Coordinating Office for the National Flood Insurance Program (NFIP) in Michigan at (517) 335-3176.

Zoning for Floodplain Protection

Floodplain zoning ordinances regulate the types of land uses that are permitted in the floodplain. Floodplain zoning districts only allow uses that are not susceptible to flood damage. Some land uses that are found to be less susceptible to flooding include recreation facilities, agriculture, conservation/education areas, and planned unit developments that cluster buildings out of the flood prone areas. Many communities with flooding problems participate in the NFIP. The NFIP sets minimum building code and subdivision standards that communities must meet to be eligible to receive federal flood insurance. These regulations are meant to protect buildings, roads, and utilities from flood damage as well as preventing these structures from exacerbating flood problems. These standards are often incorporated into their own floodplain ordinance or building code.

Planning and Public Floodplain Acquisition for Greenways and Parklands

Pro-active planning for the establishment of community greenways located in floodplain areas can create many economic benefits for a community. Park and recreation plans often target the acquisition of floodplain areas for use as passive nature recreation areas and to connect existing parks along a linear greenway, or for more intensive forms of recreation that are not permanently damaged by flooding (e.g., soccer or softball fields). Since floodplains are vulnerable to periodic flooding and the ability to develop these lands is marginal, they can often be purchased at reduced prices. Strategic long-range planning for protection and acquisition of floodplains by parks and

142

Minimum Requirements of National Floodplain Regulations

The National Flood Insurance Program is administered by the Federal Emergency Management Agency. For communities to be eligible for flood insurance the following minimum requirements must be met.

- All development in the 100 year floodplain base flow must have a permit from the community. "Development" is defined as any human-made change in the land, including new buildings, improvements to building, filling, grading, mining, dredging, etc.

- Development should not be allowed in the floodway. The floodway is defined as the channel and central portion of the floodplain that is needed to convey the 100 year flood flow of the stream. At a minimum, no development is allowed in the floodway if it will cause a harmful increase in flood flows. An engineering study is usually required to successfully meet this requirement.

- New buildings may be built in the floodplain, but they must be protected from damage by the base flood. The lowest floors of the building must be elevated above the 100 year flood elevation. Nonresidential buildings must be elevated or flood proofed. Because of the restrictions described above, buildings that are built in the floodplain are usually located outside the floodway. In addition, residential structures are prohibited in the floodway by state law.

- If repair of damage to an existing building is valued at more than 50% of the value of the original building, then it is considered a substantial improvement. A substantial improvement is treated as a new building and therefore is required to be above the 100 year flood elevation. Additions of any size are required to be elevated above the 100 year flood elevation by the building code.

For communities who are considering enrolling in NFIP, more comprehensive protection measures than those listed above are recommended. NFIP minimum requirements should be viewed as a starting point in the development of a local ordinance. Generally speaking, for true wetland protection more stringent standards need to be applied.

143

recreation commissions can contribute significantly to the protection of riparian wetlands as well as improve the quality of life benefits for the community.

Local Wetland Protection Option #4
Local Waterfront Setback Regulations

Michigan is blessed with numerous cherished waterways, from the magnificent Great Lakes, to stunning inland lakes, to trout-rich rivers. Due to a love of living near water, residential and recreational pressure to develop properties along lakes and streams is immense. Yet many of the remaining unbuilt waterfront properties contain severe environmental limitations such as poor soils for septic development, wetlands, or floodplains. Many of Michigan's wetlands are located in stream corridors and along lake shores. Areas where the land and water meet are among the most biologically significant of ecosystems— supporting diverse populations of vegetation, fish, and wildlife in a relatively small area. Undisturbed vegetation on and near the banks keeps sedimentation and flooding in check by slowing runoff and floodwaters and holding soil in place with extensive root systems. These can also be areas of great scenic beauty and attractive places for many recreational activities.

Important Elements of a Local Stream/River Corridor Protection Program

- Provide ample setbacks for sanitary facilities in corridor areas.

- Preserve a native vegetative strip immediately adjacent to the water.

- Establish structural setbacks from rivers and streams.

- Regulate road placement adjacent to the river or stream.

- Zone areas for low intensity development.

- Establish minimum lot size, frontage and width requirements.

- Prohibit new gas, oil, or salt brine wells within 300 feet of the river.

- Include reference to floodplain, soil, and sedimentation controls administered by other agencies in corridor regulations.

- Screen new structures with natural vegetation.

- Limit height of buildings so they do not intrude on natural bluff or tree lines.

- Limit commercial or industrial uses along corridors and regulate through special use permits, subject to predesignated standards.

- Promote intergovernmental coordination of regulations among communities along river and stream corridors—also coordinate efforts with state agency staff.

144

Natural Features Setbacks for Local Rivers and Streams

Although Michigan has one of the nation's premier natural river programs, it only focuses on rivers with exceptional recreational and aesthetic values and the designation process is very involved. Many of Michigan's rivers and streams will never be enrolled in this State of Michigan program, so protection efforts will fall on the shoulders of local government.

Any river or stream system can benefit from local zoning regulations similar to those used in the state and federal river protection programs. Local regulations should focus on minimizing the impacts of development on the river corridor, retaining its biological, open space, and natural character functions. Adequate community plans, maps and natural resource inventories are an essential base for local stream/river corridor regulations.

Natural Features Setbacks for Lake Shorelines

Biological and cultural functions of shorelines do not have to be at odds with one another. Proper management of shoreline development can allow the natural biological functions of the shoreline to continue while allowing human coexistence. The two most important management techniques are deep principal structure setbacks from the waterfront and the maintenance of natural vegetation along the shoreline to help stabilize banks, remove nutrients, and minimize erosion.

A key tool for local governments is greenbelts that protect natural vegetation along the shoreline. A minimum of 40 feet of greenbelt along a lake shore is a desirable goal. Lot size and dimension also have an impact on water quality protection. For new lots a minimum lot width of at least 100 feet with a minimum depth of 200 feet is desirable. Lot width-to-depth ratios of 1 to 3 are more appropriate in zoning districts adjacent to lakes and streams.

Local Wetland Protection Option #5
Local Stormwater Management

Stormwater management regulations are designed to address the challenges posed by flooding and nonpoint pollution. The term "nonpoint" refers to pollutants that originate from diffuse sources rather than a specific point or an easily identified source (e.g., from stormwater runoff vs. the outlet pipe of a wastewater treatment plant or industrial facility). Stormwater runoff can carry with it high concentrations of sediment (soil particles), hydrocarbons and other hazardous fluids like motor oil and antifreeze, pesticides, bacteria from animals, and nutrients from fertilizers.

Local governments are becoming increasingly involved in the administration of stormwater management activities, particularly in rapidly urbanizing areas where the impacts of development on water quality and quantity are most pronounced. In many areas of Michigan polluted runoff from lawns, roads, and agricultural areas can account for as much as 70% of the water quality problems of a waterway.

Research now shows that when a watershed reaches a level of 10% impervious cover (roads, parking lots, rooftops) that the water quality and fish habitat problems rapidly accelerate. By using effective site planning to reduce stormwater and soil erosion, local governments can protect wetlands and waterways from siltation, the creation of excessive imperviousness, and alterations in hydrology.

> ## Important Considerations When Developing Lakefront Setback Regulations
>
> In addition to the considerations listed for rivers and streams, consider these important elements when developing lakefront setback regulations.
>
> - Avoid structural encroachment of the surface waters except for uses traditionally dependent upon direct water access.
> - Encourage use of unmown grasses or shrubs with suckering root systems to act as filters for stormwater in areas adjacent to lakes or streams.
> - Screen unsightly or objectionable views, preferably with naturally occurring vegetation.
> - Minimize tree cutting or thinning of trees in areas adjacent to water bodies.
> - Isolate parking areas from shorelines.
> - Limit the amount of impervious surfaces allowed adjacent to the shoreline.
> - Promote intergovernmental management of shoreline areas (i.e., consistent regulation and enforcement by local governments that "share" a lake).

145

Site Planning for Stormwater Management

Site planning is an invaluable tool local governments can use when attempting to control the amount, quality, and timing of runoff to prevent its damaging effects on natural resources, private property, and public infrastructure. In the early stages of the site plan process the environmentally sensitive areas should be identified. For example, wetlands, floodplains, and steep slopes should all be identified and attempts made early on to incorporate these elements into site design as open space. The responsibility of who proposes and designs the specific stormwater and soil erosion functions during site planning is the role of the developer or landowner, yet local governments have a great deal of influence over how or what stormwater management measures are used.

Wetlands and wetland protection are an essential component in any stormwater management system. Wetlands are at times used as stormwater retention basins. This practice, although economically expedient, regularly degrades the ecological processes that sustain life in wetlands. Using wetlands as part of a stormwater management system should generally be discouraged unless the runoff from the development will not be significant or the system is engineered in such a way that allows stormwater releases into the wetland at the quantity, quality, frequency, and duration of the pre-development landscape.

Successful Stormwater Management

- Don't build what you can't maintain. Retention basins that are not regularly maintained can cause significant downstream damage.

- Use and protect the natural environment when planning a stormwater management project. Always consider the possible impact of stormwater runoff on wetlands and other natural features.

- Since everyone benefits from effective stormwater management, the economic responsibility should be shared equitably.

- Enforcing, maintaining, and building stormwater management facilities and regulations should be as fundamental as wastewater treatment and drinking water supply.

- Since drainage ways do not honor political jurisdictions, stormwater management systems should be based on watershed not political boundaries.

146

The following are a few elements that should be considered when reviewing site plans for stormwater management:

- Protect streambank and other natural vegetation and provide setbacks;

- Prohibit direct discharge of stormwater into wetlands;

- Prevent fill in wetlands, floodplains, and other natural stormwater collection areas;

- Set a limit on the percentage of impervious surfaces on a lot;

- Reduce design demands for curb and gutter, allow replacement with grassed swales where appropriate;

- Limit impervious surfaces by reducing parking area requirements;

- Require pervious surfaces whenever possible;

- Require a stormwater management plan at the site plan review stage for new, modified, or expanded developments such as on-site retention/detention for large developments; and

- Insure proper installation and maintenance of stormwater control measures to preserve the natural runoff system on and adjacent to development sites.

Urban Cooperation Agreements & Stormwater Management

Since stormwater runoff does not respect municipal boundaries, when relevant, local governments should attempt to cooperate and coordinate with surrounding units of government with regard to stormwater management. Cooperative agreements among local governments, known as urban cooperation agreements (UCA), are legally allowed under the Urban Cooperation Act of 1967. It has become increasingly common to manage and fund trans-boundary matters such as fire services, recreational facilities, water and sewer services using UCA's. Stormwater management is no different.

As a first step prior to adopting a UCA, an area-wide stormwater management plan can provide the rationale and guidelines for local regulation. Once these regional guidelines have been established it is much easier for local governments to develop their individual ordinance. UCA's can easily be applied to public works programs that would allow for construction of systems for stormwater management which might include area-wide retention basins, monitoring programs, and financing mechanism such as special assessments or utility fees.

Local Wetland Protection Option #6
Site Plan Review Regulations

Good development design strengthens economic activity, improves community attitudes, reduces nuisance impacts, decreases the cost of development, improves property values, and enhances public safety. For these reasons it is usually in a community's interest to conduct thorough site plan review. Site plans are the documents and drawings that present information showing what an applicant for zoning approval wants to achieve on a parcel of land. Because good site plans usually include information on stormwater patterns, topography, soils, and wetland locations, they can help local decision makers better assess what might be necessary to protect water resources before construction begins.

Local Site Plan Review Regulations

Site plan review regulations are provisions in a zoning ordinance for the administrative review of the physical layout of proposed projects to assure the standards contained in the zoning ordinance are complied with as each property is developed. Many local governments already administer site plan review as part of their planning process, so adding wetland review often does not add to the administrative work load.

In addition to specifying the procedures for submission and approval of site plans, site plan review regulations also identify the land uses subject to review and the individual or body responsible for administering the review. Site plan review typically requires professional assistance and trained decision makers if it is to be used most effectively. This may require hiring outside consultants with the cost borne by fees paid by applicants. Site plan review is often applied to commercial/industrial facilities, and other uses that require a more detailed review to look at number of parking spaces, structure size, and development in sensitive environmental areas such as wetlands.

147

The inclusion of standards within site plan review regulations is essential to assure effective and legally rooted review decisions. Standards typically used include: data submittal standards, nondiscretionary review standards, discretionary review standards, and conditional standards to insure ordinance conformance.

The most important of these are discretionary standards which address issues ranging from impacts on the environment and adjoining land uses, conformance with any related federal, state, or local regulations. If development does not proceed according to an approved site plan, legal means (such as performance guarantees) to require enforcement can be initiated.

Local Wetland Protection Option #7
Enforcement of Soil Erosion and Sedimentation Control

Sediment can be a significant contributor to the decline in wetland viability by reducing water depths, decreasing sunlight penetration, and smothering plant and animal species. Additionally, contaminants such as pesticides, heavy metals, oil and grease, bacteria, plant nutrients, and other chemical wastes are often attached to the sediment and deposited into wetlands.

Local Site Plan Review and Designing Developments to Protect Wetlands

For developers and landowners who desire to develop a property for residential and commercial use, wetland protection can generally be integrated into a development plan. Because of the open space provided, residential lots adjacent to protected wetlands usually fetch higher sale prices than nearby lots not adjacent to the wetland.

To plan developments that protect wetlands, an assessment of the wetland should first be conducted. This assessment would include (at a minimum):

- Wetland boundaries;
- Wetland size;
- Wetland type;
- Connections to other bodies of water; and
- Critical upland habitat that should be protected along with the wetland.

Once this is determined, the next step is to determine what type of development is compatible with protecting wetlands on the site.

The layout for the buildings and roads should be designed in a way that avoids wetlands altogether, or if unavoidable, minimizes wetland crossings as much as possible. How the upland adjacent to a wetland will be developed has important implications for the long-term health of the wetland. Important considerations include establishment of greenbelts and buffer zones around wetlands, managing the quantity and quality of stormwater that will be generated in a way that does not harm the wetland, human access and use of the wetland, and land use practices (e.g., fertilizer and pesticide use) that will be in place once the property is fully developed.

Part 91, Soil Erosion and Sedimentation Control, of 1994 PA 451, as amended, (formerly 1972 PA 347, as amended) was enacted to protect the waters of the state from sedimentation caused by unchecked soil erosion. Part 91 gives the primary responsibility for administering the statute to the counties. The County Board of Commissioners must designate a county enforcing agency such as the Drain Commissioner, Road Commission, Building Department, or the local Soil and Water Conservation District to administer the soil erosion control program on behalf of the county. Part 91 allows cities, villages, and charter townships to assume responsibility within their jurisdictions by adopting an MDEQ approved Soil Erosion and Sedimentation Control Ordinance. The costs of administering county/local erosion programs may be covered by charging fees for inspections, permits, and reviewing plans.

A significant benefit to county/local administration of Part 91 is that individuals responsible for plan review and/or inspections generally have specific knowledge of the site conditions in regard to soils, slopes, and the presence of wetlands. They are probably in the best position to ensure the protection of local resources including wetlands.

Similar to other regulatory programs, Part 91 requires permits for all regulated activities. Permits are required for all earth changes that disturb one or more acres or that are within 500 feet of a lake or stream. Plowing, tilling, and some logging and mining activities do not require a permit, but are still required to comply to the standards in Part 91. Since wetlands are often contiguous to lakes and streams, Part 91 may be a useful tool for protecting wetlands. Prior to receiving a permit, the applicant must complete an application and develop a soil erosion and sedimentation control plan to minimize erosion and off-site sedimentation.

148

Seven Principles of Soil Erosion and Sediment Control To Be Incorporated Into Every Construction Activity

1. Design and construct terrain features such as slopes and drainage ways to minimize the erosion potential of the exposed site based on the soil type, time of year, proximity to water ways, duration of exposure, length/steepness of the slope, and the anticipated volume and intensity of runoff.

2. Minimize the surface area of unstabilized soils left unprotected and vulnerable to runoff and wind at any one time.

3. Minimize the amount of time that unstabilized soil areas are exposed to erosive forces.

4. Protect and shield exposed soil areas with a cover of live vegetation, mulch, or approved erosion resistant material during the temporary and permanent control periods of construction.

5. Avoid concentrating runoff. When concentrated runoff cannot be avoided, runoff velocities must be reduced to non-erosive velocities.

6. Trap eroded sediments on-site with temporary and permanent barriers, basins, or other sediment retention devices while allowing for the controlled discharge of runoff waters at non-erosive velocities.

7. Implement a continuous inspection and maintenance program.

Local Wetland Protection Option #8
Open Space Zoning and Conservation Design

For years local governments have used such land use tools as lot width provisions, lot area requirements, and property line setbacks to attempt to maintain open space in rural and semi-rural settings. Yet as growth rates in many areas accelerate, many communities are realizing that these historical tools are not accomplishing their intended purpose. To address this growing problem Michigan communities are now using new tools that are successfully accomplishing their goals of open space protection.

Open space zoning regulations and conservation design techniques are used by communities to accommodate growth while preserving rural character and/or special resources, such as wetlands, prime farmlands, or scenic views. There are four fundamental components of open space zoning and conservation design:

1) The natural resources on the site are thoroughly inventoried and mapped;

2) A significant portion of the site is protected as permanent open space;

3) Building envelopes are sited in a manner that protects sensitive natural resources and maximizes the quantity and quality of open space on the site; and

4) Site development maintains a low visual impact-particularly along public roadways and waters.

Below is a brief description of some of the more established land use tools which can protect both open space and wetlands.

Clustering

One of the primary tools of open space zoning is clustering building sites to allow for protection of areas that contain wetlands, steep slopes, views, or agricultural lands. Clustering building sites not only has the environmental value of protecting sensitive landscapes, but provides more open space for recreation, and can preserve scenic views which contribute to higher property values. Additionally, a more compact site design can significantly lower the costs of infrastructure, surveying, and engineering.

An issue that local officials regularly face when promoting clustering in rural areas is a public misconception of what is involved in clustering. Residents of rural areas who don't fully understand the concept of clustering may initially frown upon it. The image of condominium complexes or tightly packed dwellings is often associated with clustering, but in actuality this is usually not the case in open space zoning. Rather, open space zoning reduces lot size, but the open space found adjacent to, and surrounding, the lots give a sense of much larger lots.

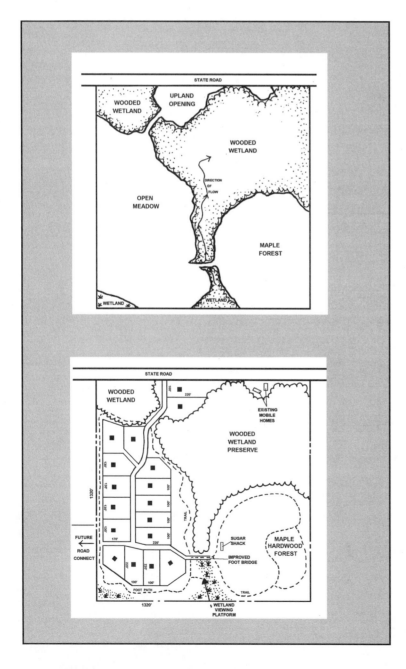

Conservation Easements and Deed Restrictions

A second tool of open space zoning is the use of conservation easements and deed restrictions for permanent land protection. (These topics are more thoroughly discussed under Option #12.) The explosive growth of the land trust movements in Michigan and nationwide is allowing local governments to create public-private partnerships in land protection. In the example to the left, the land that was preserved as open space could have deed restrictions or conservation easements placed on it to preserve it in perpetuity.

Planned Unit Developments

Planned unit developments (PUD) are authorized under state enabling acts to provide opportunities for more flexible land use and site development than is normally permitted by traditional zoning district provisions. PUD's generally encourage site design in a manner which seeks to integrate structures and uses with natural site characteristics to minimize impacts on the site and adjoining properties while enhancing the total project design with planned open space. PUD's can create larger areas of open space through clustering of units than lot-by-lot development. Design standards for PUD's are flexible and are only given real meaning when applied on a project-by-project basis.

PUD regulations can be structured to meet almost any local need. PUD rules usually encourage the use of clustering, conservation easements, and other open space zoning techniques. PUD projects must undergo a site plan review process, and thus these regulations are administratively more complex than traditional lot area and bulk regulations. The PUD process can require technical planning, negotiation skills, and knowledge of project design and site plan review to be effective.

Implementing Open Space Zoning

If a local government were to consider pursuing open space zoning, the foundation of these regulations should be embodied in the goals, objectives, and policies of the community's comprehensive plan to best assure legal validity. Open space zoning is not applicable in all situations, but is appropriate where both preservation and limited growth is desired, such as rural/suburban transition areas or rapidly growing recreational areas. Open space zoning may not be appropriate for high growth/urban areas or areas where total preservation of extensive natural resources is a primary concern. In these areas public or land conservancy purchase of lands are more appropriate.

Site development regulations should be consistent with local character, privacy, and open space access. Permitting should be no more difficult than for traditional subdivisions and if substantially easier, will result in more open space projects. In some cases density bonuses for open space projects should be considered to increase financial attractiveness of open space developments.

151

Local Wetland Protection Option #9
Performance Based Zoning

Traditional community zoning techniques are designed to allow specific land use activities – commercial, residential, or industrial – only in pre-defined geographic areas, or zones. Zoning commissions then have the task of reviewing proposed projects in reference to approved zoning maps that detail the areas where certain land uses are prohibited, authorized, or are authorized with certain conditions.

Performance zoning, on the other hand, does not divide land uses into separate zoning districts. Instead, land use is regulated by particular performance standards that developers must meet. If developers agree to meet these pre-defined standards, then a project can be sited in a broader range of geographic settings. Typical performance standards include:

- Wetland protection;
- Amount of impervious surface;
- Building density;
- Waterfront setbacks;
- Buffering requirements; and
- Open space ratios.

A significant benefit of performance zoning is that it allows communities to promote infill in underutilized urban and suburban areas, in turn limiting the progress of sprawl. The practice of infilling has the tendency to revitalize economically distressed neighborhoods by providing a greater diversity of residential and commercial uses. To ensure there is a compatibility between land uses, buffers and setbacks should be included in the community's performance standards.

The other significant benefit of performance zoning is that it gives developers a certain flexibility in designing a plan as long as all the conditions laid out by the local government are met. Developers then have a broad range of design options which they can pursue, many of which can provide significant cost savings. For example, if a developer is required to limit impervious surface and protect slopes greater than fifteen percent, the developer then can cluster buildings, mix building types, and alter road layout in efforts to meet those performance standards.

Local Wetland Protection Option #10
Performance Guarantees to Protect Wetlands

Performance guarantees are traditionally used by local governments as a legal mechanism to assure that developers establish pre-defined improvements as conditions of local project approval. Performance guarantees are a form of "insurance" to protect a community from unmarketable sites due to project abandonment or partial completion where required public or environmental improvements have not been completed.

152

Roads, sidewalks, lighting, and utilities are all common site features that local governments require performance guarantees for in the form of surety bonds, cash, or cash equivalence. The guarantee is returned to the developer when the project improvements are completed within a specified time line and an agreed upon project site plan. Performance guarantees can be used to protect wetlands by assuring that proposed land alterations are constructed as specified by community planners. For example, if a stormwater feature such as infiltration swales or detention basins are required to treat runoff before it enters a wetland, a performance guarantee will help assure that these stormwater treatment features are properly constructed. Performance guarantees enable communities to pay the cost to protect or restore wetlands or other sensitive features if the developer or contractor fails to do so.

Communities interested in utilizing performance guarantees should include in their local zoning, PUD, condominium, or subdivision ordinances standards that have been pre-defined to guide these guarantees. These standards will define the project time lines for project completion, and the resulting penalties if the predetermined standards are not met. If the project is completed to the satisfaction of the municipality then the guarantee will be released in full in a timely manner. If the developer does not fulfill the specified obligation, then the municipality may obtain the guaranteed funds and hire its own contractor to complete the project.

Local Wetland Protection Option #11
Lot Split or Land Division Regulation

Unchecked land division can remove forever large amounts of forests and farmland from production. It can also unnecessarily burden public facilities and services by the creation of vast "rural development." This rural development, which evolves over time, is now subject to local review or approval. Finally, poorly planned land divisions can create parcels that may require the destruction of wetlands to adequately site houses.

The Land Division Act, P.A. 288 of 1967 as amended (formally known as the Subdivision Control Act) does not regulate the creation of parcels greater than 40 acres in size. Local governments interested in having more control over these exempt land divisions can create local based land division and subdivision regulations.

The Land Division Act requires the approval of the Michigan Department of Environmental Quality for the preliminary plat of any subdivision containing lots within or affected by a floodplain, and any subdivision involving land abutting a lake or stream where public rights may be affected. In many cases, wetlands are involved and are brought to the attention of the developer and appropriate agencies during the review process.

> ## Elements Considered Under the Land Division Act
>
> - Location of natural or artificial drainage courses, lakes, streams, wetlands, critical sand dunes, threatened or endangered species, unusual topography, and major stands of trees.
>
> - The ratio of lot depth to width shall not exceed four (4) to one (1).
>
> - The size, shape, orientation, and existing zoning of the lots and parcels shall be appropriate for the type of development and land use contemplated. No split shall be approved which would conflict with existing drainage ditches, natural watercourses, easements, or public rights-of-way.
>
> - Parcel splits shall be approved which would preclude the feasible and efficient development, division, or access for remaining or abutting lands affected by the proposed split. No parcel shall be created solely of critical sand dune, wetland, lake or river bottom, or stream bed.

153

Local Land Division Regulations

If land division trends appear to be alarming, a local government can consider adopting a land division regulation. Local land division regulations apply to all lands. These regulations serve to prevent the creation of "unbuildable parcels" whose lot width, depth, area, shape and/or frontage do not meet ordinance minimums and ensure that access meets minimum public safety and drainage standards. They are also structured to prevent the unnecessary fragmentation of valuable natural resource areas and to prevent a proliferation of strip commercial parcels along major roadways.

Local Wetland Protection Option #12
Wetland Consideration in Public Infrastructure Projects

As communities grow it is usually necessary to upgrade and expand public infrastructure. One of the responsibilities of local government is to plan to improve public infrastructure with an eye to directing growth into areas which will have the least environmental impact. Some of the most common growth inducing actions that local government undertake are road building and widening, sewering, water main construction, and siting the locations of schools. Typically, these growth inducing actions lead to subdivision and commercial development. Consideration of the location of wetland and water resources during master planning can help direct growth inducing activities away from environmentally sensitive landscapes.

To Sewer or Not To Sewer

Below are considerations that should be taken into account when determining where future sewer projects should be allowed in areas where there is an abundance of water resources. (All conditions should be met.)

- There is an existing, documented waste treatment problem that cannot be solved by any other feasible and prudent on-site alternative;

- Dense development currently exists. More than 100 homes per mile and average lot size of less that 0.5 acres are standard criteria identified by the U.S. EPA;

- Areas which are environmentally sensitive (pertaining to water resources) are absent,

or are identified and afforded adequate protection through deed restriction, zoning, or other types of protection methods;

- Sewage is treated using current best management practices, and the treated effluent is unlikely to have a negative impact on water resources in downstream communities; and

- The diversion of water (from discharge to ground water to discharge to sewer treatment plant) will not negatively impact the hydrology or ecosystem(s) in and adjacent to the newly sewered area.

By assuring that all these conditions are met, communities can help prevent negative water resource impacts that sewering can create.

Of all infrastructure improvements sewer expansion has the greatest potential to have environmental impact when it comes to wetlands. Often times the only factor limiting building in wetlands is the inability to site fully functioning septic systems. When sewers are installed in areas with a high water table and abundant wetlands, areas considered unsuitable for on-site septic disposal, it tends to direct development into those areas.

Many Michigan communities, due to their small size or limited institutional capacity, lack any type of comprehensive planning and zoning that can help direct and control growth. In those communities it is commonly the development of a public infrastructure plan that determines where community growth will occur. In other communities where a master plan exists, or is in the process of being developed, a sewer facility plan should be included in the master plan. The extent of municipal sewers should be determined in part by the need to protect drinking water, lakes, streams, and wetlands. Indeed, the protection of these water resources is the primary reason why sewers are established.

CONCLUSION

In any of these options, there are issues that must be addressed, including mapping, wetland definitions, regulated activities, enforcement and penalties, and relationship with state and federal regulations. Unless these issues are adequately addressed in an open forum, a proposed local wetland regulation will generate much controversy. For additional treatment of these options, see the Michigan Society of Planning Officials' (MSPO) *Community Planning Handbook*, the American Planning Association's *Protecting NonTidal Wetlands*, and Tip of the Mitt Watershed Council's *Preserving Michigan's Wetlands: Options for Local Governments*. The latter publication includes model language for all the options presented in this chapter. In addition, organizations such as MSPO, The Clinton River Watershed Council, the Huron River Watershed Council, and the Tip of the Mitt Watershed Council have ongoing planning and zoning programs and can provide advice to citizens working to establish local wetland protection programs.

154

Once again, the shape and form of a local ordinance depends on a variety of factors. Accordingly, there is no one "best" way to protect wetlands at the local level. For instance, a well enforced requirement that conditions local zoning approval on state and federal permits may be more effective than a comprehensive stand-alone ordinance that is not enforced at all. The key for the local citizen wetland advocate is to build a body of support from all sectors and work to implement the most appropriate level of protection for your community. In some communities, the enactment of a wetlands protection ordinance has been a long and intensive process; in others, there was little controversy. If done correctly, the benefits to the wetland resource and the local community will be well worth the effort.

Wetland Protection Spotlight

Participating in Local Wetland Regulations
Carla Clos

"In Meridian, wetlands are protected. Period. It's pretty much accepted that if you're going to develop in Meridian, you protect wetlands. That's it."

But this wasn't always the case. In 1989, a study of the Charter Township of Meridian, located in Ingham County, found that 10% of the wetlands were completely unregulated, and were being lost at an alarming rate. These wetlands were the small, less than five acre, isolated headwater wetlands and vernal pools. Because they were small, it was economically feasible to fill them.

At this time, Carla Clos was on the township planning commission. She and others on the planning commission were concerned about the natural features present on the projects they were approving. But when they would ask the developer about the natural features, the reply was, "Don't worry about that. The state worries about the wetlands. You just need to approve the roads." None of the site plans included wetlands, and the commission would approve them, believing that these features were protected.

Unfortunately, this turned out to be exacerbating the wetland loss. Though many of the wetlands were regulated by the state, when the Michigan Department of Environmental Quality (MDEQ) considered the permit applications, they would see that the local planning commission had approved the project, therefore implicitly encouraging the project. "It was a frustration to a number of us. We wanted to protect the natural features. We found that the only way we could do that was to get involved at the local level," said Carla.

And thus began a long but successful campaign to pass a local wetland ordinance in Meridian Township. This ordinance would bring the wetlands not regulated by the state under the township's control. At first they found that they had substantial support from the township board of supervisors, and from the community. This was a high-growth community, and residents were seeing wetlands destroyed on an almost daily basis. "A lot of people would come to hearings and talk about the beautiful places that were being destroyed," Carla remembers. "We just seized on the opportunity."

But there were other interests involved, and they were extremely well-funded. Realtors, developers, and home-builders began issuing mass mailings and making dire predictions–that an ordinance would stop all growth, would lead to lawsuits, and would cost the township a half-million dollars a year to administer the program…and the township board, which had been initially supportive of the idea, began to get concerned. And so Carla and other concerned citizens began to build the public pressure for an ordinance.

They tried many different methods to increase public support for the ordinance. They didn't have the money that the developers did for mass mailings, but they did have a highly dedicated group of people, and relied on public discussion and free media. "I literally made hundreds of phone calls. If someone came to a planning commission meeting and said, 'I like trees,' I would call them up and say, 'well, if you like trees, you like wetlands,'" Carla notes. They were able to make use of the local government television channel, airing panels of scientists and wetlands experts. They found letters-to-the-editor to be very important. "No one thing motivated the public. You've just got to try anything and everything."

In 1991, after two years of debate and intense political pressure, Meridian Township adopted a wetland protection ordinance. Development is still occurring in Meridian Township, but it's being done differently. The township has found that the predictions made by the development lobby have not materialized. The Board receives very few permit applications–the developers have found it easier to just integrate wetlands protection into their design. This, in turn, has led to a very manageable cost to the government, and no lawsuits have been brought. In order to encourage protection of the wetlands under state jurisdiction, the township wetland consultants submit comments to the MDEQ on permit applications.

Since Meridian Township passed the ordinance, Carla and others have been concerned about the changes in hydrology, interruption of wildlife corridors, and isolation of wetlands that have continued to occur. In order to afford a greater level of protection to wetlands, the township today is looking at the landscape as a whole. "What have we protected if we encircle the wetlands with concrete? We may not have really protected the wetland values," Carla notes. In response to this, the Wetland Board has been changed to the Environmental Commission, and they have been working with developers to protect not only the wetland proper, but all the functions and values that the wetland provides.

Carla found that spearheading this issue has made a major change in the focus of her life. "Before this, I didn't know a marsh from a swamp. Now I'm the Deputy Drain Commissioner. The more I learned, the more I realized that these places are exceptionally important for our future–not just for the community, but for the sustainability of the whole ecological system."

Chapter **11** Nonregulatory Wetland Protection Techniques

Local, state, and federal wetland regulations are critical to the overall protection of Michigan's wetland resources. Supplementing these regulations with nonregulatory techniques can increase their effectiveness on specific properties. There are a variety of nonregulatory techniques that can be initiated by individual citizens, conservation and environmental organizations, and units of government. Nonregulatory techniques can be either binding or nonbinding, but all require cooperation and support on behalf of the landowner and the community.

BINDING NONREGULATORY APPROACHES

Many nonregulatory approaches can effectively protect wetlands in perpetuity. Others provide temporary binding agreements that can be renewed. Six such techniques are discussed here, including land donation, conservation easements, deed restrictions, purchase, eminent domain, and tax incentives.

There are many benefits to utilizing binding non-regulatory approaches to wetland protection. Federal, state, and local regulations contain exemptions for activities that can degrade wetlands. Nonregulatory programs can prohibit activities otherwise allowed by law. Donation and purchase of wetlands tends to be less controversial than regulation, and thus provides the opportunity to get even those opposed to regulation interested in wetland protection. Permanent protection options have the additional benefit of being permanent where the laws that provide legal protection can be changed. Despite all these benefits, it's obvious that we can't purchase all wetlands and that we won't be able to secure conservation easements on all of them. Legal protection across the board and voluntary protection on individual wetlands serves as an excellent combination to protect Michigan's wetlands.

Donation

The donation of wetlands to a conservation organization or a local government (with deed restrictions on the future use) has long played an important role in wetland protection. In fact, it is perhaps the most direct and cost-effective method of protecting wetlands in their natural state. By execution of a deed, the landowner gives his or her land (or a specified part of it) to a qualified nonprofit organization or government agency for conservation purposes. A donor's gift of land is considered a tax deductible contribution. Each donation of land has different tax advantages for different individuals. Different types of taxes (e.g., real property taxes, gift taxes, or income taxes) are affected differently in each situation. Landowners considering donation of wetland property should be encouraged to retain a tax attorney or accountant to analyze the tax consequences for his or her particular situation.

There are several variations on the donation theme: outright donation, bargain sale, donation with a reserved life estate, and a bequest. With a bargain sale, the land is conveyed at a price below fair market value, which may be attractive to a landowner who can not afford to convey the land without some compensation. A bargain sale is part gift and part sale. The sale price is determined jointly by the landowner and the recipient. For federal income tax purposes, it can result in both a taxable sale and a charitable contribution deduction, depending on the particular circumstances.

A donation with a reserved life estate is a donation in which the donor retains possession and use of the property for his or her lifetime. An income tax deduction is allowed for the value of a charitable contribution, which is the difference between the property's fair market value and its value under the provisions of the donation with a reserved life estate. The Internal Revenue Service takes into account the number of years that a donor with a reserved life estate is likely to enjoy the use of the property. Thus, such a donation will yield greater tax benefits to an older donor.

A bequest is a donation of land in an owner's will. Although such a donation does not enable the donor to realize an income tax deduction, the value of the bequest is deductible in determining the donor's taxable estate, which can benefit heirs by reducing estate taxes.

Donation of natural land has a number of potential income and estate tax advantages. Such a donation may also significantly reduce the costs of land ownership, such as real estate taxes. However, the extent of those financial benefits will depend upon the kind of donation, the donor's particular financial situation, and prevailing federal tax law at the time the donation occurs. The major incentive for donation of natural land is that it offers the most simple and effective tool available to the landowner who wants to protect his or her wetland. When encouraging landowners to donate their land to a non-profit organization or a governmental entity, it is important to be able to explain how the recipient organization will use the property. If the organization wants to reserve the right to sell the property in the future, it may be wise for the landowner to consider granting a conservation easement to a third party to ensure that the land will be protected by future owners.

Conservation Easements

159

A conservation easement is a voluntary agreement that is used to transfer certain rights concerning the use of land to a qualified nonprofit organization, governmental body, or other legal entity without transferring title to the land. In Michigan, Part 21 of the Michigan Natural Resources and Environmental Code (Act 451 of 1994) (formerly the Conservation and Historic Preservation Easement Act; Public Act 197 of 1980), authorizes the creation of voluntary conservation easements. A conservation easement under this statute can provide limitations on the use of, or can prohibit certain acts on, a parcel of land. The easement is enforceable against the owner of the land even if the party seeking enforcement was not a party to the original conveyance or contract. The easement is considered a conveyance of real property and must be recorded with the register of deeds in the appropriate county to be enforceable against a subsequent purchaser of the property who had no notice of the easement.

Conservation easements are flexible, effective, and allow the landowner to maintain ownership of the property. A common misconception about conservation easements is that the land must be open to public access. The public does not have access to property protected by a conservation easement unless the landowner who grants the easement specifically allows it. Conservation easements may be drafted to meet particular circumstances and objectives of an individual landowner. They can allow for uses compatible with wetland protection (e.g., bird watching, hunting, fishing, or other low-impact activities). They can identify areas on a property that will be reserved for future development. They can protect the easement area against disturbances that are not covered by wetland regulations, such as vegetation clearing. In short, conservation easements are a powerful tool that protects wetlands while enabling landowners to still use and enjoy their property.

To be eligible for a tax deduction, conservation easements must be granted in perpetuity by the landowner. Several tax benefits may be available to the grantor, including deduction of the value of an easement as a charitable contribution, as determined by the amount by which the easement reduces the market value of the property. The Internal Revenue Code normally allows an itemized deduction of up to 30 percent of an individual's adjusted gross income for such contributions. Amounts in excess of the 30 percent limitation may be carried over and deducted during the next five years (this applies to donations of land also). The easement may reduce the value of the property if it is included in the individual's taxable estate. In addition, the development restrictions placed on a property by a conservation easement may also result in reducing property taxes.

Deed Restrictions and Covenants

Deed restrictions are clauses placed in deeds restricting the future use of land. When property containing wetlands is transferred, deed restrictions can prohibit uses or activities by the new owners that would destroy, damage, or modify wetlands. A covenant is a contract between a landowner and another party stating that the landowner will use or refrain from using their land in a certain manner. Like a deed restriction, a covenant can require that landowners refrain from activities that will damage wetlands. Once placed in deeds, covenants become deed restrictions.

Mutual covenants involve agreements between nearby or adjacent landowners to control the future use of their land through restrictions agreed upon by all participating landowners. The fact that multiple landowners participate in the covenant provides greater incentive to comply with the terms of the covenant. However, getting numerous property owners to voluntarily agree on certain management practices can be very challenging.

160

Although deed restrictions and covenants have been used across the country to protect wetlands, their use in Michigan is not as effective as conservation easements. This is for primarily two reasons. First, unlike a conservation easement that is granted to and signed by an organization that has a commitment and responsibility to resource protection, the enforcement of deed restrictions and covenants is less reliable. Because deed restrictions are placed in the deed and run with the land, there is no continuity of oversight, unlike the continuous ownership of an easement holder. With a deed restriction, you're relying on the concern and commitment of some unidentified body to provide the oversight. Second, it is relatively easy for a future landowner to petition the courts to vacate a particular deed restriction. Although it is theoretically possible to modify a conservation easement, many changes are prohibited by federal regulations where income tax deductions are involved and all signatories to the easement must agree to proposed changes. It is unlikely that a qualified organization would agree to modifications of a conservation easement that would result in adverse wetland impacts. Another major difference between conservation easements and deed restrictions or covenants is that the loss in market value due to deed restrictions and covenants cannot be claimed as a charitable deduction on income tax returns.

Purchase

Acquisition of wetland property is a straightforward but costly method of protecting wetlands. Acquisition of property by public agencies ensures public access and public protection of wetlands. Because acquisition does not involve regulation, it is a politically attractive alternative. However, in addition to the cost factor, acquisition of wetlands alone does not always guarantee protection in perpetuity. Without restrictions, a unit of government might decide to convert the wetland to an alternate public use (e.g., a golf course), adjacent wetlands may be destroyed thus impacting the "protected" area, and agencies with superior powers could engage in activities that would destroy the wetland (e.g., a federal hydropower project).

If the decision is made to purchase wetlands, the purchaser should consider all the options, including purchase of fee simple title, easements and development rights, bargain sales, and other purchasing methods. A fee simple purchase provides the purchaser with permanent control and protection. The purchase of a conservation easement or development rights has numerous advantages. First, since you are only purchasing the rights to develop the property, the purchase price is lower, and second, the original owner retains title and continues to pay taxes to the local community (although the assessment should be reduced). Innovative purchasing methods should also be considered by the seller. The bargain sale provides large tax incentives to the seller while reducing the purchase price for the buyer. An option contract may also be a useful mechanism.

One of the major impediments to the purchase of wetlands is the financial burden. However, there are several state and federal programs designed to provide capital for the acquisition of land for public benefit. The following is a list of several possible sources of funds for wetland purchases.

1) **Private Sources:** Donations from private individuals or corporations in the form of specific property or money can be used to acquire wetlands. This would include grassroots fund raising efforts from local citizens, lake associations, and other community groups.

2) **Nonprofit Organizations:** The Michigan Chapter of The Nature Conservancy, Michigan Nature Association, Grand Traverse Regional Land Conservancy, Natural Areas Council of West Michigan, Michigan Audubon Society, Little Traverse Conservancy, Ducks Unlimited, Southwest Michigan Land Conservancy, and other organizations can be potential funding sources. The Michigan Chapter of The Nature Conservancy maintains a list of local land trusts and how they can be contacted.

3) **Local Municipalities:** Many local governments are willing to fund wetland acquisition programs since many of the values that wetlands provide directly benefit local municipalities and their residents.

4) **Federal Sources:** There are numerous federal programs that are designed to support wetland acquisition across the country. The following have been used to purchase wetlands in Michigan.

> a) The Federal Land and Water Conservation Fund provides monies to the state to buy open space lands which may contain wetlands. Contact the MDNR Office of Budget and Federal Aid.

> b) U.S. Fish and Wildlife Service grants under the Pittman-Robertson Act (16 U.S.C. 699) provide funds to the state for acquisition of wildlife areas and wildlife restoration. Funds are from a tax on ammunition and weapons. Contact the MDNR Wildlife Division.

161

c) U.S. Fish and Wildlife Service grants under the Dingell-Johnson Act (16 U.S.C. 777) provide funds to the state to cover 75% of the cost of fish restoration and management projects. Funds are derived from a tax on fishing equipment. Contact the MDNR Fisheries Division.

d) The Coastal Zone Management Act (16 U.S.C. 1454) provides funds for acquisition of coastal estuarine sanctuaries, including the Great Lakes. Before funds are granted, each state must have an approved coastal zone plan. For more information, contact the MDEQ.

5) **State Sources:** The following Michigan programs can be used to provide funds for wetland projects conducted by local governments.

a) Michigan Natural Resources Trust Fund provides a possible source of money to purchase select recreational, scenic and environmentally important land in Michigan. Applications can be obtained from the MDNR Recreation Services Division.

b) Proceeds from Michigan Duck Stamp sales and contests go to purchase of wetlands by the State. Contact the MDNR Wildlife Division for more information.

Eminent Domain

Eminent domain is the power of federal, state, or local municipal governments to take private property for public use. This power is founded in both the federal and state constitutions. This is the same power that allows regulatory agencies to "take" land as a result of road construction or the establishment of a park. However, the power is limited to taking for a public purpose and prohibits the exercise of the power without just compensation to the owner of the property which is taken. The private wetland owner's power is severely restricted—he or she must sell. Although this mechanism is available, it is politically unattractive and very costly. As a result, government entities seldom use it to protect resources. For a further discussion regarding regulatory takings, see Chapter Thirteen.

Tax Incentives or Private Landowner Subsidies

There are several existing programs that provide economic incentives for landowners to protect and enhance wetlands. Essentially, these programs provide tax reductions in return for short-term wetland "easements" to encourage farmers to protect wetlands.

On the federal level, these include the Conservation Reserve Program (CRP), the Wetland Reserve Program (WRP), and the Wildlife Habitat Incentive Program (WHIP). CRP is administered by the Farm Services Agency and provides an incentive to encourage farmers to enroll highly erodible land and/or land contributing to serious water quality degradation into the reserve for 10 to 15 years. WRP and WHIP are administered by the Natural Resources Conservation Service. WRP is a voluntary program that offers landowners a chance to receive payments for restoring wetlands. Under WRP, landowners are provided cost-share funds to restore wetlands in return for a conservation easement. WHIP provides an incentive for property owners to develop and improve wildlife habitat on their property. Though cost-share assistance is not available for wetland restoration, it is available for developing and maintaining the area adjacent to the wetland. In addition, the Swampbuster provisions of the Farm Bill eliminate federal subsidies to farmers who convert wetlands for agricultural purposes. Although the combination of these incentive and disincentive programs help to protect wetlands, the protection provided is by no means permanent.

163

On the state level, Michigan's Farmland and Open Space Preservation Act (P. A. 116 of 1974) provides tax breaks for landowners who agree to not develop land. As wetlands constitute open space, protecting them would allow a farmer to qualify for the tax relief. As in the federal tax incentive programs, the agreements between the individual and the state are for a 10-year period.

DESIGNING DEVELOPMENT TO PROTECT WETLANDS

Typically, most wetland advocates find themselves trying to stop a poorly planned development. Getting involved early in the development process to ensure the creation of a good plan that protects wetlands may be new to most wetland advocates.

Wetlands can be integrated into development plans in a way that ensures aquatic habitat protection and enhances the quality of the development. In many cases across Michigan, residential lots adjacent to protected wetlands fetched higher sale prices than nearby lots not adjacent to the wetland.

On a large parcel of land slated for development, citizens can play a critical role in advocating for the protection of wetlands. The key is to ensure that wetland protection is considered early on in the site planning process.

To plan development to protect wetlands, the first step is to conduct an assessment of the wetland that would include (at a minimum): wetland boundaries, wetland size, wetland type, connections to other bodies of water, and critical upland habitat that should be protected along with the wetland. Once this is determined, the next step is to determine what type of development is compatible with protecting wetlands on the site while still meeting financial desires. The layout for the buildings and roads should be designed in a way that avoids wetlands and minimizes wetland crossings as much as possible. How the upland adjacent to a wetland will be developed has important implications for long-term health of the wetland. Important considerations include establishment of greenbelts and buffer zones around wetlands, managing the quantity and quality of stormwater that will be generated in a way that does not harm the wetland, human access and use of the wetland, and land use practices (e.g., fertilizer and pesticide use) that will be in place once the property is fully developed.

After a plan for the property has been developed that will protect the wetland over time, there are many opportunities to help put that plan in place. Implementing the protection measures through a conservation easement can result in substantial tax benefits. Likewise, donating the portion of the property that is to be protected to a qualified organization will result in tax benefits.

Ensuring that upland practices such as lawn care are compatible with wetland protection also provide a challenge when attempting to design developments to protect wetlands. The best way to do this depends on the pattern of ownership in the development. With a condominium-type ownership pattern, the developer retains responsibility to manage the property. However, in a traditional subdivision ownership pattern, unacceptable land use practices may need to be prohibited through deed restrictions. A neighborhood or property owners' association can serve to enforce the deed restriction.

VOLUNTARY NONBINDING PROGRAMS

164

The nonregulatory approaches listed above provide binding mechanisms to protect wetlands for either the short or long term. In addition to these mechanisms, there are several approaches that encourage wetland protection in a nonbinding, nonregulatory manner. These programs provide public support for wetland protection activities and also serve to educate landowners and the public of the need to protect wetlands.

Michigan Natural Areas Registry

The Michigan Chapter of The Nature Conservancy promotes the preservation of important natural areas, including wetlands, through voluntary nonregulatory agreements between landowners and The Nature Conservancy. The Michigan Natural Features Inventory (MNFI), a program partially supported by funds from The Nature Conservancy, provides a listing of significant natural areas in the state. The Nature Conservancy staff provides outreach to the landowners of significant areas to develop positive relationships and voluntary protection agreements. To qualify for the Registry, a property must be either ecologically significant, such as an unusual wetland or old growth forest, be a relict plant community (survivors from climates and ecosystems of the past), or be habitat for rare, threatened, or endangered plants or animals. The Nature Conservancy should be contacted concerning properties which might be eligible for registration.

Natural Heritage Stewardship Award Program

Coordinated by the Michigan Natural Features Inventory, this program promotes the voluntary preservation of endangered or threatened species and their habitat. Currently, the program focuses on threatened species that inhabit the Great Lakes shoreline and interdunal swale wetlands, including Houghton's goldenrod, dwarf lake iris, and Pitcher's thistle. The program uses information from the MNFI to target properties which may have significant habitat. The purpose of the project is to contact landowners and provide information regarding how to protect and enhance significant habitat areas either on their property or on nearby state land. Since wetlands are the home for more endangered and threatened species than any other landform, this program can help to raise awareness and encourage proper stewardship of wetland areas.

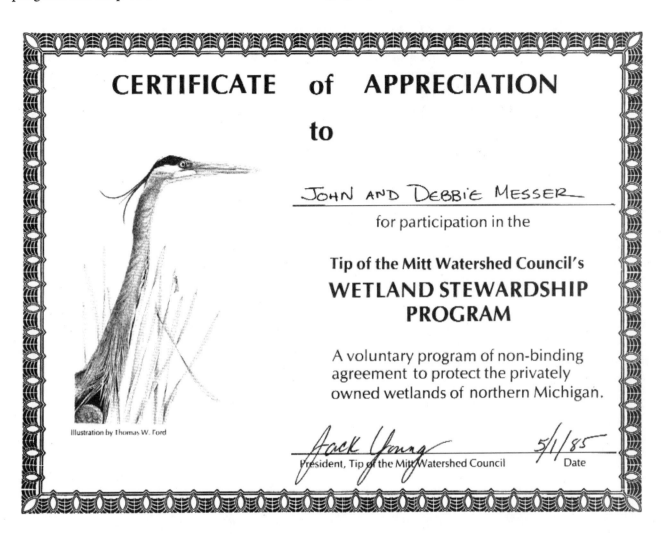

CERTIFICATE of APPRECIATION

to

JOHN AND DEBBIE MESSER

for participation in the

Tip of the Mitt Watershed Council's
WETLAND STEWARDSHIP PROGRAM

A voluntary program of non-binding agreement to protect the privately owned wetlands of northern Michigan.

Jack Young   5/1/85
President, Tip of the Mitt Watershed Council   Date

Illustration by Thomas W. Ford

165

Wetland Stewardship Programs

In Northern Michigan, the Tip of the Mitt Watershed Council has developed a Wetland Stewardship Program to involve landowners in wetland protection who may not be willing or ready for permanent protection. The Watershed Council has identified wetland owners in their service area and encouraged them to become wetland stewards. The goal of the program is to protect wetlands through voluntary commitments from the owners of the resource.

The Watershed Council's Wetland Stewardship Program promotes the protection of wetlands through voluntary, nonbinding agreements between wetland owners and the Watershed Council. The wetland steward agrees not to drain, dredge or fill, or in any other way destroy his or her wetland. They also agree to notify the Watershed Council when they plan to sell the land or if they decide not to participate any longer in the Stewardship Program.

In return for becoming a Wetland Steward, the Watershed Council provides assistance regarding land management, advice on other protection measures, and a certificate of appreciation. Hopefully, the wetland stewards also receive the satisfaction and pride which come from knowing they have helped protect Michigan's wetlands.

THE ROLE OF CITIZENS IN NONREGULATORY PROTECTION EFFORTS

Just as citizens are critical to the regulatory process, individuals or local wetland protection teams can be essential in promoting nonregulatory protection. Local wetland protection advocates can initiate acquisition, conservation easement, or restoration programs in their community, obtain information and assistance on protection techniques, and work with state agencies or the Michigan Chapter of The Nature Conservancy to promote large acquisition projects. In addition, a local wetland protection advocate can promote management and protection through wetland stewardship programs or other landowner award programs.

The Grass River Natural Area (GRNA) in Antrim County is an example of a successful cooperative wetland purchase effort. The GRNA is managed by a local nonprofit organization along with the Antrim County Board of Commissioners and provides the opportunity for thousands of visitors each year to experience wetlands. With the assistance of The Nature Conservancy and the Soil Conservation Service, over 1,100 acres of land have been acquired by purchase, direct donation from individuals, and by transfer from the State of Michigan. The Three Lakes Association was the original sponsor of the project and has continued its involvement throughout.

There are numerous similar projects throughout Michigan that were made possible by dedicated local citizens who initiated the efforts. Grassroots education to provide public support and the involvement of numerous agencies and organizations were also key to their success.

166

Wetland Protection Spotlight

Southwest Michigan Land Conservancy
Renee Kivikko

Southwest Michigan is rich in wetlands, with more fen-type wetlands than any other part of Michigan, as well as a great diversity of other wetland types–bogs, wet meadows, marshes, shrub-carr, and cedar and tamarack swamps. Like so many other areas in the state, however, Southwest Michigan has been experiencing rapid growth and development pressure, which has greatly altered and impacted hydrology and drainage regimes.

Witnessing the rapid encroachment of development on the region's remaining wetlands and open space, and considering the lack of a local conservancy servicing the nine counties that make up Southwest Michigan, a group of volunteers came together in the early 1990s to address the need for a local land conservancy. These were individuals who were self-trained naturalists, people who had experience working with other conservancies, and other people in the area who were concerned about threats to the region's natural areas and wanted to protect them.

The Southwest Michigan Land Conservancy was incorporated in Spring 1992, with the mission to "protect the diversity, stability, and beauty of Southwest Michigan by preserving our natural and scenic lands." The Conservancy works to accomplish their goals primarily by accepting and encouraging land donations and conservation easements.

The group has met with great success since their inception, protecting more than 2,000 acres of natural and agricultural land. One of their most successful projects created easements on a 700-acre parcel of land which includes two lakes, a diversity of wetland types, several stream systems, and valuable upland habitat. The project began with the donation of a 555-acre easement that included the lakes. The land had been purchased by a private foundation, with the intent to turn it into an environmental institute and learning center. The easement is bordered by another 153 acres protected by easement. The Conservancy is working with other landowners in the area to further increase the protected acreage.

The Jephtha Lake Fen, another project the Conservancy has completed, provides an example of a bargain sale. The land has been in the Olson family since the early 1900s, and farmed up until the 1960s. The landowner wished to protect the area, but could not afford to simply donate the land. The Conservancy seized this opportunity to work out a bargain sale of the property. The landowner received an income tax donation for the difference between the appraised value and the sale price of the land. The Conservancy received a unique and beautiful parcel, and the landowner was able to ensure that the land that she loved was protected.

167

But it hasn't all been smooth sailing. Renee Kivikko, former executive director of SWMLC and now the Regional Director for the Land Trust Alliance, has found that one of her biggest hurdles is explaining to landowners and the public how local conservancies work. "Because The Nature Conservancy is so well known, people confuse the two." Renee found that it takes time to explain the philosophy of local land conservancies and how they operate, and for the landowners to become comfortable with them. "Most people, if they are really interested, will have the motivation right out, but it's just a conversation you have to have," Kivikko said.

SWMLC uses many tactics to promote their organization and to encourage land protection–partnering with other organizations, building relationships, targeted outreach, and media exposure. Their targeted outreach campaigns have proven to be one of their more effective programs. SWMLC chooses a "target area" and determines the important natural features and community values within that area. Then they do a series of direct mailings, one every couple months for 9-12 months, and increase the number of programs done in that area. "Once you get one landowner actively interested, more landowners in that area will come forward," said Kivikko.

The Southwest Michigan Land Conservancy has learned much from its activities. The biggest lesson, says Kivikko, "is that no two projects are alike–even if you think they should go the same, they don't. You always learn from the first project and there's always something to learn from the next. There's nothing cookie-cutter about this kind of work."

For more information about the
Southwest Michigan Land Conservancy, contact:
6851 Sprinkle Road
Portage, MI 49002
Phone: (269) 324-1600
Fax: (269) 324-9700
e-mail: conserveland@swmlc.org
website: www.swmlc.org

Chapter 12 Wetland Protection and Management on Public Land

A s a citizen, you are part owner to over 7.1 million acres of state and federal land in Michigan. Michigan residents are blessed with the largest amount of public land of any state east of the Mississippi. These lands provide the resource base for countless outdoor recreational pursuits and a thriving tourist economy. Although enjoyed and appreciated by millions each year, very few citizens actually get involved in providing input to the agencies responsible for managing these lands. There is an estimated 1.3 million acres of wetland in state or federal ownership in Michigan. If we are to ensure that Michigan's wetland resource base is protected, Michigan citizens must participate in the management of wetlands on public lands.

The most direct impacts, and the greatest opportunity for citizen involvement in wetland protection on state and federal land are related to forest management activities. This chapter outlines the basic ways you can get involved to ensure that wetlands are given the consideration they deserve when state and federal agencies make their forest management decisions.

FEDERALLY-OWNED WETLANDS

There are two federal agencies–the U.S. Forest Service (Department of Agriculture) and the U.S. Fish and Wildlife Service (Department of the Interior)–that administer the vast majority of federally-owned wetlands in Michigan. The Forest Service manages nearly three million acres in three national forests–the Ottawa, in the Western Upper Peninsula, the Hiawatha, in the Middle and Eastern Upper Peninsula, and the Huron-Manistee, which has two sections–the Manistee, in the Western Lower Peninsula, and the Huron, in the Northeastern Lower Peninsula. The Fish and Wildlife Service manages two major national wildlife refuges–the Seney in the Upper Peninsula, and the Shiawassee in the Eastern Lower Peninsula, in addition to several smaller refuges which are managed by the staff of the larger ones. All combined, the Fish and Wildlife Service manages 112,133 acres in Michigan. These wildlife refuges consist primarily of wetlands. While all three national forests do include wetlands, the Hiawatha in particular contains large wetland holdings, much of them forested.

It is important to note that significant wetlands also occur in the three parks managed by the National Park Service (NPS)–Isle Royale National Park, Pictured Rocks National Lakeshore, and Sleeping Bear Dunes National Lakeshore. The marshes and swamps in Isle Royale and Pictured Rocks provide critical habitat for Michigan's moose population, whereas the interdunal wetland swales in Sleeping Bear Dunes National Lakeshore comprise some of the rarest wetland types on the planet. Although the management of these parks by the NPS are typically consistent with wetland protection goals, there is an ongoing role for citizen input and oversight. For example, a proposed "scenic drive" in Pictured Rocks National Lakeshore threatens to impact wetlands, and a golf course proposed near Sleeping Bear Dunes National Lakeshore could have had long-term impacts on wetlands and water quality of the Crystal River. In both cases, citizen involvement has been critical in staving off development that would impact the ecological integrity of the wetlands within the park system.

The laws and regulations that the Fish and Wildlife Service and the Forest Service must follow in managing these public lands provide a good opportunity for public involvement. Both agencies are required to follow procedures for public input as laid out in the National Environmental Policy Act of 1969 (NEPA). Both agencies are also required to follow the Endangered Species Act. In addition, management of the national forests is controlled by the National Forest Management Act (NFMA) and the Multiple Use-Sustained Yield Act (MUSY). Procedures for management of the national wildlife refuges is outlined primarily in the National Wildlife Refuge System Administration Act of 1966 and the Refuge Recreation Act of 1962. NEPA, however, is the policy which has most relevance to the public input process.

The NEPA Process

The National Environmental Policy Act (NEPA) was enacted in order to codify the decision-making procedure for "major federal actions" which may have an "adverse environmental impact." Most activities on federal lands are subject to the NEPA process. NEPA gives the responsibility to develop non-agency specific regulations to the Council on Environmental Quality (CEQ), a three-person council appointed by the President of the United States. The way the process is carried out for each agency varies slightly, but, for the most part, is very similar.

Generally, if the agency believes that a proposed project may have an adverse environmental impact, one of two documents must be completed. One is an Environmental Assessment (EA); the other is an Environmental Impact Statement (EIS). Some activities, such as development of a Forest Plan, automatically require an EIS. Others, such as individual timber sales, will generally undergo an EA to determine the need for an EIS.

The Environmental Assessment

The public input process begins with a public notice in the Federal Register, known as a "scoping notice." This notice gives a basic outline of the proposed project, a list of the alternatives being considered, and should include maps of the project area. The public will have at least 30 days after the posting of the scoping notice in the Federal Register to comment. The purpose of scoping is to identify issues of concern to interested parties, should the project be approved. When commenting, it is most helpful to identify exactly what you feel is problematic with the project. Also, you can offer additional alternatives to be considered (the agency is required to consider a "no-action alternative," i.e., the results of not implementing the project, in addition to a general "range of alternatives"). This is also a good opportunity to ask questions about the project. Sometimes, particularly when a proposed project is considered controversial, the agency will hold a scoping meeting with the public. Next, the agency will issue a Draft EA, after which follows a 30-day public comment period.

A "Decision Notice" (DN) is issued after the public comment period. Unless you have successfully convinced the agency to withdraw their proposal (if that's your wish), they will issue a "Finding of No Significant Impact" (FONSI,) or they will develop an EIS.

171

If you do not agree with the agency's decision, the next step would be an administrative appeal. You will have 45 days after the release of the Decision Notice to file an appeal. Your appeal will likely require additional research in that you will need to show that the project is not legal. This could be because the project is not consistent with the Forest Plan, the Endangered Species Act, NEPA, or some other federal law. There are several groups in Michigan that can assist you with this process. It may be helpful to check with Northwoods Wilderness Recovery, Superior Wilderness Action Network (SWAN), and Heartwood, Inc. (see Appendix A for contact information) to find out if they are already appealing the project.

If your appeal is denied, and you still feel that the project is not legal, the only recourse left at this point is litigation. An important thing to remember is that you can only address concerns in your lawsuit that you addressed in your appeal. Many groups have found attorneys and paralegals who are willing to work for a reduced fee or even free. The Michigan Environmental Law Center provides initial legal consultation, serves as a clearinghouse for legal information, and connects citizens with public interest lawyers who are willing to accept clients for reduced rates (see Appendix A for contact information). Even if you do find free or inexpensive legal help, the costs of a lawsuit can escalate quickly. Again, check with the groups mentioned above to find out if they are already planning to litigate.

The Environmental Impact Statement

If the agency decides to develop an Environmental Impact Statement for the project, the process is quite similar. An EIS is like an EA in many ways, but is far more in-depth. The public comment process begins with a Notice of Intent (NOI), which is much like a scoping notice. Again, the public has 30 days in which to provide comment. After the comment period, the agency will release a Draft EIS. A 90-day public comment period follows. At the end of the comment period, the agency will issue a Record of Decision (ROD) and final EIS. Following this, the public has 45 days to appeal the decision and final EIS.

If the agency performs an Environmental Assessment, and decides to prepare an EIS, then the process is the same. A new scoping period begins with the Notice of Intent.

The NEPA Process

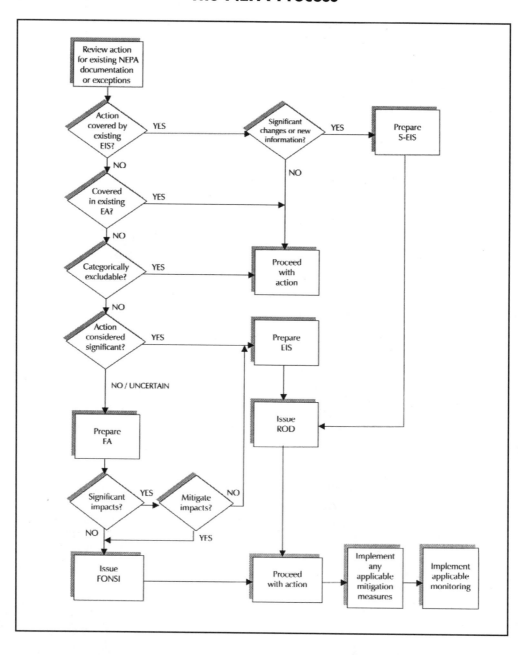

172

Tips for Working with the NEPA Process

1. Get on the "scoping lists" for the national forest or national wildlife refuge in which you are interested. You'll need to write a letter to the national forest or national wildlife refuge. This will keep you informed of all upcoming projects on the forest or wildlife refuge. For work on national forests, you'll also want to get a copy of the forest's Land and Resource Management Plan (Forest Plan) and accompanying EIS. You'll find it helpful to refer to this document when submitting comments and appeals.

2. Keep copies of all correspondence.

3. If you can, visit the site. Maps accompany many EA's and EIS's. Knowing the area will help you to provide useful comments.

4. Cite articles, studies, and other references if you can. If you don't have any of this information, that's okay too. The important thing is that you make your concerns known.

5. Review other people's comments. If you go to the office of the agency, you can look through the files on the project and find out who else has submitted comments. This will give you an idea of how many people are supportive versus how many are opposed. It will also give you some ideas for potential allies.

6. Keep Track of Deadlines! While sometimes you can get an extension, it is very important that you submit your comments by the stated deadlines.

7. Become familiar with applicable laws. Many of these laws are listed in this chapter. Knowing them will help you to determine when a proposed project is illegal.

173

STATE-OWNED FORESTED WETLANDS

In the northern two-thirds of Michigan, the vast majority of state-owned wetlands are forested, and administered by the Michigan Department of Natural Resources Forest Management Division. These forestlands are widely used for recreation, hunting, and fishing. These lands are also managed for timber extraction, which has many possible impacts on wetlands.

While much of Michigan's swampland was logged at the turn of the century, over the past hundred years these areas have largely recovered to become functioning, diverse ecosystems. Logging, as it is practiced today, has a much greater impact on wetlands than it did a hundred years ago. Heavy machinery threatens the delicate soils and the microclimates present in many wetlands, deer overpopulation decreases cedar regeneration and changes the composition of the forest, and the continued extraction of nutrients locked in the trees threatens the future fertility of the forest. In order to determine the type and scope of projects, including logging on the state forests, the MDNR conducts inventories and makes management decisions for the state forests.

Brief Overview of Forest Management Division's Tasks and Responsibilities

Management of state forests is very detailed and structured in Michigan. Every year one-tenth of state forest lands are inventoried (approximately 400,000 acres). Information that is acquired during an inventory includes size and age of trees, species composition, forest health, wildlife including threatened and endangered species, recreational activities, plus much more.

"Citizen involvement in the Open Houses can be extremely valuable. At an Open House in Emmet County, citizens pointed out the presence of a trail commonly used by people in the area that was in the middle of a proposed thinning stand. MDNR staff were not aware of this trail. After learning about the trail, we added in a buffer strip on both sides, where thinning wouldn't occur."

Mike Mang, MDNR Forest Manager

To make management on state forests easier and better, forests are subdivided into smaller units, called compartments. Forest compartments are generally 2 to 3 sections in size (1,280 acres to 1,920 acres) but vary depending on other physical features such as forest cover type, rivers, and roads. The results from the detailed inventories are reviewed by Forest Management Division, Wildlife Division, Michigan Natural Features Inventory (for input on threatened and endangered species), and often Fisheries Division. After the review, management recommendations are developed for the compartments inventoried. Management recommendations range from prescribing clear cutting to no action at all. To help the Forest Management Division best manage these resources, they sponsor two different types of public forums to allow citizens to share their ideas on how the state's forests should be managed.

Forest Management Open House

Open Houses, just as the name implies, are an opportunity for citizens to meet with MDNR foresters and wildlife biologists in an informal manner to discuss and ask questions about where and what MDNR forest management activities are planned. The inventories, compartment maps, and recommended management actions for specific compartments are available for the public to look at and provide suggestions to the MDNR staff.

174

There are no formal presentations or public comment periods at Open Houses. Instead, the informal atmosphere allows people to meet one-on-one with MDNR resource managers who work on state forest lands in their immediate area.

Compartment Review Process

Following the Open House, MDNR foresters take information and comments collected at the Open House and if necessary, modify management recommendations and actions into a finalized compartment plan. The compartment plans are then presented at another public forum, a Compartment Review.

Management plans for forest compartments are presented in a formal presentation at the Compartment Reviews. Information about the findings from the forest inventory are presented such as tree species diversity, age and class (size) of trees, presence of threatened or endangered species, and other special features. If timber activities are planned, the MDNR presents a "prescription" as to how this will occur. The Compartment Review involves open discussions regarding management for each compartment being reviewed. The public is welcome to participate in these discussions. In addition, written comments are accepted, but must be received on or before the date of the Compartment Review.

The MDNR will once again review public comment and if appropriate, modify compartment plans and logging plans. If a citizen is dissatisfied with the MDNR's plans after the Compartment Review, a grievance can be filed.

The Appeals Process

The public is entitled to appeal the prescriptions made at the formal Compartment Review, as well as delayed decisions, and subsequent significant changes in prescriptions. The appeal must be postmarked no later than 45 days after the Compartment Review, or 45 days after the date of the "memo of advisement" for delayed decisions or changes in prescriptions. In order to file an appeal, you must have participated in the Compartment Review–either by attending, or by submitting comments. The appeal must state how the decision fails to consider comments previously provided, or how it violates laws, regulations, or policies.

In addition, a loophole allows "emergency actions," which include "matters affecting public safety or welfare, or significant potential loss of resources, such as salvage after fire, storm, or insect and disease outbreak, or for emergency deer feeding," to be exempt from the normal process of public notice, review, and decision-making. You may still, however, request a "mini-review" to be conducted "when time permits," and submit comments as to whether there may be more value or less impact in simply allowing the effects of a natural disturbance to remain as is.

The appeal is decided solely by the MDNR Field Deputy, within 30 calendar days after the closing of the 45-day appeal period. The Field Deputy may extend the decision-making period for an additional 30 calendar days. The Field Deputy will then issue a written decision to the appellant.

After this appeal, there are no other opportunities for the public to influence the decision administratively. At this point, the only option left is a court case. It is important to note that judicial review will generally be denied if the person or organization filing the suit has not first appealed the project.

Understanding Compartment Review Maps

- All compartment maps are oriented so that North is at the top of the page.

- A one-acre square is approximately 208 feet by 208 feet.

- Most sections are made up of 640 acres. There are typically 36 sections in a township.

- The maps list the location of the compartment by township, range numbers, and section, e.g., T34N, R4W, SEC. 19. The compartment area in the example is located in Township (T) 34 North (N), Range (R) 4 West (W), Sections (SEC) 19, 20, 29 & 30. The location of a township in Michigan is based upon the Michigan Meridian and Baseline. County plat maps contain township and range information for property. They also have a description on how to locate properties using the township and range numbers. The Meridian runs North and South and the Baseline runs East and West. The two meet in southcentral Michigan in Jackson County. The example given above, T34N, R4W, means the township (T) is 34 townships north (N) and 3 townships or ranges (R) West (W) of the Meridian.

175

Reading Compartment Maps

Understanding proposed forest management activities requires learning how to read forest compartment maps. MDNR staff can help explain how to do this at Open Houses. However, to better prepare you for an Open House we have compiled some helpful tips for reading the maps. An example of a compartment review map from a State Forest in southern Emmet County will be used to guide the process of interpreting compartment maps.

The purpose of the compartment review maps is to show the different stands of trees (or forest type description) with an attached recommendation for management. The forest stands are determined based on the different types of trees present. Boundaries for forest types are marked on the map and are represented by the irregular polygons. Within each polygon is the stand number (usually in small print) and a letter followed by a number. The letter is an abbreviation for a type of tree, e.g., M, represents northern hardwoods and R, represents red pine. The legend for the Forest Compartment Map includes the codes that the MDNR uses to describe the different forest types.

The number following the letter describes the size density of the forest, commonly called the stocking of the stand. The code for size density describes the tree size and the density of the forest. There are three size classes for trees: sapling, poletimber, and sawtimber. A sapling is any tree less than 5" in diameter; poletimber or pole is all trees 5" in diameter to 9.9" in diameter; sawtimber is 10" in diameter and up. All these diameters are measured at 4 feet from the ground (also commonly referred to as diameter at breast height or DBH).

176

The density of a stand is determined by measuring the basal area. Basal area is the amount of area in a cross section of a tree at its DBH. For example, a tree with a 10" DBH has a basal area (actual stem cross-sectional area) of 0.545 square feet. Basal area is usually recorded on a per acre basis and is calculated by foresters using a special prism. Using three different breakdowns of basal area, a stand is determined to be poorly, medium, or well stocked. Using our example compartment map, many of the stands are labeled M6, describing northern hardwood forests of poletimber that is well stocked.

Prescribed treatments for the forest stands are labeled on the maps, with different types of shading. A prescribed treatment takes into account the method of cut such as thinning or final harvest (commonly called a clear cut), as well as the merchantability of the timber. Generally, there isn't a detailed written explanation about the treatment; however, MDNR Forest Management staff can share their reasoning for recommending a particular treatment at the Open Houses.

Species Codes

A. Aspen (upland)
B. Paper Birch
C. Northern White Cedar
D. Treed Bog
E. Swamp Hardwoods
F. Upland Spruce Fir
G. Grass
H. Hemlock
I. Local Use (Explain in remarks card)
J. Jack Pine
K. Rock
L. Lowland Bush
M. Northern Hardwoods
N. Marsh
O. Oak
P. Balsam Poplar, Swamp Aspen, Swamp Paper Birch
Q. Mixed Swamp Conifers
R. Red Pine
S. Black Spruce (swamp)
T. Tamarack
U. Upland Brush
V. Bog or Muskeg
W. White Pine
X. Non-stocked
Y. Sand Dunes
Z. Water

0 Non-stocked (less than 17%)

1 Seedling-Sapling, 100-399 trees/acre, (18%-39% stocked)

2 Seedling-Sapling, Medium, 400-699 trees/acre, (40%-69% stocked)

3 Seedling-Sapling, Well, 700+ trees/acre or a minimum of 70% stocked

4 Poletimber (5" to 9.9" DBH), 10-39 sq.ft. Basal Area, poorly stocked

5 Poletimber (5" to 9.9" DBH), 40-69 sq.ft. Basal Area, medium stocked

6 Poletimber (5" to 9.9" DBH), 70 and over sq.ft. Basal Area, well stocked

7 Sawtimber (10" DBH and up), 10-39 sq.ft. Basal Area, poorly stocked

8 Sawtimber (10" DBH and up), 40-69 sq.ft. Basal Area, medium stocked

9 Sawtimber (10" DBH and up), 70 and over sq.ft. Basal Area, well stocked

MDNR Forest Compartment Map

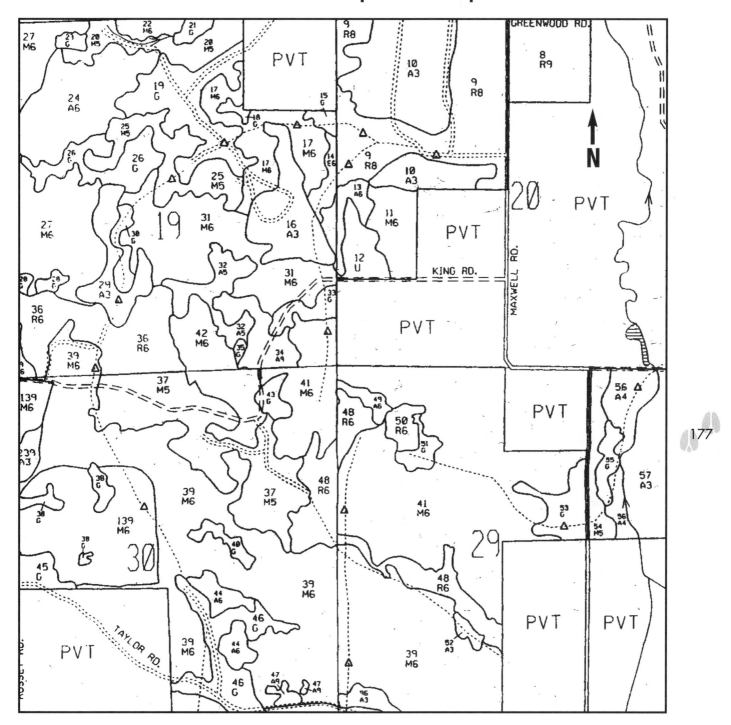

177

Integrated into a Compartment Review is an accounting of wildlife species and habitat in the forest. If a landowner in the area knows of any species that would be of particular concern, please let the MDNR Wildlife Biologist know. Often you are the best contact the MDNR has with wildlife. For more information on MDNR Forest Management, Open Houses, and Compartment Reviews contact the MDNR Forest Management Division office nearest you.

OTHER STATE-OWNED WETLANDS

In the southern third of Michigan, management of state-owned wetlands is much different. These wetlands are administered largely by the wildlife management division of the Michigan Department of Natural Resources. Some of these wetlands are forested, but the majority are marshes with open water, managed primarily for waterfowl.

Unfortunately, there is very little room for public input into the management of these wetlands. There are no requirements for public comment on projects in these areas. Generally, prior to implementing a project, MDNR Wildlife Management Division staff will hold an informal meeting with a local hunting and/or fishing club, reflecting the fact that many of these areas were purchased with revenues generated by hunters and anglers. Fortunately, the MDNR staff are generally open to public input. You may be able to informally participate in management decisions for these areas by contacting and getting to know the appropriate MDNR staff persons in your area. Certainly a need in the management of these lands is an increased consideration of non-game wildlife and ecological values associated with these wetlands.

178

CONCLUSION

Publicly owned wetlands provide a wealth of ecological functions that benefit the citizens of Michigan and numerous recreational opportunities that support a thriving tourist economy. Citizen wetland advocates can play a critical role in ensuring that these wetland continue to serve their ecological functions and are managed in a way that allows a sustainable use for generations to come. In addition to our shared responsibility to protect these public lands, we also have a shared responsibility to enjoy them. By getting out and visiting our wetlands (either canoeing, birdwatching, duck hunting, fishing, whatever!) we experience and learn more about our shared natural heritage and provide proof to elected officials and agency staff that these areas are valued.

Wetland Protection Spotlight

Protecting Michigan's Wild and Scenic Rivers
Doug Cornett

Many government projects take years and even decades to reach the implementation stage. Most often, citizens are asked what they think late in the process. Unfortunately, this important phase of decision-making is often looked upon by agency personnel as a formality, long after a decision has been made. Momentum builds and so much time and money has been committed that even the most ill-conceived project is almost impossible to stop.

-- Doug Cornett

The proposed Nahma Junction Roadside Rest was almost another unstoppable project. Located in Michigan's Upper Peninsula on US-2 between Manistique and Rapid River, the Sturgeon River site is within a congressionally-designated National Wild and Scenic River corridor and owned by the Hiawatha National Forest. The Michigan Department of Transportation planned to build a roadside rest to accommodate 250,000 visitors a year.

179

Hiawatha District Ranger Bob Walker thought the plan was a good one. The Hiawatha would get space in the facility to "inform and educate the public" on Wild and Scenic Rivers, Research Natural Areas, and the Forest Highway 13 Scenic Byway.

In March 1999, Ranger Walker issued a Scoping letter for the project. Before any public input, Walker went as far to say that he expected "no significant impact" and that no Environmental Impact Statement was necessary. Further, he expected the decision could be made in a few short months, and planned to approve the project by late summer.

Doug Cornett first called a botany consultant who knew the area well, and asked his opinion. He had concerns because the oxbow lake and wetlands constituted prime habitat for rare and endangered plants and the site had never been thoroughly surveyed. However, his biggest concern was a known pre-historic archeology site about 6,000 years old. By chance, the botanist had talked to the archeologist who found the site, shortly after the 1980 discovery. This was almost 20 years before the first public comment was taken!

Doug obtained the archeologist's report and then decided to visit the proposed building site. When he arrived there on a Tuesday morning in late March, survey markers for the building and road were already in place. The west corners of the building would be about 30 feet from the top of an erosion-prone sand bluff above the Sturgeon River, and cover the site of test pits from the 1980 archeological survey.

An oxbow lake, designated as a Candidate Research Natural Area, lies about 100 yards to the south of the knoll. The building's septic system would drain toward the oxbow.

Armed with photos of the site, and convinced that this proposal would significantly degrade values the Sturgeon Wild and Scenic River designation was meant to protect, Doug set out to get as many people as possible to protest this proposed roadside rest area.

Doug wrote a comment letter and Action Alert, and then over the next couple of weeks sent the Alert and a sample letter to as many individuals and e-mail listserves as he could find. He targeted not only the Forest Service, but also Congressman Dale Kildee, who penned the Michigan Wild and Scenic River Act. A lot of folks responded - some as far away as California, Washington, and Florida. All were outraged. Congressman Kildee voiced concerns to MDOT and the Forest Service.

Late in June, Doug unexpectedly received a letter denying MDOT's special-use application! In an about-face, Walker rejected the application stating "…after reviewing public response it is my conclusion that construction of a major public use area within the Sturgeon River Wild and Scenic River Corridor and adjacent to the Lower Sturgeon River Candidate Research Natural Area would be premature. The lack of both a comprehensive management plan for the Sturgeon River and an establishment report for the CRNA raises serious questions about our abilities to protect and enhance the river's outstanding remarkable values…" Doug notes that, "Although we have a law meant to protect Michigan's Wild and Scenic Rivers, without citizen oversight that law is often meaningless. We cannot rely on agencies to protect the public trust, citizens must be vigilant and ready to defend the Wild."

For more information, contact:
Doug Cornett
Northwoods Wilderness Recovery
P.O. Box 122
Marquette, MI 49855-0122
website: www.northwoodswild.org

Chapter 13

Some Thoughts on Key Wetland Issues

There is no question about it—although practically everyone will say how important wetlands are, the regulation of private activities in wetlands generates controversy. This controversy arises for many reasons, paramount among them the issue of trying to balance private gain against the public interest. This chapter attempts to shed light upon some of the more common controversial issues related to wetland protection. The discussions here are not meant to be comprehensive treatments of the subject matter or to cover all controversial wetland issues, but rather to serve as "talking points" to prepare the wetland advocate for discussions on these issues.

THE IMPACT OF WETLAND REGULATIONS ON ECONOMIC GROWTH

A common criticism of wetland regulations is that they halt economic development and community growth. Since only ten to fifteen percent of wetland applications to the state and less than ten percent of the federal wetlands dredge and fill applications are denied (and many of these are reapplied for and issued with modifications), wetland regulations are not "halting" a significant amount of economic development. Granted, there are costs related to the wetland regulatory process, but these costs are minimal when

compared to the other costs of development, and pale in comparison to the long-term economic value that would be lost if wetlands were degraded without any regulatory review.

Many municipalities in Michigan with wetland regulations are among the fastest growing communities in the state. Growing municipalities like West Bloomfield Township, Meridian Township, Hayes Township, and the City of Novi have adopted wetland protection ordinances with no negative impact on economic development. For example, in the early 1990s the city of Novi issued over four times as many residential building permits in the five years after adopting an ordinance than in the previous five years.

Protecting wetlands contributes to the development of more liveable communities by providing public benefits such as critical fish and wildlife habitat, recreation opportunities, valuable open space in residential areas, and buffers between incompatible land uses. Residential lots that border on protected wetlands often are more desirable and fetch higher prices than other properties. Developers who realize this and integrate wetland protection into their developments have the opportunity to increase their profits.

THE IMPACT OF WETLAND REGULATIONS ON AFFORDABLE HOUSING

Opponents of wetland protection often cite that wetland regulations lead to a lack of affordable housing. Upon closer review, it becomes apparent that the economic costs of regulatory review are minimal compared to other costs of property development. Many wetland development projects are situated on wetlands that are adjacent to lakefront property—some of the most expensive real estate in Michigan. "Affordable" housing projects are rarely proposed for these properties. Furthermore, additional costs of wetlands development arise from the site engineering (dredging, filling, etc.) that must be done to prepare a wetland site for development. These costs can be avoided by appropriate site plan review and regulation that directs development out of wetlands. There are many factors that influence the lack of affordable housing, perhaps the most significant of them are the economics of the building trades industry. There is substantially more profit margin on larger, more expensive homes than there is on smaller "affordable" homes.

COSTS OF LOCAL WETLAND REGULATIONS TO LOCAL GOVERNMENT

In situations where a community wishes to provide additional protection to wetlands by enacting local wetlands protection provisions, a common criticism is that the local wetlands regulations are too expensive for the local community to bear. Here are two responses to this argument. First, there are many different local wetlands protection options (See Chapter Ten), each involving different levels of staffing and financial resources to implement. The local unit of government can select an option that is compatible with existing or foreseeable resources.

Second, there are ways in which to structure the ordinance so that the financial burden of the regulatory process is borne by those seeking to degrade wetlands. This can be done by charging application and processing fees that cover the costs of the regulatory review, or by the applicant setting up an escrow account to cover the costs. Depending on the project size and complexity, the actual costs of adequate regulatory review could range from less than a hundred to several thousand dollars. As long as the escrow is set at an adequate amount, the local government does not have to pay excess costs in complex cases that involve extra administrative work. Any money left in the escrow account after regulatory review can be returned to the applicant or put towards performance guarantees for any required mitigation. In addition, the escrow account can be set up so that added funds must be supplied by the developer if the permit process is to continue.

LOCAL WETLAND REGULATIONS

To some anti-government special interest groups, the very concept of local wetlands protection regulations is a controversial issue. The reasons they criticize local wetlands ordinances are varied. Below, a few of the most common criticisms of local wetlands ordinances are presented, and short responses provided.

Opponents of local wetlands regulation say that municipal wetlands regulation has all too often been unreasonable, excessive, and administered with lengthy delays and multiple hearings. These claims have not been substantiated with any factual information or convincing statistics. In fact, Michigan's wetland protection statute dictates that local wetland permits must be reviewed by the same body and in the same timeframe as other local approvals for a particular development. Given the fact that local wetland regulations ensure that wetlands are considered early in the development planning process, thus avoiding costly delays in dealing with wetlands after the site planning has been completed, local wetland ordinances my indeed speed up the overall regulatory review process.

183

Opponents of local wetlands regulations have also stated that the local control of wetlands is used for economic and racial exclusionary purposes, and that local wetlands boards are composed of lay people who do not have an environmental or technical background. There is absolutely no data to support the first claim. In regards to the second point, local boards who make decisions on all local land use issues are seldom environmental professionals. Accordingly, these boards rely on the findings and recommendations of professional staff. In the case of wetlands regulations, local wetlands boards often pay for professional wetland consultants with escrow accounts set up and paid for by the applicant. The information upon which the boards base their decisions is thus gathered in a technically sound and professional manner.

Another platform from which opponents of local wetlands regulation speak is that of the duplication of permits. Depending on the type of local wetlands regulation, two wetlands permits may in fact be required before work that degrades wetlands can begin. Opponents of local wetlands regulation state that this creates undue time and cost constraints. Supporters of local wetlands regulation usually respond with one of three comments: 1) the cost is minimal compared to the costs of the wetland functions that are lost when wetlands are

destroyed; 2) local wetlands review is integrated into the normal zoning review process and therefore does not add an additional time constraint; and 3) wetlands provide values that are both important to the local municipality, the state, and the country as a whole, and as a result, local, state, and federal permits should all be required for activities that degrade wetlands.

THE VALUE OF SMALL WETLANDS

Michigan's wetland protection law exempts numerous wetlands that are isolated from surface waters, many of which are small. It is important to note that this was not due to some finding by the legislature that isolated or small wetlands are not valuable, but rather a political compromise made to pass the bill. Small wetlands can be extremely important ecological resources for many reasons, including flood storage, endangered species habitat, and local refuge habitat for a variety of animals (especially in urban areas). Recognizing this, and realizing that varying ecological systems might require local management of wetlands, the original drafters of Michigan's wetland law wisely authorized local governments to have the legal authority to protect these valuable resources. In the absence of local regulations, the Act does authorize the MDEQ to regulate small isolated wetlands if a determination is made that the wetland is important for the protection of natural resources in the state and informs the landowner of that determination. Although the MDEQ has developed a process and identified potential sites, very few landowners have been notified. The fact that locally important wetlands can be effectively managed by local municipalities is as true today as it was in 1979. For this reason, among others, the enactment of local ordinances should be promoted to protect wetland resources not adequately protected by state law.

184

THE VALUE OF BUFFERS

One of the shortcomings of Michigan's wetland protection law is that it fails to protect ecological buffers between upland activity and wetlands. The ecotone that occurs at the boundary between wetland and upland serves as important wildlife habitat and is important to water quality by attenuating silt and contaminants associated with runoff. Other states' wetland regulatory programs protect this important zone.

Under the current state and federal regulations in Michigan, earth change activities can be permitted right up to the edge of the wetland without a permit. With this sort of development, the ecological benefits of the buffer zone are lost and the wetland is directly impacted by the adjacent development. Local zoning requirements such as building setbacks or required vegetated strips can effectively protect wetland buffers. Here is an excellent example of where local wetland protection efforts can protect the ecological integrity of wetlands.

THE DEGRADATION OF WETLANDS FROM STORMWATER

One of the most useful natural functions of wetlands is that of maintaining the water quality of lakes, rivers, and streams by removing silt and other contaminants from runoff. This natural function is sometimes put to work to treat stormwater before it is discharged to surface or ground water. Although this seems like a good "use" of wetlands, studies have shown that stormwater discharge to natural wetlands can alter the hydrology, water quality, topography, vegetation, and biological communities.

For these reasons, direct discharge of stormwater to natural wetlands should be avoided. However, there are many ways to structure a system of stormwater management that utilizes wetlands. The negative impacts of stormwater on natural wetlands can be reduced through the use of retention ponds located in uplands or the conveyance of stormwater through grass lined swales. These mechanisms help to remove the sediment and pollutants from the stormwater before it enters the wetland, and can serve to minimize damage due to hydrologic changes. The key is to design the system so that stormwater entering the wetland after development is similar in quantity to stormwater prior to development. Artificial wetlands can be created specifically for the purpose of stormwater management. In this case, there are no issues regarding adverse impacts on natural wetlands, as the artificial wetlands are created and managed for this purpose. Additionally, the wetlands that are created provide functions and values (e.g., fish and wildlife habitat and open space) not provided by other means of stormwater management.

185

THE DUBIOUS VALUE OF WETLAND CLASSIFICATION SCHEMES

The term "wetland classification" has been used to represent two different concepts. In one, a wetlands classification scheme developed by the U.S. Fish and Wildlife Service is used as a sort of taxonomical key to describe different wetland types. Alternatively, as in this discussion, wetland classification refers to the concept of "classifying" wetlands into ranked categories based on their functions and values to society, and basing the amount of protection provided to these wetlands on these rankings. In efforts to "streamline" wetlands regulations, this concept of classification is presented as an attractive mechanism to focus regulatory efforts on wetlands with a "high" ranking. However, there are several problems with wetlands classification that question its benefits to wetlands protection.

First, there are likely to be biases in the ranking criteria. For example, given the variety and abundance of species using wetlands, how does one rank various types of habitat against each other? Are marshes better than swamps? Is variety or abundance "better" than a rare or endangered species? In regards to functions, is the urban wetland that traps sediment from entering the Rouge River more "valuable" than a cedar swamp that is used by deer for winter cover in the Upper Peninsula? It is extremely difficult to answer these questions in an objective manner.

Second, most functions are not easily assessed. All wetlands serve multiple functions to some extent, and their values depend on where they are situated in the landscape and the characteristics of the watershed. To accurately measure all the functions and values that each wetland provides would be prohibitively expensive and administratively impossible. However, without accurate assessments of functions, the validity of any classification scheme falls apart. Another way to look at this is to consider the context of the functional evaluation. In the context of permit review, the direct impacts of the proposed project on wetland functions can be assessed. Outside of the context of specific activities on specific wetlands, functional evaluation becomes extremely subjective.

The third, and perhaps most controversial issue related to wetlands classification, is the concept of providing unequal protection to different classes of wetlands. In several bills introduced to amend the Federal Clean Water Act, wetland classification schemes were proposed to be used as a mechanism to eliminate protection for "lower" classes of wetlands, or to weaken protection so it is rendered ineffective. This is ludicrous from a wetland protection perspective. All wetlands provide some functions valuable to society. Given that Michigan has lost over half of its pre-settlement wetlands, schemes that would promote the degradation of more wetland acreage, regardless of the type and "value," should be opposed.

In addition to these, any classification scheme will have to be linked to some sort of detailed inventory initiative (see Proper Use of Wetland Inventories and Maps). Given the problems inherent with inventories, and the difficulty of developing a classification scheme and applying that scheme to a particular wetland, wetlands classification would add time delays and costs to wetland regulations.

186

WETLANDS CREATION CAUTIONS

The concept of creating wetlands has been put forth as a way to solve practically all problems with wetlands regulation. It is important to realize the distinction between wetland creation and wetland restoration. Wetland restoration refers to the rehabilitation of wetlands that have been degraded or hydrologically altered. Wetland creation refers to the construction of wetlands where they did not exist before.

The three most common reasons for wetland creation in the United States are wastewater treatment, coal mine drainage control, and replacement of wetland loss. In Michigan, the most common reason has been for the mitigation of unavoidable losses permitted through state and federal wetland regulatory programs. There has been little follow-up of these mitigation creation projects and there are few methods available to determine the "success" of a created wetland in replacing the functions lost with the destruction of the original wetland.

Like wetlands properly created and managed for the purpose of stormwater management, wetlands created for the purpose of wastewater treatment add to the existing resource base and represent a positive way for humans to utilize the functions that wetlands provide. The critical issue of wetland creation is in regards to mitigating wetland losses. The creation of wetlands where they did not exist before can be extremely costly and has been shown to have a low rate of success from an ecological perspective. For these reasons, wetland creation should only be used to offset wetland losses when there are absolutely no other mitigation alternatives. In addition, there must be stipulations to ensure that the losses are appropriately replaced by the creation project, including requiring two acres of created wetlands per every one acre lost (since at least half of the creation projects fail in some way), monitoring and maintenance provisions, and financial commitments (bonds or escrow accounts) to ensure that the project is successful in the long term.

THE PROBLEMS ASSOCIATED WITH WETLAND MITIGATION BANKING

"Wetland mitigation banking" is a term used to refer to the creation, or restoration of wetlands by a developer to serve as a "bank" with "credits" to compensate for future wetland impacts. The concept of the mitigation bank is attractive to landowners, developers, and economists as it attempts to integrate a "market-based" element into wetlands regulation. The concept has generated much debate since its inception.

On the positive side, mitigation banks can encourage the creation and restoration of large wetland areas, which generally have a lower cost per acre than smaller wetland restoration projects. Mitigation banks also provide a greater flexibility to developers, whereby instead of designing and implementing their own mitigation plans, they can purchase or use existing credits. One benefit of Michigan's current mitigation banking program is that wetlands are built in advance and developers can only use the credits once the bank is proven successful. This is not the case under typical mitigation requirements.

On the other hand, mitigation banking projects have many disadvantages. Mitigation banks often encourage the cheapest and easiest wetland creation, enhancement, or restoration projects. Thus, marshes or shrub-scrub swamps are created to mitigate for the loss of other wetland types. This loss of one wetland type for another does not benefit the state or nation's severely degraded wetland resource.

187

To a large extent, wetlands derive their values from their location in the landscape and their relationship with other wetlands and waterbodies. Mitigation banks replace wetlands lost in one location with wetlands located in another. Many wetland functions are site-specific and are lost when the wetland is destroyed. These cannot be replaced by wetland credits in a mitigation bank at some other site. This disadvantage is amplified by the fact that mitigation banks would encourage developers to propose off-site mitigation, as this sort of mitigation is less expensive than performing on-site and in-kind mitigation.

In the regulatory process, the existence of mitigation banks may allow developers to exert considerable pressure on regulatory agencies to forego thorough alternatives analysis and impact avoidance. Developers may argue that because mitigation is achieved through their "credits" in the "bank," they should receive a permit to dredge or fill wetlands that otherwise may not be issued.

This potential for pressure was realized during the development of the administrative rules that address mitigation banking in Michigan. Accordingly the rules clearly state that applicants are subject to sequencing restrictions in which all alternatives are utilized to first avoid, then minimize, impacts on wetlands. In the case of unavoidable wetland impacts, mitigation for wetland impacts should be done in accordance with the sequencing process set forth in Michigan's Wetland Protection Act and administrative rules (see Chapter Eight and the appendices). As mitigation banks become established, citizens can play an important role in reviewing their success and ensuring that agency staff adhere to the sequencing process.

PROPER USE OF WETLAND INVENTORIES AND MAPS

Wetland inventories and maps can be extremely useful items, but only if their inadequacies are understood. Chapter Three discusses the wetland maps that are widely available throughout the state. From the regulatory perspective, wetland maps have many shortcomings. On the local level, creation of a wetlands inventory is required as part of establishing a local wetland permitting program. Wetland inventories can provide an excellent means by which to inform landowners that they may have regulated wetlands on their property. However, wetland inventories, no matter how comprehensive, are not a viable substitute for on-site wetland investigation of wetland boundaries. Accordingly, wetland inventories serve a very limited regulatory purpose. This is not a problem, as long as the regulated community realizes the limited utility. When wetland inventories are misused or misperceived to serve as delineating the boundaries of jurisdictional wetlands, problems arise. When the state finishes the wetlands inventory, or when a local government produces a wetlands inventory, it is critical that the purpose and its shortcomings be clearly spelled out... wetland inventories are not jurisdictional maps. Otherwise, individuals may use the excuse, "My wetland is not on the inventory map," to avoid the regulatory process.

Portion of a Legend From a Wetland Map

ANTRIM COUNTY COMPOSITE WETLAND AREAS
Map Data:
This map is a composite of three sources of wetlands information:

a. The National Wetland Inventory, conducted by the U.S. Fish and Wildlife Service using aerial photography and topographic data. Note: National Wetland Inventory digital data is available for most of the county (excluding only the south-eastern edges).
b. The U.S. Soil Conservation Service Soil Survey of Grand Traverse County which identifies hydric soils and soils with hydric inclusions.
c. The Michigan Resource Inventory System (MIRIS) Land Cover interpretation from 1978 aerial photographs.

These three data layers were combined using PC ArcInfo (GIS software).

The Composite Wetland Area Map project was conducted in coordination with the Michigan Department of Environmental Quality with funds from the U.S. Environmental Protection Agency.

DISCLAIMER: This map has not been field checked and should only be used for general planning purposes. This map should be used to supplement a field inventory by a qualified wetland expert. This map is not a complete inventory of all the wetlands in this area. Regulated wetland areas may exist that are not included on this map.

Data for the base features on this map were developed by the Michigan Resource Information System (MIRIS), Department of Natural Resources, 1978 PA 204. These roads, section lines/numbers, and water features were digitized from the U.S.G.S. topographic quadrangle maps.

The major and minor watershed basin boundaries were delineated on U.S.G.S. topographic quadrangle maps and digitized by the Department of Environmental Quality, Land and Water Management Division. The sub-watershed basin boundaries were delineated on U.S.G.S. topographic quadrangle maps and digitized by the Northwest Michigan Council of Governments.

MICHIGAN
DEPARTMENT OF ENVIRONMENTAL QUALITY

Map produced by:

NORTHWEST MICHIGAN COUNCIL OF GOVERNMENTS
August 1997

INADEQUATE ENFORCEMENT OF WETLAND REGULATIONS

Presently in Michigan, when a violation is identified, the MDEQ staff may issue a cease and desist letter to the responsible individual which stipulates required remedies. If the responsible individual complies with the terms of the letter, many times no further enforcement action is needed. If further enforcement action is needed, legal actions to enforce wetlands regulations must be brought about by the enforcing agent, either through the County Prosecutor or the Attorney General. Currently, there is a lack of effective court action, primarily for three reasons: 1) the lack of sufficient staff to both adequately review permits and enforce the state law, 2) the difficulty of getting appropriate action from County Prosecutors, and 3) the work load of the Attorney

General's office. If a County Prosecutor is unwilling to take the case, and the Attorney General's office does not have the time, MDEQ staff are out of options to pursue enforcement.

Furthermore, there are no citizen suit provisions in the Michigan Wetland Protection Act which would allow citizens to file suit in a court of competent jurisdiction for an injunction or other process against any person to restrain or prevent violations of Michigan's wetland protection statutes. However, citizen suits to enforce Section 404 are authorized by Section 505 of the Clean Water Act. Citizens seeking to use this as a remedy must file suit in federal court. Indirectly, it is possible to use this provision to enforce Michigan's Wetland Protection Act by filing suit in federal court against the EPA for improper oversight of the MDEQ's administration of the assumed Section 404 program.

There are a variety of ways to improve the enforcement of Michigan's Wetland Protection Act. Perhaps the most direct would be to increase the staffing levels to the point where a sufficient amount of staff were devoted to enforcement activities. Other improvements include granting the authority for MDEQ staff to issue appearance tickets, and authorizing citizens to sue to enforce the provisions of the state's wetland law. Both of these options would involve amendments to the state law.

Michigan's criminal code allows the issuance of appearance tickets for minor offenses, including misdemeanors, where the maximum penalty is a $500 fine and/or 92 days in jail. The authority to issue appearance tickets would provide the MDEQ a viable enforcement tool for minor offenses and to deter minor wetland violations. However, there are several concerns that must be addressed when amendments to authorize this tool are introduced. The first is that the definition of a "minor offense" in regards to wetland activities must be clearly defined. The second is that appearance tickets eliminate the possibility of pursuing restoration or further penalties under the criminal code. However, civil action for relief of the same violation would be possible.

189

Amending the various resource management statutes to include citizen suit provisions provides a way to help ensure that the statutes are indeed complied with and enforced by the enforcing agent. Citizen suit provisions would enable citizens to file for an injunction to restrain or prevent violations of the specific statutes, and to require restoration of ecosystem damage. Although the Michigan Environmental Protection Act does authorize citizens to sue to enjoin environmental impairment, it is seldom used. Integrating citizen suit provisions into the resource management permitting statutes would make suing for specific performance under a particular statute more straightforward.

THE ISSUE OF REGULATORY TAKINGS

One of the most contentious aspects of wetlands protection is the "takings" issue. Governments have the power of eminent domain which allows them to "take" property when it is in the public interest and provided that the landowner receives just compensation. In some cases, landowners claim a regulatory taking has occurred when they are deprived of the preferred use of their land due to the application of wetlands regulatory standards. Although these claims resonate with deep-seated American values derived from the Fifth Amendment of the Constitution, the courts have consistently ruled that individual landowners do not have the unrestrained right to engage in activities which adversely impact the public interest.

In general, to determine if a regulatory taking has occurred, two findings must be made by the court: 1) that the regulatory statute does not substantially advance legitimate public interests, and 2) the government regulations deny a landowner essentially all economically viable uses of his or her land. Although there is no set formula to determine if a regulation or governmental action constitutes a taking, there are several court cases which help to define this. In the only two court cases in which the U.S. Supreme Court deemed a taking had occurred through the administration of Section 404 of the Clean Water Act, (Florida Rock Industries v. United States, and Loveladies Harbor v. United States), the landowners had been deprived of 95% and 99% respectively of the value of their land. In Michigan, cases such as Blue Water Isles, Inc. v. Department of Natural Resources and Bond v. Department of Natural Resources, support the MDEQ's authority to deny development activities in wetlands pursuant to state regulations.

In the past decade, several legislative initiatives in Michigan have sought to amend the Wetland Protection Act so that the simple designation of an area as wetlands would constitute a regulatory taking. This concept does not meet the required "denial of all economically viable uses" test, and would diverge significantly from court decisions regarding this issue. The Michigan Court of Appeals has held that the mere designation of property as wetlands by the MDEQ does not constitute a taking of the property (Bond v. Department of Natural Resources and Carabell v. Department of Natural Resources). In Carabell, the court established that the test for determining if there was a taking of property was whether the wetlands designation "deprives the owner of an economically viable use of his land," not whether the owner was deprived of the most profitable use of his or her land. In another takings case (K&K Construction v. Department of Natural Resources), the Michigan Supreme Court ruled that consideration of takings claims must be given to the regulatory impact on the entire parcel, not just the portion that contains wetlands.

190

The takings issue has been overinflated in recent years by the "Wise Use" movement. The Corps processes over 50,000 permits throughout the United States each year. Since the Clean Water Act was passed in 1972, only two permit decisions have been ruled a takings by the United States Supreme Court. It is a simple fact that the vast majority of wetlands regulatory actions do not deprive the landowner of all economic uses of their land, and thence, a regulatory taking does not occur. The same holds true for Michigan's wetland protection law. Since there are several economically viable uses which do not even require a permit, it is extremely difficult for a landowner to demonstrate that the designation of an area as wetlands or a denial of a permit for a particular economic use constitutes a taking.

Notwithstanding these facts, the issue of regulatory takings has successfully been raised by anti-environmental forces in opposing local wetland ordinances. Local government officials, fearing the costs of litigation, are often swayed by the misinformation campaign waged by takings advocates. Local citizens have the opportunity to provide sound information to local government officials so they can appropriately consider the threat of takings lawsuits in the context of the benefits that may be gained from wetland protection at the local level.

THE BEAUTY OF AN UNGROOMED BEACH

The fluctuation of Great Lakes water levels is very important to the health of coastal wetlands. During periods of low water, wetland vegetation colonizes the exposed bottomlands, providing excellent habitat for waterfowl and shorebirds. During high water levels, these vegetated flats are inundated, and the flooded vegetation provides excellent habitat for fish. After several years of high water, the wave and ice action can remove the vegetation…and when the water levels recede, the exposed shorelines are then revegetated. Coastal wetlands, and the plant  and animal species that rely on this unique habitat, are particularly adapted to this dynamic system.

During the low water levels of 2000-2002, a coalition of coastal property owners calling themselves "Save our Shorelines" (or SOS for short), began a movement to allow riparian landowners to "groom" the vegetated Great Lakes bottomlands on their property. Although "grooming" sounds innocuous, the actual activities that they wanted to engage in were far from benign. For example, one method of grooming involves dragging a disc behind a tractor to rip up and kill all vegetation on the shoreline.

Thanks to a coalition of organizations such as the Tip of the Mitt Watershed Council, Michigan Environmental Council, the Lone Tree Council, and others, the legislation that was introduced to exempt grooming activities from state law was defeated in 2002. That does not mean, however, that the beach grooming issue will go away.

There are two main arguments against beach grooming. The first is ecological. These coastal wetlands comprise the most important ecosystem in the Great Lakes. They provide habitat for more than four dozen fish species and two dozen waterfowl species. They provide important nutrient and pollutant uptake from the water. They absorb wave action along the shoreline thus reducing erosion and suspension of sediment and provide for tourism and economic benefits to the whole region through recreational fishing and waterfowl hunting.

The second is a bit more complicated and deals with the interpretation of the public trust doctrine. The Great Lakes and their bottomlands are held in trust by the states for the public. Riparian property owners on the Great Lakes technically own land to the ordinary high water mark. The land below the ordinary high water mark is considered public trust bottomlands. Although landowners have what is called "exclusive use" of the exposed lands below the ordinary high water mark (meaning they can cross the exposed lands to get to the water's edge and they can restrict access across the exposed lands by others), it is simply not theirs. SOS is attempting to re-interpret their rights to impact public trust bottom-lands in ways that are contrary to the public trust doctrine and that could have enormous ecological impacts.

191

If we are to maintain a healthy Great Lakes ecosystem, and ensure that the public trust bottomlands that are shared by all citizens are not taken by a few coastal property owners, wetland activists must fight current and future efforts to exempt beach alteration from state and federal laws. In addition to staunch advocacy, citizens can launch a campaign to promote the beauty of ungroomed bottomlands!

AVOIDING THE RACE TO THE BOTTOM

As you have seen in previous chapters, there are many similarities between state and federal wetland regulations. In both arenas, the case is made for wetland protection based on protecting the functions and values that wetlands provide. In both arenas, the political forces attempting to remove or weaken wetland regulations are powerful.

The ability to maintain sound wetland laws and administer them effectively largely depends on the political will of the United States President and Michigan's Governor. Since wetland regulations were originally instituted, citizen activists and environmental and conservation groups have had to fight to keep them on the books. And the battle wages on.

By using a twisted form of logic, wetland protection opponents in Michigan have argued that Michigan's wetland laws should not be more stringent than federal wetland laws. The reasoning most often takes two forms. First, the argument is that the federal agencies "know" more than state agency staff, and therefore it doesn't make sense to protect wetlands to a greater extent than what federal experts deem necessary. Second, in order to compete with other states in the country, Michigan should not regulate wetlands any more than federal law.

192

Thus, every time there is a federal lawsuit or a change in the administration of federal wetland laws, there is a call to weaken Michigan's state wetland program. Michigan's wetland advocates must strenuously fight this "race to the bottom."

Michigan's wetlands are essential to the quality of life of Michigan residents. Although the functions that our wetlands provide do indeed improve water quality, reduce floods, and provide habitat (especially for migratory birds) in ways that benefits the country at large, the majority of the functions our wetlands provide benefit Michigan's residents directly. Accordingly, Michigan state law should protect wetlands regardless of the federal role in wetland protection.

Chapter 14 Local Organizing for Wetlands Protection

Working to protect wetlands on an individual basis can be very draining. Although individual action is critical to the protection of Michigan's wetlands, building support and engaging others in wetland protection efforts can increase your effectiveness.

The initiation and coordination of a citizen wetland protection team provides an ongoing mechanism to protect wetlands in a proactive manner. Often, the threat of immediate environmental damage draws citizens into action. Then, after a particular issue has been addressed, wetland advocates often go back to their daily lives, not to be motivated until the next development proposal threatens wetlands in their area. Local groups can continue their momentum and capitalize on the contacts and experiences gained by focusing on proactive activities.

Citizen teams can provide an effective mechanism for public involvement in wetland protection. There are numerous activities that citizen teams can get involved in, including:

1) Inventorying critical wetland areas;

2) Receiving wetland permit application notices and responding to public notices from regulatory agencies;

3) Monitoring the area for unauthorized wetland alterations;

4) Assessing cumulative wetland losses in a watershed;

5) Documenting functions and values of local wetlands; and

6) Educating other citizens.

It's not easy, but organizing a group of citizens to take advantage of these opportunities can lead to the long-term protection of wetlands. It can also be personally rewarding. Organizing for wetland protection allows you to get involved in your community, meet new people, hone your skills, learn new things, and improve the lives of fellow community members.

This chapter provides some tips on how to build community support for wetland protection. Regardless of what kind of group you form, how big it is, or the specific issues you plan to tackle, chances are you'll find many of the techniques described in this chapter useful. In addition, the list of resources at the end of this chapter will give you a more in-depth look at these methods for organizing.

194

Deciding to Act

You may be one person, working to save a wetland in your backyard, in your neighborhood, your town, your county. Maybe you used to watch birds and frogs in this place, maybe you fear that the loss of this wetland will cause your land to flood, maybe you fear that the golf courses, strip malls, and second homes overtaking the woods and fields and wetlands that you've grown to love will destroy the beauty that was the reason you came here in the first place. Maybe there's no specific looming threat, but you want to get in at the beginning to ensure that wetlands in your area continue to be protected. This is how the vast majority of grassroots groups begin–with one person concerned that something undesirable is going to happen to them, to the place where they live. This thing may threaten your health, your children's health, your family's quality of life. It's hard to say what compels one person to act to change things, when another person in the same situation may choose to throw up his or her hands and say, "I haven't the time, I haven't the skill, nothing's going to change no matter what I do."

Regardless of why, you've decided it's time to act. You may immediately go to your friends and neighbors and solicit their support. Or maybe you'll try to go solo. Maybe you'll succeed in getting what you want, maybe you won't. No matter what you're working on, though, chances are you'll be more effective, and enjoy the work more, if there are other people taking on some of the tasks, and showing support.

Initiating a Wetland Protection Effort

Most groups begin with just a few people. One person or a couple, seeing the need to form a group, will begin to talk to friends and neighbors. Later, they may begin putting out flyers, posting notices in the local paper, creating brochures. Maybe you only start with three people, but three minds are better then one, and that allows you to do three times the work.

There are many active citizen organizations around the state monitoring activities in wetlands in their area. Many organizations across the state are active in initiating, training, and coordinating local citizen wetland protection efforts, including Clean Water Action, Michigan United Conservation Clubs, Huron River Watershed Council, Lake Michigan Federation, and Tip of the Mitt Watershed Council (See Appendix A). In addition, the Tip of the Mitt Watershed Council coordinates the Michigan Wetland Action Coalition, a loose coalition of individuals and groups working to protect wetlands across the state.

If you are interested in forming a wetland protection team, a good first step is to contact existing organizations to see if there are already efforts in your area, and if not, to help you organize one. Lake associations, watershed councils, or environmental and conservation groups are all likely places to start. Do not let the lack of a group in your area deter you. Many of the groups who are coordinating local citizen wetland protection teams in other areas of the state can provide information to get you started.

Recruitment

The factors that motivate individuals to get involved with working to protect wetlands, or any other resource, are as unique as the individuals themselves. Wetlands touch us in many ways throughout our lives. Wetlands provide such a multitude of functions and values that everyone can find something there to motivate their involvement in protecting them. One of the best ways to motivate citizens to protect wetlands is to focus the efforts of the group on a specific geographic region. Not only does this make the efforts of the citizen team more relevant to the individual members, but it makes monitoring and response activities more effective and easier to coordinate. Depending on the size of the region, it may be best to divide it into geographic areas such as watersheds, lakes, rivers, townships or counties, and to assign at least one committee member as the monitor of each area.

There are many tactics to build your organization and increase involvement. Here are a few ideas to help recruit support.

Presentations

A great place to find new members is from other organizations. Many organizations welcome presentations from other groups and individuals. And don't just stick to environmental groups— service clubs, churches, sportsmen's groups, recreation groups, senior centers, garden clubs, and colleges and universities are all great places to find people who are interested in wetland protection.

195

Advertising

Advertise your meetings and events! This, of course, does not mean that you have to pay for newspaper or TV ads. Put up flyers on local community bulletin boards at libraries, supermarkets, co-ops, community centers, and so on. Talk to your local paper and public radio station about listing or airing a notice. And don't forget about alternative press.

Make it Fun

It's easier to get new people to come to an event first than to a meeting, and, many times these events can be fundraisers as well. Be creative. Picnics, spaghetti dinners, dances, field trips, concerts, canoe floats—your imagination is the limit!

Ask!

When new people come to your events or meetings, let them know what they can do to help. This is important when making presentations as well. Ask people to become members. Make them feel welcome at meetings. There's nothing worse than going to a meeting and feeling like you're "out of the loop." Avoid being cliquey.

Meetings

One thing that almost all groups have in common is meetings. There are infinite numbers of ways in which people meet and make decisions. You may decide to invite everyone to all meetings, to break up into committee meetings, to hold meetings weekly or monthly, or even yearly. To make decisions, you may vote or use a "consensus process" (see side bar.) You may run the meeting through Robert's Rules of Order or through a looser conversational style. How and when your group meets depends largely on the size of the group, its purpose, the commitment and involvement of the members, and how they feel comfortable operating.

Tips for Successful Meetings

Have an agenda ahead of time - The agenda will help keep the discussion on track. You may find it helpful to place time limits on discussions.

Have a good facilitator - Generally, it is helpful if the facilitator does not feel strongly about or personally invested in a subject. The facilitator should remain neutral. It can be helpful to rotate the role of facilitator—this allows other members to feel empowered, and avoids the facilitator interjecting his/her opinions into the process. The facilitator generally helps to restate proposals, call on people to speak (though sometimes another person may be designated for this task), focus the discussion, formalize decisions, and look for consensus (in consensus-style decision-making.)

Keep it fun/Keep the energy going - If people are getting tired, stressed, or unfocused, it's probably time to take a break. Some groups will relieve stress and tension by singing, back rubs, ritual, games, or just some alone-time.

Avoid and address bad process - Personal attacks, guilt trips, domineering, snide comments, etc. are unacceptable and need to be addressed as such, when they occur.

Consensus Decision-Making

Consensus decision-making was formalized by the Quakers in the 18th century, but has been used in one form or another throughout history, and is used by many groups today. The philosophy behind consensus decision-making is that it avoids the trap that occurs in voting, where there is always an unhappy minority. Consensus process, however, does sometimes take more time and patience than voting.

Consensus Process, Step-by-Step

1) State the problem
   (What are we talking about?)

2) Clarify the question
   (What needs to be decided?)

3) Discussion
   (What are all the viewpoints?)

4) Proposal
   (What action will the group take? Incorporate all viewpoints.)

5) Discussion
   (Speak to proposal—clarifying questions, good points, concerns.)

6) Modify proposal (by "friendly amendments") or withdraw proposal

7) Check for consensus (Re-state proposal first.)
   a) Call for concerns
   b) Call for objections within consensus (Reservations/Stand-asides—"I don't like it, but I can live with it.")
   c) Call for blocks (on strong moral grounds) If the proposal is blocked, it should be dropped, discussed further, or sent to committee.

8) Consensus reached
   (Show visual/verbal agreement.)

9) Decision implemented
   (Who does what?)

An important role in consensus decision-making is the facilitator. The facilitator helps to focus discussion, restates proposals, keeps an eye on the time, limits or engages speakers, and helps the group keep to the agenda.

197

Focus the discussion - This falls largely on the facilitator, but it can happen that the facilitator becomes enmeshed in a side discussion. It's every participant's responsibility to point out a discussion that has digressed from the original.

Tools for Meetings

Brainstorming - The only rule in brainstorming is that ideas are not analyzed until the brainstorm is over.

Go-Rounds - This is where everyone states, briefly, what they think about an issue. This allows an opportunity for the more quiet people to be heard, and for everyone to feel included.

Small group discussions - Often it is useful to designate a committee or working group to develop a plan or a proposal. In consensus decision-making, often when there is great disagreement about an issue, those with the strongest feelings on both sides of the subject will have a discussion to find a compromise that they are comfortable with. This compromise proposal is then taken to the full group for approval.

Evaluations - Find out what people thought about a meeting—what went well, what could be improved next time. This can be an oral "check-in" at the end of the meeting, or participants can write down their comments.

Working from the Grassroots

"Grassroots" is a term that has come into wide usage in the past decade, but one which is difficult to define. Generally, it refers to a bottom-up approach to change, as opposed to top-down. Grassroots groups and movements take advantage of sheer numbers of people, as opposed to large amounts of money. The truth is that no matter how much money a group has, those that they are opposing can always come up with more. In addition, grassroots organizing allows us to get involved in our communities, to meet new people, hone our skills, learn new things, and feel a sense of having improved our lives and our community.

Local wetland protection groups are a prime example of the effectiveness of grassroots organizing. There are many, many different kinds of local wetland protection groups, working on the entire spectrum of wetland issues. Some groups focus on stopping or revising poor development proposals or drainage projects. Others work toward passing local wetland ordinances. Some concentrate on education, and some on preserving land through purchases and conservation easements. Many groups work on several or even all of these routes to wetland protection.

Developing Strategy

A strategy for your group lays out the path by which you plan to reach your goals. It also helps you determine which are the best goals for your group. Like every other topic discussed in this chapter, there are many ways in which you can develop strategy. No matter how you choose to map out your strategy, the important thing is that you do it. Whether you plan for the next week, the next year, the next ten years, or all of these, developing strategy will save you time and you will be more effective. There is far too much philosophy and there are too many methods regarding strategic planning to discuss here, but helpful exercises can include asking questions, brainstorming, using strategy charts (see below for an example), and working step-by-step. The resources section of the appendices lists some excellent resources for helping your group to develop strategy.

198

MIDWEST ACADEMY STRATEGY CHART				
After choosing your issue, fill in the chart as a guide to developing a strategy. Be specific. List all possibilities.				
GOALS	**ORGANIZATIONAL CONSIDERATIONS**	**CONSTITUENTS**	**DECISION MAKER**	**TACTICS**
What are the long-term goals of your campaign? What is the intermediate goal for the campaign? What specifically will constitute a victory? What short-term or partial victories can you win as steps toward your intermediate goal?	In specific numbers, list the resources that your organization brings to the campaign. In the same terms, list the ways in which you want this campaign to strengthen your organization. List any internal organizational problems.	Who cares about this issue enough to join in the campaign? Into what already existing groups are they organized? Which individuals or organizations will be willing and able to help your campaign? Who will actively organize against you?	Who has the power to give you what you want? What power do you have over them? *Remember, a decision maker is always a person or persons.* Is there a secondary decision maker or someone who has power over your primary decision maker? What power do you have over them?	How can you demonstrate the power you have over your decision maker? Tactics must be: -Directed at a specific decision maker. -Backed up by a specific and explicit form of power. Tactics include: -Direct actions with the decision maker -Public hearings -Voter registration, education, and turnout -Strikes -Letter writing, postcards, and petitions

Should your group incorporate?

The following is a list of benefits and drawbacks to incorporating.

+ Limited Liability: The individuals who control the corporation are not, except in unusual situations, responsible for the legal and financial obligations of the organization. This, however, requires that the leaders of the corporation act reasonably and responsibly. Incorporation also won't necessarily prevent you from being sued individually; it would just give your attorney another "defense." Most lawsuits of this kind are harassment suits anyway, designed to tie up the organization and frighten individuals.

+ Continuity: The continued existence of a corporation is not dependent upon continued participation from individual members.

+ Tax Exemption: An organization that has an annual income of greater than $5,000 must incorporate in order to receive tax-exempt status. This is one of the strongest reasons for incorporation.

- Cost: It is highly advisable that you seek legal assistance in incorporation (as well as filing for tax-exempt status.) This can get expensive, unless you are able to find reduced-cost or free legal help. In addition, there are fees that will need to be paid throughout the process.

- Time: This process can also take up a lot of time. There are many decisions that your group will have to make about structure and process (which can be a good thing), and a lot of paperwork.

- Obligations: There are many obligations that you will be taking on when you incorporate. You will have to keep close track of your finances and file several reports annually. You are also obligated to follow the rules governing your organization as laid out in your bylaws. This can be a good thing, but for some groups it is an unnecessary hindrance.

Accountability

Some groups are afraid to hold public officials accountable for their actions. Other groups are so absorbed in "the bad guys" that they forget to notice and recognize the people who have helped them and who are supportive of their work. In order to maintain a democracy, public officials need to be held accountable to the people who have elected them, and in order to build relationships that will benefit our work, we need to commend those that take positive action. Of course, this doesn't mean that we should personally attack those we disagree with. This generally just detracts from the real message, and may cause a poor image for you and your group.

Accountability is a two-way street. Grassroots groups that are working to hold elected officials and agency staff accountable must also realize their responsibility to be accountable. Maintaining or exceeding the same levels of honesty, integrity, and decency that we expect from elected officials will help to ensure that wetland advocates are given the respect that they deserve.

To Incorporate or Not to Incorporate

After awhile, almost inevitably the question will be raised as to whether your group should incorporate or not. This process is lengthy, and depending on whether you can get free legal help, can be rather costly as well.

A corporation is a legal entity with rights, privileges, and liabilities separate from those of the individuals who compose its membership. Only the corporation, and not those who form it, invest money in it, or serve as its members, bears the responsibility of its actions.

199

There are numerous factors to consider when deciding on whether or not your group will incorporate (see side bar). If you do decide to incorporate, you will likely also be applying for nonprofit status, which requires another round of decision-making.

In summary, unless you have a good reason for doing it, such as planning to be in existence for some time and being able to raise money through sources for which you must be tax-exempt, it is probably not worthwhile for you to incorporate. You'd probably be better off spending the time, money, and other resources on directly accomplishing your goal.

Nonprofit, Tax-Exempt Status

Most likely, your group will be applying as a tax-exempt nonprofit if it chooses to incorporate. And, most likely, you will choose to incorporate either as a "501(c)(3)" or "501(c)(4)" (these numbers refer to sections of the internal revenue tax code for nonprofit organizations.) The status that you choose will depend largely on how much lobbying your group intends to do. It is to your advantage to incorporate as a 501(c)(3) group if at all possible.

The major difference between 501(c)(3) and 501(c)(4) groups is the tax-deductibility of contributions, and the amount of lobbying that the group is able to do. Basically, donations to a 501(c)(3) group can be deducted from the donor's income taxes. This is especially important if you intend to raise money through "grants" from foundations or corporations. A 501(c)(3) group, however, is limited in, though not precluded from, the amount of lobbying that it can do. There are two "tests" regarding lobbying under this form that your group can choose. One is the "no substantial part" test, the other is the "lobbying expenditures" test.

Under the "no substantial part" test, the law states that "no substantial part" of the activities of a 501(c)(3) organization may consist of carrying on propaganda or otherwise attempting to influence legislation. The problem with this is that no one really knows what constitutes "no substantial part." It is very vague, and open to interpretation. If your group plans to focus on lobbying, this is probably not a good choice.

Basically, the "lobbying expenditures" test states that a group may spend up to 20% of the amount they spend on their tax-exempt purposes on direct lobbying. Whichever test you choose, should you choose to become a 501(c)(3) organization, you may not engage in any partisan political activities, regardless of whether there are any expenditures associated with this activity. (Partisan political activity is that which favors or opposes a candidate or candidates for office.)

The amount of lobbying that a 501(c)(4) group is allowed to do is not limited. A 501(c)(4) organization may also support or oppose candidates for office, to a limited extent. The primary purpose of a 501(c)(4) is required to be "social welfare." This requirement refers to all activities of the organization, not solely expenditures. A 501(c)(4) may engage in partisan political activity only if the group's primary activity remains social welfare, not the political work. Keep in mind that contributions to 501(c)(4) groups are not tax deductible by the donor.

By-Laws

Both incorporation and application for nonprofit status require that your group form by-laws. By-laws are the "rules" which outline the structure of your group and its manner of acting. Even if you are not applying for nonprofit status or incorporation, these steps can be useful to your group. If you will be applying for nonprofit status or incorporation there are things that will need to be addressed in your by-laws. This is too complex a process to delve into in this chapter. It is advisable that you obtain legal assistance in this process, if only to read over your by-laws. In addition, though the temptation may be strong to simply adopt another group's by-laws, this is not advisable, as, though your groups may be similar, chances are your philosophies and means of operation are not identical, and your by-laws should reflect this.

These guidelines for incorporation and nonprofit status are only a very rough overview. Before taking on either, it is highly recommended that you consult a lawyer. Minimally, a lawyer should look over both your articles of incorporation and your by-laws. In addition, if your group is not clear on whether your activities are considered lobbying and/or partisan political activity, legal advice should be sought as well.

An Alternative: Fiscal Sponsorship

Fiscal sponsorship is an arrangement where a 501(c)(3) organization accepts donations on behalf of a group or individual that is doing charitable work but does not have formal tax exempt status. This arrangement generally works best for short-term groups and projects which wish to raise money from funders who will only give money to tax-exempt groups.

This arrangement requires that the sponsor have "complete discretion and control" over funds, and it holds the sponsor legally responsible to ensure that its payments to the group or project further the sponsor's tax-exempt purposes. Of course, your ability to make use of this alternative requires that you are able to find a willing sponsor. Fortunately, this is generally not difficult. Many groups, particularly larger groups, are willing to sponsor projects. Unfortunately, some funders are not willing to give money to a fiscal sponsor. If your group plans to be raising large amounts of money and/or plans to be around indefinitely, you should probably become an independent tax-exempt organization.

201

SOME ORGANIZING TOOLS

Now that you have a group, a group structure, and a mission, in order to lay out your strategy, you'll need to consider the tools available to you. How are you going to get your message to those whom you want to influence, and to get more people involved in your campaign? What are the methods by which you can reach your goals?

Working with the Media

"Free media" can be one of the best ways to get information out to a large number of people, to get decision makers' attention, and, like the name, it's free (in that you don't directly pay for it–but everything has costs, of course.) The term free media applies to coverage that you don't pay for, i.e., that is not advertising. This type of media coverage is also generally more believable to the readers, as

Effective Press Releases

- Keep it simple, direct, and brief but be sure to include all the essentials.
- Use a headline that will get attention and highlights your message.
- Use a catchy, engaging first paragraph.
- Get to the point, and then elaborate.
- Be sure of your facts.
- Convey a sense of urgency (if you can honestly do so without hyperbole.)
- Keep words simple, and short.
- Avoid jargon and define acronyms.
- Try to use clear and concise sentences.
- Don't make assumptions—assume the reader is not familiar with the issue or your group.
- Keep the release to no more than two pages.
- Include visual aids (photographs, graphs, etc.) when possible.
- Make sure you have someone else look at it for typos, grammatical errors, readability.

there is not the blatant self-interest that underlies paid advertising. The drawback, however, is that you don't have ultimate control over what is printed or aired. Often, the interest of the media is different from yours. For example, the news media will often focus on the controversy of a project (or seek to generate controversy) to make a story "newsworthy," whereas you may want to focus on collaboration. For these reasons, it's important to develop and articulate your message clearly and carefully.

Your Message

When writing a press release, talking with a reporter, or to a video camera, whether you're at a press conference, demonstration, or town meeting, it's generally best to focus on one message, the single most important point you're trying to convey. Depending on the reporter or talk show host or whomever, they may try to steer you off-topic. Or you may be so excited about all the wonderful things your group is doing (as well you should be!) that it's easy to drift away from the point that you're trying to convey.

The Press Release

There are many great in-depth sources for writing press releases. In a nutshell, a press release is a notice sent to the media announcing some news. The news aspect is what's important here. In order for the media to run a story, there needs to be something new, and interesting. Undoubtedly, there are many things that your group is doing or plans to do or has recently done that are new and interesting. A couple common problems that groups run into when writing press releases is that 1) they write a release that doesn't contain any news (for example, a group that has been trying to get the township to buy a parcel of land for the past five years writes a press release stating that they have been trying to get the township to buy a parcel of land for the past five years) or 2) the group has news, but hasn't reported it in a way that seems newsworthy. (For example, the press release tells the history of the last five years of the group, and only touches on the real news–that the state has given the township a Trust Fund grant–as a footnote at the end of the press release.)

Letters to the Editor

The Letters to the Editor page is one of the most widely read pages of the newspaper. This is a place where you can say what you want people to hear, the way you want to say it. Again, message here is important, particularly because you usually have only 400-500 words to work with. One tactic that many groups have found helpful is to have different people write many letters. This can be particularly useful when dealing with a non-supportive or even hostile press. An Op-Ed (short for "opposite the editor") piece is generally allowed to be longer, and gives you more room to make the case. Competition for this space, however, can be high, and therefore it's useful to contact the newspaper's editor first before taking the time to write the article.

202

Editorials

An editorial gives the newspaper's stance on an issue. By providing information on an issue and your group's viewpoint, you can encourage the editors to take a particular stand on that issue. Again, letters to the editor sent before asking a paper to write an editorial on your issue can come in helpful here, because they show that there is support within the community for your position. Setting up a meeting with the editor or the editorial board of the newspaper will give you the opportunity to explain your position and solicit the paper's support. It's generally best to keep these meetings small.

Broadcast Media

Visuals can always help your media coverage, regardless of the specific medium. It's helpful to include photos when talking to newspaper reporters, or meeting with editorial boards. When working to get television coverage, the need for visuals is even greater. Press conferences and demonstrations can help to provide images for what you are saying. At a press conference, be sure to avoid the "talking heads" trap (in other words, make it visually interesting) and keep speakers few and brief. You may also be able to get a television reporter out to the place you're working to protect.

Relationships with the Media

All of the above media tactics are best employed when you have developed a good relationship with reporters and editors. One thing to be conscious of is that the relationship is mutual. The media person is helped by a good story, and you are helped by increasing the visibility of your group, your project, and your issue. Be careful not to swamp an outlet with press releases, just for the sake of getting out a press release. And, of course, don't rule out media ideas just because you don't know anyone at the newspaper/television station/radio station etc.; what you have to say is always more important than who you know.

Your Mailing List

A good mailing list is essential to any group. This is the list that you will use to disseminate information about your group, about your work, keep people updated, and solicit funding. Mailing lists can range from the extremely simple—one list and everyone always gets everything—to very complex lists, which sort out different groups of people based on membership status, interests, so on and so forth.

Here, many of the tips for recruitment come into play as well. At presentations, always, always, send around a sign-up form for your mailing list. Petitions are a great way to show support for your cause, and to build your list. You can swap lists with other groups, or pay a "list broker" for the use of a list. When people contact you, ask if they would like to be on your mailing list. Another type of list, an electronic listserve, is addressed later on in this chapter (see The Internet.)

Want an Effective Newsletter?
Ask yourself these questions...

- Who is the target audience?

- Will this only be used internally (i.e., sent to members only) or as an outreach tool?

- Will the newsletter give only updates on the group, or will it include information on the issue? Both?

- What will be gained by creating and maintaining a newsletter?

- What will it cost us?

- Is our time and money better spent elsewhere?

The Newsletter

A newsletter can be a great way to keep in touch with members and to publicize your cause and your group, or it can be an unwieldy monster that eats up more of your time than it's worth. When determining the scope of your newsletter, the size, and whether you want to have one at all, it's helpful to answer a few key questions (see box on this page.) A newsletter can be a 20-page, full-color, professionally laid out and printed affair, or a one-page update that you hammer out on your word processor and get photocopied at your friend's office. But neither one is worth the time or expense unless you have a good reason for doing it.

Action Alerts

Action alerts serve to involve members, and to show support or opposition to proposed legislation, development, or other policy. It's important to give the recipients enough information that they can make a rational case for the action you wish them to take, but not so long or jargon-filled that they are turned off. Depending on the knowledge base of the people you are targeting (are these members of a wetlands-protection coalition? Your group's members? The local birdwatchers' club?), the action alert can be long or short. But, as with most things, brief is usually better. Another thing to think about when drafting press releases is whether you are lobbying or not (see Lobbying sidebar). If you are lobbying, you'll need to consider how much money your group is spending on the action alert, and the "20% Rule."

Letter Writing Campaigns

Letter writing can be a very useful means to affect decisions. The general equation that lawmakers consider is that one letter equals one hundred constituents who feel the same way. Probably the best target for a large campaign is legislation and policy. This is because letters written in support of an idea or a specific legislation or policy, backed up by a few facts, can make the case for public support or opposition. This doesn't work quite as well with comments on permit applications, for example, because the agency generally does not have to take into consideration the public sentiment. Large numbers of letters written against a specific permit, however, can influence the "public interest" test. There is often concern about when letter writing becomes lobbying, and therefore an issue for 501(c)(3) tax-exempt groups. The Lobbying sidebar explains guidelines and definitions for lobbying.

There are many ways to get people to write letters. A couple are discussed above–media (here letters to the editor can be really handy), and action alerts mailed to your mailing list. In addition, your group can sponsor letter-writing parties, which may encourage people to write letters who otherwise wouldn't, had they just been mailed an action alert. These can be fun events, and increase the members' feelings of involvement and personal investment. Tabling is another great way to reach out to new people. You can encourage people to write letters, you can distribute information, or put out a donation jar, and it gives you the opportunity to talk to people face-to-face. Chances are there are numerous events in your community that could provide tabling opportunities. Local festivals (such as food and harvest festivals), arts and craft fairs, and music festivals are a few examples.

The Internet

In recent years, the Internet has become a great tool for activists, but has also created some problems. This can be a great way to keep each other updated and to discuss issues between meetings (particularly if your meetings are few and/or the members of your decision-making body live far away from each other.) There are, however, some drawbacks to this form of communication.

One tool that many groups have found useful is "listserves." Listserves are electronic mail (e-mail) lists that allow everyone on the list to send a message to everyone else on the list. There are many different kinds of listserves—from an open list, whereby anyone who wishes may subscribe, to a closed list, where a moderator approves list participants. Listserves can be very useful for sharing information and making decisions. They can also lead to an overload of mail, and tensions in the group. (A major problem with electronic communication is that there is no inflection, and it is so fast. It's easy to send a message but then think better of it later. Many hard feelings have been caused as a result of this!)

Webpages have also become a very common tool for groups—from the smallest grassroots groups to the largest national and international organizations—to disseminate information. As the Web gets more and more popular, more and more people spend time "surfing" it. People interested in your issue may find your webpage during a search. You can also link your page to other related pages, and thereby increase the visibility of your page, and include the webpage in literature "for more information." This can all lead to more members, and the education of more people about your issues. A good webpage, can, however, be very time-consuming to create, and if not updated regularly, can be fairly useless. Many of the same questions that you can ask your group about a newsletter can be asked when deciding whether or not to create a webpage.

205

Direct Action/Civil Disobedience

Grassroots activism runs a wide spectrum from meeting with government officials to purchasing land to letter writing to civil disobedience. Civil disobedience has long roots in this country—the Boston Tea Party, Henry David Thoreau's famous refusal to pay taxes, the Freedom Riders of the Civil Rights Movement in the 1960's, peace protesters and student demonstrations in the '70's— and continuing today with massive demonstrations against globalization, nuclear power plants and weaponry, and with the growth of the Earth First! movement.

The term "direct action" is a broad term and includes any action where a person is directly working to effect a change, and generally involves large numbers of people. This spans the spectrum from writing a letter, accountability sessions (where decision-makers are brought to a group's meeting and demands and information is presented,) holding a picket sign, to street theater, to locking one's neck to a bulldozer. It's important to recognize that none of these techniques is inherently better or worse than any other. Each has a role to play in working toward social and environmental change. Each group needs to decide when is the right time to play any given card, if at all. "Locking down" to a gate or bulldozer is pointless and will only backfire if no one has written a letter first.

Lobbying – The Rules for 501(c)(3) Groups

Many 501(c)(3) groups fear that they will lose their 501(c)(3) status if they engage in anything that can be called "lobbying." "Lobbying," however, is a broad term. The ability of a 501(c)(3) group to engage in lobbying in the legal sense is limited, though not prohibited. There is a fine line between lobbying and education. As a 501(c)(3), you can freely engage in education. For example, you can inform people about an issue, about a piece of legislation, and how a legislator voted on a given issue or bill. You can encourage your members and others to let their legislators know how they feel about an issue. However, telling or implying to people what to tell their legislators about a bill is crossing the line to lobbying. Using staff time, materials, etc. to ask a legislator to support/oppose a specific piece of legislation is lobbying. Asking a legislator to support wetland protection, however, is not. The same holds true for ballot initiatives. Influencing how someone should vote is lobbying; educating them about the pertinent issues is not.

The 20% Rule

As a 501(c)(3) group, you can still engage in lobbying, but you are limited in the amount of lobbying you can do. Your organization can spend 20% of your total expenses on lobbying. You are further restricted in the kinds of lobbying you can do. You are only allowed to engage in "grassroots lobbying" (lobbying the public) up to 25% of your overall lobbying allowance.

Direct lobbying refers to communications with members or staff of a legislative body, or with other government officials or staff who are involved with the formulation of legislation expressing a given view on a specific piece of legislation.

Grassroots lobbying refers to activities that encourage others to contact legislators. These actions target the general public or segments of the general public. Grassroots lobbying also must include the following three factors to be considered such:

  The communication refers to specific legislation;

  The communication reflects a view on the legislation; and

  The communication has a "call to action" which encourages the recipient to take action with respect to such legislation.[1]

[1] Minnesota Council of Non-Profits. For more information, see their website, www.mncn.org/lobbying.htm

Lobbying

Lobbying can take the form of writing a letter, making a phone call, or meeting with a decision maker. In the broad sense of the term, lobbying means encouraging a decision maker to take a certain position on an issue. In the legal sense of the term, lobbying is "All attempts including personal solicitation to induce legislators to vote in a certain way or to introduce legislation." Some larger groups have full-time professional lobbyists, but any group or individual can lobby their decision makers, and it can be far more effective for a constituent to write, call, or visit a lawmaker than a paid professional.

BUILDING RELATIONSHIPS

Getting to know the decision makers that affect the wetland(s) you are working to protect can be one of the most fruitful endeavors for your group. This could include your local planning commission, township board of supervisors, local MDEQ officers, soil and water conservation district, and developers. It may be helpful to meet these folks, explain what your group is trying to accomplish, solicit their support, and see in what capacity you can work together.

After meeting with these folks, keep in touch. If they are supportive of your work, actively engage them in your campaign. If they are doing the right thing, publicize their actions. Mention them in press releases, your newsletter. Send thank-you notes. And, as mentioned above, if these decision makers and others are not supportive, or, worse, are actively working against your goals, hold them accountable. Let them know that they are not working in the public interest and why, but do this civilly… even if you are attacked, it doesn't help your cause to seem irrational.

In sum, it is much easier and can be more successful to work with people rather than against them. You've set out a goal that you want to reach, and will need to determine the

206

Tips for Grassroots Lobbying

1) Consider gathering representatives from several organizations in your community to meet with your elected official as a group. This will convey wide-based support for your issue. Keep the group small and decide ahead of time who will say what. Do advanced preparation to ensure you deliver a unified and assertive statement.

2) Act confident and assured of your position.

3) Don't be late for appointments.

4) Dress nicely.

5) Always be friendly, never hostile. Compliment them for positive work done and concerns expressed in the past. Speak about your issue with conviction, not hostility.

6) Show you are serious about your issue. Know the facts. Be able to give your lobbying pitch in five minutes or less. First tell your elected official what you want him or her to do, and then state your arguments and the facts. Relate to him or her the consequences for your community (his/her constituents) of accepting or not accepting your proposal.

7) Never overstate or exaggerate your case. Doing so may put you in the position of having to answer questions you don't have honest answers to. Be able to back up everything you say or you'll risk losing your credibility.

8) Listen carefully to questions asked. Be open to questions and respond with hard facts and a sense of understanding. If you don't know an answer to a question, admit it and promise to look into it and get back to them. Always follow through on any commitments made.

9) Keep the discussion focused. Don't let the legislator evade the issue by changing the subject. If they do, tactfully re-focus the discussion and ask them how they plan to address your issue.

10) Show your sincere appreciation to legislators who support your position. Assure them of this issue's importance to people in your community and to the legislator's constituents. This will encourage them to work harder for your goals.

11) Ask legislators to commit to the issue and to take action on it (if they clearly support your cause.) Inquire if they will actively support your policy position, propose legislation, or whatever you are asking of them.

12) Always follow up with a thank-you letter and any information you promised during the meeting. Establish a good working relationship with the legislator and his or her staff. Never underestimate the importance and influence of legislative aids and staff.

207

best way to do this. You'll find it rewarding to work with some people, and others you just will not be able to work with. It is, however, in your best interest to try the positive approach first.

FUNDING YOUR GROUP

Again, the amount of time you spend on and the methods you use for fundraising will depend on your group's needs and constraints. There is an almost infinite number of ways that you can raise money, ranging from bake sales to membership dues to major donors to foundations. The following outlines a few different categories of fundraising, and provides a short list of creative fundraising ideas. The most important thing to remember in fundraising is that in order to get money, you have to ask for it. In order to sustain funding, you must do something positive with the money you are given.

Memberships

Memberships, for many small groups, is the main source of funding. Memberships can be a wide range of amounts. The most common minimum range is $15-$35. Some groups offer different categories, which could be student/low income, general, individual, family, supporter, etc. Some groups offer an alternative whereby a person can become a member by putting in a given number of hours of work, rather than paying up front. Many groups offer "perks" for membership, which could include a newsletter, voting privileges, maybe a tote bag.

Foundation Grants

Grant writing can be time consuming, but can give big returns. Foundations and other grant makers range from very small to very large. As a small grassroots group, you'd probably be best advised to work with the smaller funders first. There are many books and periodicals about how to write grant proposals, and how to determine the best prospects. And there's the saying that "for every project there is the right funder." Often, it's just a matter of finding that "right funder." Unfortunately, it takes time to research foundations and other grantmakers to determine which would be the best for you to approach. There are, however, a few major drawbacks when it comes to foundation grants. Chief among these is that, with some exceptions, the monies are generally restricted in some way. For example, most foundations do not provide funds for lobbying. Another drawback is that there can be a very long turn-around time. It may be months to a year after submitting a proposal before you receive funds.

Corporate Donors

208

There are varying views on corporate donors. Some groups feel that corporations are a great source of funding and should be utilized. Other groups reject this money, as they feel that it encourages "greenwashing" (a practice by which a corporation seeks to improve its public image more through good public relations rather than through improved environmental practices.) Some corporations have made commitments to environmental protection and social welfare and have built their businesses on this foundation (e.g., Working Assets, Real Goods, and Seventh Generation) or have made a real commitment to providing support for environmental protection (e.g., Patagonia, REI, and Aveda.)

Government Funding

Many state and federal agencies offer grants to organizations for a wide range of wetland-related projects. Sometimes they are narrowly-defined, sometimes they are very broad. Perhaps the best source of information on government grant funding opportunities is the EPA's Great Lakes National Program Office website–www.epa.gov/glnpo.

Major Donors

These are usually people who are already on your membership list. Many people who could give more often don't...unless they're asked. It might take a letter, a phone call, maybe a face-to-face visit, but taking the time to build these relationships can result in substantial donations. Discussions among your board and staff can lead to ideas for potential donors.

"Grassroots Fundraising"

This is where imagination and creativity (not to mention some savvy publicity skills!) come into play. Often, event fundraisers can double as opportunities for member recruitment, education, and visibility-raising. There are countless options in this category including benefit concerts, dances, picnics, dinners, auctions, raffles, walk-a-thons (and every imaginable variation thereof,) garage sales…the list goes on. Your imagination is the limit!

ADVOCACY TIPS FOR WETLAND ACTIVISTS

Michigan's wetland advocates have had great success across the state in promoting wetland protection. There have also been situations where wetland advocates "lost" the battle. In both cases, the activists have learned from their experiences. Below are some of the lessons learned that can help you in your efforts.

Educate Yourself

You certainly don't need to be an expert to organize, but the truth is that generally emotional pleas are not going to get you very far. There is a learning curve involved, but don't let the technical or legal information overwhelm you. And don't be afraid to ask questions. As the West Valley Coalition has written, "Any information in the world can be obtained by making enough phone calls and keeping your sense of humor."

Draw in Diverse Groups and People

Don't forget about other groups and people who may be allies. Church/religious groups, sportsmen's clubs, businesses (especially those who are dependent on recreation and tourism), and service clubs can all help to get out your message and to show diverse support for your work.

Realize the Bigger Picture

209

Taxes and quality of life issues are often more compelling to folks than the environmental ones. Some people may not be concerned about the loss of a heron rookery, but may be concerned that dams and levees will need to be built to keep flooding from occurring due to a loss of wetlands. A common argument against wetland protection is that more development will create a bigger tax base. Many studies have, however, found that the costs of the infrastructure needed for new housing developments is far greater than the increase to the tax base.

Be Creative

Opportunities abound to educate people on the need for wetland protection, and about your issue. It's just a matter of seeing them. Also, people get tired of the same old thing. New activities, events, and tactics will keep members and the public interested and involved.

Build Coalitions and Networks

Coalitions and networks can bring many more people into an issue, as well as avoid the problem of every group re-inventing the wheel. And be creative here. As stated above, look for possible allies that have not been approached before and bring them in. As Alan Puplis said in Chapter One, there are issues that people will agree on, and issues that they won't, but strong coalitions can be built around the common cause. Coalitions can be difficult to forge, but when successful, the effort is always well worth it.

Have Fun/Keep A Sense of Humor

A good chuckle now and then can help keep things in perspective and lower stress. Take time out for a picnic or a camp out, or a hike through the wetland(s) that you're working to protect. Enjoy your work. It's easy to get too serious and determine that there just isn't time for the fun stuff, but, in the long run, taking a break now and then will keep spirits up and people involved.

It Takes All Kinds

Make sure that the quiet people are given the opportunity to speak, and that the shy ones feel empowered. All kinds of people are needed for a citizen's group–laid-back people, screamers, take-charge types, shy people…and everyone has a role to play and skills to bring, whether it be making phone calls, writing letters, high-visibility public speaking, or baking cookies for the meeting. Make sure that everyone feels appreciated.

210

Be Honest

Be honest with yourselves in what your motives are, and what you are capable of doing. Be honest with the public and with decision makers–don't exaggerate or make up facts. This might get attention, but will likely come back to haunt you in the end. Your personal integrity is essential to maintaining the integrity of your cause.

Remain Civil and Respectful

Even when holding someone accountable, it is wise to avoid personal attacks. When you remain clam in the face of being attacked, you will look much better and the other person will look that much more foolish.

Avoid Burn-Out

It's easy to feel that the weight of the world is on your shoulders. It's key to remember that the world will keep spinning and the sun will still rise even if you fail on this particular issue. Take time out with your family and friends, or take a hike or an afternoon kayak trip. As an organizer, your long-term presence is important, so take care of yourself and make sure that you are enjoying what you are doing. Make sure that you're not taking on more than your share of the work. If you are, take the time to delegate tasks and to teach others how to do what needs to be done. It may take a little time now, but in the long run it will save you a lot.

WHERE TO GO FOR MORE HELP

The goal of this guidebook is to provide you with critical information that will assist you in working to protect wetlands in your community. As you can see, there are numerous ways to promote wetland protection. From school-aged education to commenting on dredge and fill permits, from establishing local wetland protection ordinances to promoting voluntary protection by landowners, there are nearly as many ways to protect wetlands as there are wetlands. Obviously, this guidebook is only a start. As you work on a particular wetland protection or restoration project, you will find that you need more information to increase you effectiveness. Here are some thoughts on where to go for more help.

Environmental Organizations

There are over 100 environmental and conservation organizations working to protect or enhance wetlands in Michigan. These organizations and individual wetland advocates are linked together as part of the Michigan Wetlands Action Coalition, a project coordinated by the Tip of the Mitt Watershed Council. The Coalition serves as an informational clearinghouse and communication network for wetlands protection in Michigan.

Appendix A includes a brief overview of the organizations that are actively involved in wetlands protection. The organizations listed responded to a questionnaire that was sent to wetland protection advocates across the state. Although there was an attempt made to ensure that all organizations working to protect wetlands were listed, some may have been missed. Each organization profile includes address, phone, wetland resource materials on hand, a brief narrative about their activities, and their geographic area. If you are involved with a wetland protection organization that does not appear on this list, please write the Tip of the Mitt Watershed Council.

These organizations can provide a wealth of expertise to citizens working to protect wetlands. To find out who to call, look over the list of organizations and select those that serve your area or can provide the expertise that you need.

Agency Staff

Citizens often feel like they are "on the other side of the table" from agency staff (especially when agency staff have issued wetland permits that citizens feel should have been denied). However, agency staff can serve as valuable resources for citizen wetland advocates. Responding to citizen inquiries is part of their responsibility as public servants. See Appendix B for a list of federal and state agencies that work on wetland protection. Contact the office nearest you for information.

Often, the responsiveness of agency staff to a particular issue is based on prior relationships. If you don't know your local MDEQ or Corps staff person, call them up to schedule a meeting. Making the connection before an issue becomes controversial will help to ensure that lines of communication are open when you most want them to be.

Private Consultants and Academic Experts

You may find yourself in a situation where organizations or agency staff can not provide you with the information you need. This often occurs in the case of finding expert witnesses for a lawsuit.

If so, it may be helpful to contact one of the hundreds of private wetland consultants in Michigan who provide these and other services on a fee-for-service basis or experts in the academic field.

In spring of 2000, the Tip of the Mitt Watershed Council compiled a list of experts as part of its coordination of the Michigan River Network and the Michigan Wetland Action Coalition. Because local grassroots organizations are vital to water resource protection in Michigan, and because many of these groups operate on minimal funding, the "River and Wetlands Experts Directory" is intended as a tool to help grassroots organizations access important information to strengthen their water protection efforts. The directory provides a list of water resource professionals who responded to a request for information to be included in a directory of experts in wetland and river protection in Michigan. This directory is available both in this hard copy version, and on the web at www.glhabitat.org/mrn and www.glhabitat.org/mwac.

The response to the request for experts for this directory has been outstanding, however, inclusion in this directory is in no way an endorsement of any of the consultants listed. This directory should be a starting point for your personal research into consultants who may fit with the goals and work of your organization.

Selecting Expert Advice

Working to protect and restore wetlands often involves a complex interplay of many policy and technical issues. For local-based citizen groups, the advice of experts can be very valuable in developing protection strategies, designing projects, or interpreting data. For some projects, all that citizen groups need is an experienced "sounding board" to bounce ideas off of. For other citizen-based efforts, substantial legal, technical, or organization advice is needed.

There is an inherent difficulty in finding a qualified consultant since "wetland consultants" are not required to be certified, licensed, or bonded in Michigan, especially if you want one who will be willing to fight for environmental protection (which may alienate them from their "bread and butter" clients). The U.S. Army Corps of Engineers and the Society of Wetland Scientists each have certification programs, and many wetland consultants in Michigan have become certified through these programs. Although no official list of consultant services is available, the Michigan Department of Environmental Quality maintains a list of consultants who have submitted their names to the MDEQ. Being included on this list in no way implies endorsement of a consultant's services by the MDEQ. In addition to this list, environmental consultants are sometimes found in the yellow pages of your telephone book, or by asking the advice of individuals or associations who commonly call upon consultants to assist them with wetlands work.

The process of selecting an expert and actually contacting them is one that should be taken seriously. Ask yourself the following questions when selecting an expert for advice:

1) **Do you really need expert advice?**
   In order to answer this, your organization or citizen effort must have a clear objective of what it wants to accomplish. With clear goals in mind, you can then determine if there are people already within your group that have the skills to move the organization

toward meeting its goals. If not, is this a piece of information that some additional research could uncover? Often, citizen groups will find that they already have the expertise they need...but if not, go on...

2) **What sort of advice do you need?**
It is important to be clear about what information you need and from what source you want it. This will depend on the nature of your project or issue and will guide your selection of possible experts to call upon. It will also be helpful in clarifying your expectation for the expert.

3) **How much are you willing to pay?**
Knowing your budget (or if you even have one) is an important factor in choosing whom to call. Most environmental consultants will be willing to spend a few moments on the phone hearing about your project in order to consider working with you.

4) **What is the universe of options?**
Once you know if you need an expert, what sort you need, and how much you can pay, you can leaf through the MRN/MWAC directory, review your local yellow pages, and call your local environmental colleagues to see who might be a potential option. Once you have this list, prioritize it and start calling.

5) **Do their credentials and references stack up?**
As you call them, and especially if you are going to hire them for an important project, you need to do a little research. Just like any fee-for-service business, there are some really great environmental consultants and some that...well...you know. Here are some things to keep in mind:

   - What is the academic and experiential background? Is it relevant to your needs?

   - Is the expert's environmental philosophy consistent with yours?

   - If the expert you are considering is a private consultant, who are their primary clients? Are there potential conflicts of interest?

   - Ask the expert for the names of former clients...and call them to find out their experience.

   - If you want the expert to produce a product, ask for samples of similar projects to examine quality.

6) **Make the connection.**
Once it seems like you've analyzed each of your options adequately, then make the selection and go from there!

Granted, all you may need is to chat for 10 minutes with someone who has a bit more experience than you do. If you are in that situation, then this involved selection process may be more than you need. However, if you need more substantial assistance, and the nature and scope of your project will be in part determined by the expert

213

you bring on, then you must put a lot of thought into the decision. By going through this process, you can make your decision based on solid information. The expert will benefit from knowing that they have a knowledgeable, careful consumer and a valuable client. And, most importantly, you will be sure that you are getting your money's worth!

Wetland Protection Spotlight

Humbug Defense Task Force
Bruce Jones

On August 31, 1999, the Army Corps of Engineers denied a permit to Made in Detroit, a developer who had proposed to build 340 houses and a nine-hole golf course on the "Humbug Complex," which includes a marsh and island. The public outcry against this project, which would have destroyed one of the last natural areas and some of the last coastal wetlands in heavily-populated, heavily-industrialized Southeast Michigan, was unprecedented. This was due, primarily, to the tireless effort of the Humbug Defense Task Force, a coalition of environmental and sportsmen's groups, and members of the community.

Laying the Foundation

A firm believer in community rights, Bruce Jones became the first president of the Grosse Isle Land and Nature Conservancy, founded in 1993. Through his work with the Conservancy, he became well-acquainted with the lower river ecosystem. Realizing that in order to effectively protect this unique ecosystem they needed to learn more about it, the Conservancy and several other groups held the first Lower River Ecosystem Conference in 1994. At this conference, which included various agency staff, conservation clubs, and concerned citizens, they developed a "Conservation Crescent" which includes the east side of Grosse Isle, Stoney Island, Gibraltar Bay, and the Humbug Complex. They then began to work to protect this area.

Threats Escalate, Permit Denied

In August 1998, the threats to the area became urgent when a development company, Made in Detroit (MinD), submitted an application to the Michigan Department of Environmental Quality (MDEQ), which holds a conservation easement on Humbug Island, to alter the terms of the easement and to fill wetlands. After several permit attempts and denials by both the Corps of Engineers and the MDEQ, and a lot of public involvment, the Corps denied the developer's permit but granted a modified permit, which protects the wetlands and created shoreline buffer zones.

214

Unfortunately, the upland areas are largely unprotected under the Corps' modified permit, which allows only a much scaled-down version of the original project. Bruce and the Task Force hope that this scaled-down project will not be economically viable and MinD will pull out, allowing the possibility of the entire area being protected for the long term.

Organizing to Protect Humbug

The first public hearing about the proposed development was held in September, 1998, and was attended by approximately 1,200 people, most of them in opposition to the development. It was after this meeting that the Humbug Defense Task Force was developed. The Task Force is a "nebulous group," as Bruce describes it. There are no officers, no leaders as such–the meetings are lead basically by whoever gets there first. While a loosely structured group, the Task Force has been very successful in gleaning information about the Humbug Complex, the laws, and sharing this information with the public and with decision makers.

The Task Force has used many methods to publicize this issue. They have made extensive use of the local newspapers, with letters to the editor and numerous articles about the issue, due in part to a good relationship with the Detroit Free Press. The group has also reached out to a very diverse group of people. They've spoken to church groups, service groups, have drawn in fishermen and hunters, and people concerned more about the possible effects on their taxes than the effects on the environment. They've made use of several e-mail lists which has allowed them to get information out quickly to many people, as well as communicate with agency staff and folks at the Fish and Wildlife Service who could provide them with information. They've delivered flyers door-to-door, and taken out ads in the local newspapers (in part to counter misinformation in ads taken out by MinD.) Over 2,000 letters have been written in opposition to the project. (Contrast this with 42 written in support.) In essence, as Bruce describes it, they have tried to take a "common sense approach"–to show the community that this project is not in the public interest, and to make that message very clear.

To raise money and to further increase their visibility, one talented and creative man in the Task Force has designed several very successful fundraisers. These have included two spaghetti dinners, a 50/50 raffle, and a Saturday morning bingo group.

Lessons Learned

Bruce Jones has gained a much greater appreciation for the area and for nature in general due to his work on this issue. "I have a much healthier respect for our relationship with the natural world around us, and the fact that humans need the quiet, peace, and tranquility of natural areas to renew our spirits. And a greater respect for the differences in perspectives. My perspectives, living here on 1-1/2 acres are going to be much different than someone living in the inner city."

Bruce also believes strongly in the necessity of educating yourself and then educating others. "I can't underestimate the necessity of getting all the facts you can and then understanding them. And the communication and education that comes from that."

215

APPENDIX A: Michigan Organizations Involved in Wetlands Protection

Across Michigan there are countless individuals and numerous environmental and conservation organizations working to protect or enhance wetlands. Many of these organizations and individuals have united to form the Michigan Wetland Action Coalition. The Coalition serves as an informal clearinghouse and communication network for wetlands protection in Michigan.

The purpose of this Appendix is to provide the reader with a brief overview of the organizations that are actively involved in wetlands protection. The organizations listed responded to a questionnaire that was sent to wetland protection advocates across the state. Although there was an attempt made to ensure that all organizations working to protect wetlands were listed, some may have been missed. If you are involved with a wetland protection organization that does not appear on this list, please contact the Tip of the Mitt Watershed Council for more information regarding the Michigan Wetland Action Coalition.

Each organization profile includes contact information, wetland resource materials on hand, a brief narrative about their activities, and their service area. If you are looking for assistance with wetlands protection activities in your region, refer to the organizations' service areas to locate a local organization. If you are in a region that is not served by a local organization, contact one of the statewide wetland protection organizations. If you are seeking specific expertise or resource materials, refer to the narrative information or materials available.

BEAR CREEK WATERSHED COUNCIL
P.O. Box 357
Bear Lake, MI 49614-0357
PH: (231) 362-2812

The Bear Creek Watershed Council works to correct streambank erosion problems. The Council is also collecting information and mapping wetland areas within Manistee County. They comment on state and federal dredge and fill applications.

Service Area: Manistee County

Materials Available: No materials available at this time

CENTRAL LAKE SUPERIOR WATERSHED PARTNERSHIP
1030 Wright Street
Marquette, MI 49855
PH: (906) 226-9460
FX: (906) 228-4484
E-mail: lindq@portup.com
Website: www.superiorwatersheds.org

The Central Lake Superior Watershed Partnership (CLSWP) provides technical, educational, and financial assistance including, but not limited to: wetland identification, wetland restoration, landowner information, GIS mapping, exotic species identification and removal (i.e., purple loosestrife), monitoring habitat protection (i.e., conservation easements in cooperation with the Central Lake Superior Land Conservancy), garbage and large debris removal through the Adopt-A-Stream program and more.

Service Area: 20 major watersheds in Marquette County

Materials Available: County soil surveys, national wetlands inventory maps, U.S.G.S. topographic maps, locally produced wetland maps, MIRIS maps, watershed maps, model local ordinances, slide shows, brochures, guidebooks, textbooks, video tapes

CITIZENS FOR ALTERNATIVES TO CHEMICAL CONTAMINATION (CACC)
8735 Maplegrove Rd
Lake, MI 48632-9511
PH: (989) 544-3318
FX: (989) 544-3318
E-mail: nuntan@pilot.msu.edu

CACC reviews and comments on water quality permits and land use applications in central Michigan, with a strong emphasis on the impact of oil and gas development. CACC board and members watchdog wetlands issues in their communities throughout Michigan.

Service Area: Great Lakes Basin

Materials Available: County soil surveys (Clare, Isabella), guidebooks, model local ordinances (Riparian), watershed maps

CITIZENS FOR ENVIRONMENTAL PROTECTION
P.O. Box 1284
Niles, MI 49120-8284
PH: (269) 683-6213

Citizens for Environmental Protection works with other area groups to support specific legislative actions. The group sponsors conferences and workshops to bring information about water quality and wetland issues to the general public.

Service Area: Cass and Berrien Counties

Materials Available: Brochures

CITIZENS' WETLANDS PROTECTION COMMITTEE PITTSFIELD CHARTER TOWNSHIP
6201 W. Michigan Avenue
Ann Arbor, MI 48108
PH: (734) 944-1637
E-mail: clerk@pittsfieldtwp.org

Charged by the Township Board with proposing solutions to a high priority environmental problem, the Wetlands Protection Committee set a goal to produce an innovative township ordinance and incentive-based protective measures. To achieve their objectives, the group attended seminars, researched libraries and the internet, toured local wetlands by foot and photographs collected maps, read federal regulations, state law and ordinances from other local communities, and drafted the RFP for a wetlands inventory.

CLEAN WATER ACTION AND CLEAN WATER FUND

1200 Michigan Avenue, Suite A
East Lansing, MI 48823
PH: (517) 203-0754
FX: (517) 203-0760
E-mail: elansingcwa@cleanwater.org
Website: www.cleanwateraction.org/mi

Clean Water Action and Clean Water Fund work to assist citizens in their understanding and use of state and federal wetland laws and regulations. Citizen inquiries are fielded by Clean Water staff and volunteers and appropriate next steps are identified. Clean Water Action also addresses wetland protection in the legislative arena by lobbying for stronger protections.

Service Area: Statewide

CLINTON RIVER WATERSHED COUNCIL

1970 E. Auburn Rd
Rochester Hills, MI 48307-4803
PH: (248) 853-9580
FX: (248) 853-0486
E-mail: contact@crwc.org
Website: www.crwc.org

The Clinton River Watershed Council (CRWC) provides coordination, technical assistance, and information and education services to individuals, community groups, businesses, and local governments to protect and improve the Clinton River and its watershed. The Council completed a functional assessment of wetlands in the Stony Creek subwatershed in 2000. Thirteen watershed communities currently have wetland ordinances.

Service Area: Primarily Oakland and Macomb counties

Materials Available: Local and model ordinances, brochures, guidebooks, slides, U.S.G.S. topographic maps, National Wetland Inventory maps, watershed maps, water monitoring materials, expert contacts

CONCERNED CITIZENS FOR WEST BLOOMFIELD

5572 Stanhope Avenue
West Bloomfield, MI 48322
PH: (248) 626-4867

Concerned Citizens for West Bloomfield helped establish the township's Wetland and Watercourse Ordinance and the Wetland Review Board. Regularly monitors the local wetland permit process. Helps citizens report and follow up on unpermitted activities within wetlands and lands adjacent to wetlands and lakes.

Service Area: The Charter Township of West Bloomfield

DEGRAAF NATURE CENTER

600 Graafschap Rd.
Holland, MI 49423-4549
PH: (616) 355-1057
FX: (616) 355-1069
Website: www.degraaf.org

DeGraaf Nature Center is an Outdoor Classroom. The Center sponsors educational programs to area schools and the general public, they provide educational materials to teachers and the public, and they have hands-on exhibits in nature centers.

Service Area: Schools in West Ottawa and West Allegan Counties and residents of that area

Materials Available: Brochures, guidebooks, slide shows, stream table demonstration, textbooks, videotapes

DETROIT AUDUBON SOCIETY

1320 North Campbell Rd.
Royal Oak, MI 48067-1555
PH: (248) 545-2929

Detroit Audubon Society (DAS) will hold conservation easements, accept donated properties statewide, and will assist in developing a local land trust. DAS will comment on dredge and fill applications and assist citizens with their comments. DAS will also assist in site documentation, especially wildlife species.

Service Area: Southeast Michigan

Materials Available: Brochures, locally produced wetland maps, slide shows, textbooks, U.S.G.S. topographic maps, videotapes, watershed maps

DUCKS UNLIMITED, INC.
GREAT LAKES/ATLANTIC REGION OFFICE (GLARO)

331 Metty Drive, Suite 4
Ann Arbor, MI 48103
PH: (734) 623-2000
FX: (734) 623-2035
Website: www.ducks.org

Ducks Unlimited, Inc. is a private, non-profit organization dedicated to conserving wetland habitat for waterfowl and other wildlife. Its mission is to fulfill the annual life cycle needs of North American waterfowl by protecting, enhancing, restoring, and managing important wetlands and associated uplands. GLARO's staff biologists and engineers work with landowners and cooperate with other organizations and agencies to implement Ducks Unlimited's wetland restoration programs.

EAST MICHIGAN ENVIRONMENTAL ACTION COUNCIL (EMEAC)

21220 W. 14 Mile Rd.
Bloomfield Hills, MI 48301-4000
PH: (248) 258-5188
FX: (248) 258-5189
E-mail: emeac@aol.com
Website: www.emeac.org

The East Michigan Environmental Action Council actively participates in public review and comment procedures regarding the Michigan and federal wetland protection programs, and occasionally participates in administrative procedures and litigation to protect particular wetland areas.

Service Area: Southeast Michigan

Materials Available: Brochures, model local ordinances

FERNWOOD

13988 Range Line Road
Niles, MI 49120-9020
PH: (269) 695-6491
FX: (269) 695-6688
Website: www.fernwoodbotanical.org

Fernwood provides environmental educational programs which include wetland ecology and protection. Fernwood also provides assistance to individuals interested in conservation easements and land donation.

Service Area: Southwest Michigan

Materials Available: Slide shows, brochures, guidebooks, videotapes, programs

FLINTSTEEL RESTORATION ASSOCIATION

610 Apache Drive
Wakefield, MI 49968
PH: (906) 229-5074
FX: (906) 229-5074
E-mail: flintsteel@skyenet.net
Website: www.flintsteel.org

The organization provides consultation and testing services for the public in areas of wetland, stream, and lake restoration and protection.

Materials Available: County soil surveys, U.S.G.S. topographic maps, watershed maps, guidebooks, textbooks, model local ordinances, testing equipment

Service Area: Western Upper Peninsula, northern Wisconsin

FRIENDS OF ROSE TOWNSHIP

9601 Fish Lake Road
Holly, MI 48442
PH: (586) 634-7668

The Friends of Rose Township (FRT) comments on dredge and fill applications and assists citizens with their comments. The FRT also provides information about habitat preservation, grassroots wetlands protection initiatives, and educational materials.

Service Area: Oakland County and surrounding area

Materials Available: County soil surveys, national wetlands inventory maps, U.S.G.S. topographic maps, MIRIS maps, locally produced wetland maps, watershed maps, brochures, guidebooks, textbooks, model local ordinances

FRIENDS OF THE CRYSTAL RIVER

P.O. Box 123
Glen Arbor, MI 49636
PH: (231) 386-9285
FX: (231) 386-9485
E-mail: rivermouth@friendsofthecrystalriver.org
Website: www.friendsofthecrystalriver.org

Friends of the Crystal River explores ways and means of preserving the natural, ecological, historic, recreational, aesthetic and educational values of the Crystal River and its adjacent lands. They maintain and improve the water quality, and educate the public regarding the use and enjoyment of this classic wetlands nature resource. They raise and disburse funds, and take other necessary action for the accomplishment of this purpose.

Service Area: Crystal River, Glen Arbor, MI

Materials Available: Watershed maps

FRIENDS OF THE ROUGE

24401 Ann Arbor Trail
Dearborn Heights, MI 48127
PH: (313) 792-9627
FX: (313) 792-9628
E-mail: execdirector@therouge.org
Website: www.therouge.org

Friends of the Rouge (FOTR) focuses their efforts on the Rouge River watershed. FOTR works with local governments, neighborhood groups, and other volunteer organizations, and provides basic information on wetland protection to landowners.

Service Area: Rouge River watershed (Wayne, Oakland, Washtenaw Counties)

Materials Available: Locally produced wetland maps, watershed maps, slide shows, brochures, guidebooks, adopt-a-stream, water quality monitoring

FRIENDS OF THE ST. JOE RIVER ASSOCIATION, INC.

P.O. Box 354
Athens, MI 49011
PH: (269) 729-5174
FX: (269) 729-5045
E-mail: algs@net-link.net
Website: www.fotsjr.org

Friends of the St. Joe has been concentrating on its water quality monitoring program, but has plans to begin a wetlands program in the near future.

Service Area: The St. Joseph River Watershed

Materials Available: Watershed maps

GRAND TRAVERSE REGIONAL LAND CONSERVANCY

3860 North Long Lake Road, Suite D
Traverse City, MI 49684
PH: (231) 929-7911
FX: (231) 929-0433
E-mail: info@gtrlc.org
Website: www.gtrlc.org

The Grand Traverse Regional Land Conservancy is a non-profit, land protection organization dedicated to the preservation of sensitive, natural, scenic and agricultural lands in Northwest Michigan. Located in the heart of several major watersheds, the Conservancy is especially dedicated to working with the landowners to protect their lands using several different conservation options.

Service Area: Antrim, Benzie, Grand Traverse, Kalkaska, and Manistee Counties

Materials Available: County soil surveys, U.S.G.S. topographic maps, MIRIS maps, locally produced wetland maps, watershed maps, website, brochures, guidebooks

GRASS RIVER NATURAL AREA

P.O. Box 231
Bellaire, MI 49615
PH: (231) 533-8314
FX: (231) 533-4448
E-mail: grna@torchlake.com
Website: www.torchlake.com/grna

The Grass River Natural Area (GRNA) protects Grass River area wetlands through the acquisition of land or conservation easements, and is an educational resource offering guided hikes, classes and educational books. The 1,100 acre preserve is open to the public year round.

Service Area: Grand Traverse Bay region

Materials Available: brochures, guidebooks, books, videotapes

219

GREAT LAKES AQUATIC HABITAT NETWORK AND FUND
(a project of Tip of the Mitt Watershed Council)
426 Bay Street
Petoskey, MI 49770
PH: (231) 347-1181, ext. 106
FX: (231) 347-5928
E-mail: jill@watershedcouncil.org
Website: www.glhabitat.org

GLAHNF empowers citizens to take action at the community
level to protect and restore wetlands by providing consultation
and financial resources, sharing information, and fostering
communication between citizens and organizations working
to protect aquatic habitats.

Service Area: Great Lakes Basin

GROSSE ILE NATURE AND LAND CONSERVANCY
P.O. Box 12
Grosse Ile, MI 48138
PH: (734) 675-6657
FX: (734) 675-0307
E-mail: bjones6657@aol.com

The Grosse Ile Nature and Land Conservancy (GINLC) has been
the leader in developing partnerships for the protection and preservation of the remaining natural habitat in the lower Detroit River.
To date they have acquired the 120 acre Hennepin Marsh along
with several wetlands within the island of Grosse Ile and have been
instrumental in the designation of a two-mile shoreline in Gibraltar
Bay as a natural area and in the acquisition of Stony Island by
MDNR.

Service Area: Grosse Ile primarily, but not limited to it

Materials Available: County soil surveys, U.S.G.S. topographic
maps, locally produced wetland maps, slide shows, brochures

220

HEADWATERS ENVIRONMENTAL STATION
HCR 1 Box 98A, Keweenaw Bioregion
Toivola, MI 49965
PH: (906) 288-3000
Website: www.headwaters-env-station.org

Headwaters Environmental Station is a non-profit 501(c)(3)
Educational Institute, founded solely for the purpose of teaching
environmental/ecological education, focusing on the ecology and
natural history of watersheds and basins. Headwaters coordinates
the ICF annual crane count for Houghton/Keweenaw Counties,
offers Ecological Land Inventories to private and corporate
landowners and Resident Ecology Research Internships on
Gratiot Lake and the Little Gratiot River in cooperation with
the Gratiot Lake Conservancy.

Service Area: The Keweenaw Bioregion Watershed

HEADWATERS LAND CONSERVANCY
P.O. Box 783
Gaylord, MI 49734
PH: (989) 731-0573
E-mail: headwaters@gtlakes.com
Website: www.otsego.org/hwlc

The mission of the Headwaters Land Conservancy is to use a
participatory approach to securing and sustaining the quality of
life enjoyed by present and future residents of northeast lower
Michigan. The Conservancy seeks to foster an open-space
philosophy and preserve ecologically sensitive areas, scenic
landscapes, and historic features - together with associated natural
resources, archaeological legacy, and recreational opportunity. HLC
accepts donations of land and conservation easements that meet
their criteria.

Service Area: Alcona, Arenac, Alpena, Crawford, Iosco,
Montmorency, Ogema, Oscoda, Otsego, Presque Isle,
Roscommon Counties

Materials Available: brochures, guidebooks

HURON RIVER WATERSHED COUNCIL
1100 North Main Street, Suite 210
Ann Arbor, MI 48104-1059
PH: (734) 769-5123
FX: (734) 998-0163
E-mail: lrubin@hrwc.org
Website: www.hrwc.org

The Huron River Watershed Council (HRWC) comments on
dredge and fill applications, assists citizens with their own review
and comments, trains individuals to assess water quality and
watershed land use patterns, and provides guidance for individuals
wishing to get involved in local land use planning. The Council
assists communities to develop master plans and ordinances which
promote wetland protection and can provide computer mapping
of wetlands and other natural features.

Service Area: Parts of Oakland, Livingston, Ingham, Jackson,
Washtenaw, Wayne & Monroe Counties in the Huron River Basin

Materials: County soil surveys, national wetlands inventory maps,
U.S.G.S. topographic maps, MIRIS maps, watershed maps,
guidebooks, textbooks, videotapes, permit applications, model
local ordinances

INDEPENDENCE LAND CONSERVANCY
P.O. Box 285
Clarkston, MI 48347
PH: (248) 625-8193
FX: (248) 625-9170

The Independence Land Conservancy (ILC) is a regional land trust
serving Northwest Oakland County. Celebrating 25 years (1997) of
preservation of open space, the ILC protects 21 properties, (about
350 acres) in Independence and Springfield Townships through
outright ownership and scenic easements. As an all-volunteer
organization, the ILC has endorsed and is guided by the "standards
and practices" of the "Land Trust Alliance."

Service Area: Northwestern Oakland County

Materials Available: Brochures, model conservation easements

INDIAN SPRINGS METROPARK NATURE CENTER
5200 Indian Trail
White Lake, MI 48386
PH: (248) 625-7280
FX: (248) 625-6639

The Indian Springs Nature Center provides wetland programs and
exhibits that are generally centered around the Huron Swamp which
is located in the park. These wetlands are the headwaters of the
Huron River and home to many wetland plants and animals. The
Nature Center's programs often discuss the importance of such
areas for biodiversity and water quality.

Service Area: Oakland County

Materials Available: Textbooks

INLAND SEAS EDUCATION ASSOCIATION
101 Dame Street
P.O. Box 218
Suttons Bay, MI 49682
PH: (231) 271-3077
FX: (231) 271-3088
E-mail: info@greatlakeseducation.org
Website: www.greatlakeseducation.org

Inland Seas Education Association (ISEA) provides Great Lakes
education programs for students and adults aboard tall ships. Over
45,000 people have taken part in ISEA shipboard programs since
1989. ISEA also offers a free wetland education program summer
evenings at the Suttons Bay Marsh.

Service Area: Statewide; local Grand Traverse area for wetland programs

Materials Available: Videotapes, reference material on Grand Traverse Bay and Great Lakes, brochures, Schoolship Log (newsletter), annual report

IZAAK WALTON LEAGUE OF AMERICA, MICHIGAN DIVISION
6260 Blythefield NE
Rockford, MI 49341
PH: (616) 866-8475, 1-800-453-5463
E-mail: jtrimber@earthlink.net
Website: www.mich-iwla.org

The Izaak Walton League of America provides resource and educational materials on wetland ecology, preservation, legislation and technical assistance on wetland issues. It offers hands on involvement in wetland conservation projects through its Save-Our-Streams program. Quarterly newsletters on wetland issues are available at the National website at www.sos.iwla.org. The IWLA hosts a biannual wetlands conference.

Service Area: The Izaak Walton League of America is a national conservation organization. The Michigan Division has membership across the entire state.

Materials Available: Slide shows, brochures, guidebooks, video tapes, model ordinances, and newsletters

KALKASKA CONSERVATION DISTRICT
605 N. Birch St.
Kalkaska, MI 49646
PH: (231) 258-3307
FX: (231) 258-3318
E-mail: kswcd@torchlake.com
Website: www.kscd.org

Service Area: Kalkaska County

Materials Available: County soil surveys, U.S.G.S. topographic maps, brochures, textbooks, videotapes

KEWEENAW LAND TRUST
P.O. Box 750
Houghton, MI 49931
PH: (906) 487-2149
E-mail: cwalck@mtu.edu
Website: www.keweenawlandtrust.org

The Keweenaw Land Trust is a community partner dedicated to preserving the quality of life in the Keweenaw through land conservation. It holds conservation easements and properties for the benefit of wildlife, watersheds, and the general public good. At present, the Keweenaw Land Trust owns 30 acres called the Paavola Wetlands, near Hancock with a 10-acre pond, and 200 acres called the Six-Mile Creek Preserve at the head of the Keweenaw Bay near Baraga, a forested wetland. It involves the schools, the Boy Scouts, the Audubon Club and other groups for protection and enjoyment of the wetlands.

Service Area: Keewenaw, Houghton, Baraga, and Ontonogon

Materials Available: County soil surveys, locally produced wetlands maps, watershed maps, brochures, guidebooks, textbooks, biological inventory of properties

LAKE ERIE CLEAN-UP COMMITTEE INC.
47 East Elm Avenue
Monroe, MI 48162-2648
PH: (734) 242-0909

The Lake Erie Clean-Up Committee works to stop pollution of Lake Erie and all fresh water lakes and streams, and to inform the public of the need for greater pollution controls to prevent the return to old methods of the past and to encourage industry to do more research. "Our Great Lakes are a fragile part of our ecosystem and we must continue to protect them."

Service Area: West shore of Lake Erie including downriver Detroit, Monroe County and north Maumee Bay

Materials Available: Locally produced wetland maps, watershed maps, remedial action plan, brochures, Water Resources Development Act of 1996

LAKE MICHIGAN FEDERATION
700 Washington Ave., Suite 150
Grand Haven, MI 49417
PH: (616) 850-0745
FX: (616) 850-0765
E-mail: michigan@lakemichigan.org
Website: www.lakemichigan.org

The Lake Michigan Federation (LMF) provides general assistance to citizens and groups in the area of wetland protection strategies.

Service Area: Lake Michigan shoreline counties

Materials Available: Brochures, guidebooks, textbooks, videotapes, newsletter

LAKE ST. CLAIR ADVISORY COMMITTEE, INC.
P.O. Box 272
Mt. Clemens, MI 48046
PH: (586) 725-8827

The Lake St. Clair Advisory Committee is a conservation group dedicated to the preservation of the waters, wetlands, fish, and wildlife of Lake St. Clair, its waterways and environments. The Committee participates in groups preparing the St. Clair River and Clinton River Remedial Action Plans.

Service Area: United States shoreline of Lake St. Clair

Materials Available: Brochures, fishing guides

LAND CONSERVANCY OF WEST MICHIGAN

1345 Monroe NW, Suite 324
Grand Rapids, MI 49505
PH: (616) 451-9476
FX: (616) 451-1874
E-mail: lcwm@naturenearby.org
Website: www.naturenearby.org

221

As the local land trust for the central West Michigan area, the Land Conservancy preserves wetlands and riparian lands through acquisition and conservation easements. The Conservancy assists watershed groups and local governments in identifying and preserving priority lands.

Service Area: Kent, Ottawa, Oceana, Muskegon, Newaygo, Northern Allegan County

Materials Available: brochures, guidebooks, textbooks, presettlement maps, model local ordinances, inventory of Grand River corridor in Kent and Ottawa

LAND STEWARDSHIP CENTER
P.O. Box 225
Columbiaville, MI 48421
PH: (810) 793-5303
E-mail: clark@hew-era.com

The Land Stewardship Center is part of the Great Lakes Bioregional Land Conservancy. They restore wetlands, host wetland restoration workshops, and maintain sustainable agriculture demonstrations open to the public.

Service Area: The "Thumb" region of Michigan, especially Capeen County

LEAGUE OF WOMEN VOTERS OF MICHIGAN

200 Museum Dr., Ste. 104
Lansing, MI 48933
PH: (517) 484-5383
FX: (517) 484-3086
E-mail: lwvmi@voyager.net
Website: www.lwvmi.org

The League of Women Voters of Michigan (LWVMI) advises callers on how to obtain copies of pending legislation and public acts and how to lobby legislators. LWVMI has available booklets and videos on the Planning Process and how to participate in the Planning Process entitled: *This Land is Ours* and *Keeping This Land Ours.*

Service Area: Statewide

Materials Available: Booklets and Videos – *This Land is Ours* and *Keeping This Land Ours* (booklets are free in limited quantities, plus shipping and handling. Videos are 1/2 hour videos and are $20 each, plus shipping and handling).

LEELANAU CONSERVANCY

P.O. Box 1007
Leland, MI 49654
PH: (231) 256-9665
FX: (231) 256-9693
E-mail: conservancy@leelanau.com
Website: www.theconservancy.com

The mission of the Leelanau Conservancy is to conserve the land, water, and scenic resources of Leelanau County. The Conservancy publishes three issues per year of the Leelanau Conservancy. They conduct 20 field trips on their preserves annually. LC accepts donations of land and conservation easements that meet their criteria and offers free ecological evaluations of qualified wetland parcels. The Leelnanau Conservancy monitors water quality in Leelanau County's major inland lakes and streams, maintains a water quality database, and is currently developing a computer model to predict trends.

Service Area: Leelanau County

Materials Available: Locally produced wetland maps, watershed maps, slide shows, brochures, guidebooks, videotapes, model local ordinances

LIAISON FOR INTER-NEIGHBORHOOD COOPERATION (LINC)

P.O. Box 40
Okemos, MI 48805-0040
PH: (517) 349-4306
FX: (517) 347-3060

LINC is a civic improvement organization that promotes the protection of natural resources and sound land use planning through community involvement, networking, and governmental participation.

Service Area: Meridian Township and surrounding areas

Materials Available: Brochures

LITTLE TRAVERSE CONSERVANCY (LTC)

3264 Powell Road
Harbor Springs, MI 49740
PH: (231) 347-0991
FX: (231) 347-1276
E-mail: ltc@landtrust.org
Website: www.landtrust.org

The mission of the Little Traverse Conservancy is to protect the natural diversity and beauty of northern Michigan encompassing Charlevoix, Emmet, Cheboygan, Chippewa, and Mackinac counties by preserving significant land and scenic areas, and fostering appreciation and understanding of the environment. They publish quarterly the Update. The Conservancy gives numerous

field trips and accepts donations of land and conservation easements that meet their criteria. They also assist other groups to pre-acquire, handle negotiations, secure donations/bargain sales, and also assist with grant applications.

Service Area: Charlevoix, Cheboygan, Chippewa, Emmet, Mackinac Counties

Materials Available: Brochures

MICHIGAN ASSOCIATION OF CONSERVATION DISTRICTS

201 N. Mitchell Street, Suite 204
Cadillac, MI 49601
PH: (231) 876-0328
FX: (231) 876-0372
E-mail: info@macd.org
Website: www.macd.org

The Michigan Association of Conservation Districts is a nongovernmental, nonprofit, 501(c)(3) organization established in 1940 to represent and provide services to Michigan's 82 Soil and Water Conservation Districts. Many of the local districts have some form of wetland program, including review of dredge and fill permits, wetland restoration, educational workshops, and assistance in applying for permits.

Service Area: Statewide

Materials Available: Through local conservation districts: county soil surveys, USGS toP.O. maps, watershed maps, brochures, guidebooks

MICHIGAN AUDUBON SOCIETY

6011 W. St. Joseph Hwy.
Suite 403, P.O. Box 80527
Lansing, MI 48908-0527
PH: (517) 886-9144
FX: (517) 886-9466
E-mail: mas@michiganaudubon.org
Website: www.michiganaudubon.org

Michigan Audubon Society was established in 1904 and is the oldest environmental organization in Michigan. They have 45 chapters around the state that provide a grassroots base of knowledge and activities for the public. The Society is affiliated with two major nature centers, Sarett Nature Center and F. Ponds Nature Center, and owns 5,000 acres of sanctuary land. MAS was responsible for saving the tip of the Tawas Point from development, and can when necessary formulate action with the help of its 9,000 members.

Service Area: Upper & Lower Peninsulas of Michigan

Materials Available: Slide shows, brochures, guidebooks, videotapes, natural history bookshop with great selection of children's books

MICHIGAN ENVIRONMENTAL COUNCIL

119 Pere Marquette, Suite 2A
Lansing, MI 48912
PH: (517) 487-9539
FX: (517) 487-9541
E-mail: mec@voyager.net
Website: www.mecprotects.org

The Michigan Environmental Council (MEC) monitors the overall condition of Michigan's wetlands and Wetland Protection Program. We comment on significant permit applications, rule changes, and legislation. We assist citizens by helping them collect information on wetland programs and permits, and by putting them in contact with local groups involved in similar issues.

Service Area: Statewide

Materials Available: Brochures and newsletter

222

MICHIGAN ENVIRONMENTAL LAW CENTER
P.O. Box 984
Traverse City, MI 49685-0984
Website: www.michenvirolaw.org

The Michigan Environmental Law Center helps provide legal assistance, including litigation services, to the public in order to protect and restore environmental quality in Michigan.

Service Area: Statewide

Materials Available: Legal resources

MICHIGAN LAKE AND STREAM ASSOCIATIONS, INC.
P.O. Box 249
Three Rivers, MI 49093
PH: (269) 273-8200
FX: (269) 273-2919
E-mail: info@mlswa.org
Website: www.mlswa.org

The Michigan Lake and Stream Associations, Inc. (ML&SA) serves as a communication link between hundreds of individual lake associations throughout Michigan. ML&SA advises citizens on understanding wetland regulations and on the best approaches to avoid or minimize wetland destruction.

Service Area: Statewide

Materials Available: Brochures, guidebooks, model local ordinances, slide shows, U.S.G.S topographic maps, videotapes, watershed maps

MICHIGAN NATURE ASSOCIATION
326 E. Grand Ave.
Williamston, MI 48895
PH: (517) 655-5655
E-mail: mna@greatlakes.net
Website: www.michigannature.org

The Michigan Nature Association (MNA) owns and protects 159 nature sanctuaries in 54 counties throughout Michigan. MNA projects take place in their preserves and sanctuaries that protect rare and endangered species, unique scenic vistas, critical wetlands, old growth forests, shorelines, bogs, geological formations and other natural features that make Michigan unique. Two-thirds of their holdings are wetlands. The mission of the MNA is two part: 1) to carry on a program of natural history study and conservation education, and 2) to acquire, maintain, and protect natural areas in the State of Michigan or areas adjacent thereto. MNA accepts donations of land and conservation easements that meet their criteria.

Service Area: Statewide

Materials Available: Guidebooks, preserve and sanctuary maps, brochures

MICHIGAN NATURAL AREAS COUNCIL
c/o Matthaei Botanical Gardens
1800 N. Dixboro Road
Ann Arbor, MI 48105-9741
PH: (734) 461-9390
E-mail: mnac@cyberspace.org

The Michigan Natural Areas Council is made up of individual members statewide, including naturalists, scientists, academics, etc. The Council's focus is to promote the protection of significant natural areas in Michigan and to provide information to the public. The Council conducts biological surveys of wetland natural areas and also testifies at state legislative committee hearings.

Service Area: Statewide

Materials Available: Newsletter, reconnaissance

MICHIGAN ORGANIC FOOD & FARM ALLIANCE
P.O. Box 626
Gaylord, MI 49734
PH: (269) 445-8769
FX: (269) 445-9887
E-mail: macmerrill@aol.com
Website: www.moffa.org

Michigan Organic Food & Farm Alliance (MOFFA) works with growers and farmers to eliminate use of harmful, toxic fertilizers and pesticides across the state. MOFFA puts on workshops, seminars, conferences on organic and sustainable farming practices and appropriate food systems, in addition to management practices/ natural habitat retention, etc to enhance wetland and water quality protection.

Service Area: Statewide

Materials Available: Brochures, slide shows, videotapes, organic growing standards/practices

MICHIGAN UNITED CONSERVATION CLUBS
2101 Wood Street
P.O. Box 30235
Lansing, MI 48909
PH: (517) 371-1041
FX: (517) 371-1505
E-mail: muccpolicy@mucc.org
Website: www.mucc.org

The Michigan United Conservation Clubs (MUCC) routinely comments on dredge and fill applications and assists citizens with their comments. MUCC's Wetland Watch program provides local activists across the state with public notices and technical assistance free of charge. MUCC Lansing staff work to protect wetlands at the local, state, and federal level. In addition, MUCC has over 500 affiliate organizations across the state, many of which also work on wetlands.

223

Service Area: Statewide and Federal

Materials Available: Brochures, guidebooks, slide shows, U.S.G.S. topographic maps, video tapes

MICHIGAN WATERFOWL ASSOCIATION
P.O. Box 163
Marquette, MI 49855
PH: (906) 225-5066

The Michigan Waterfowl Association provides a $750 dollar annual conservation scholarship to a Northern Michigan University student majoring in biology or wildlife management. They also provide 650 ($1,300) subscriptions to Tracks Wildlife magazine to area middle schools, mallard and wood duck nesting program, 410 acre flooding, and sponsor a water quality research project at the high school.

Service Area: Marquette County and surrounding area

Materials Available: Brochures, videotapes

MICHIGAN WILDLIFE HABITAT FOUNDATION
6380 Drumheller Road
P.O. Box 393
Bath, MI 48808
PH: (517) 641-7677
FX: (517) 641-7877
Website: www.mwhf.org

The Michigan Wildlife Habitat Foundation provides citizens with design, technical, and funding assistance, supervision of fish and wildlife habitat restorations, and community improvements. The Foundation sponsors an annual training seminar to teach people to recognize drained wetlands that can be restored or improved.

Service Area: Statewide

Materials Available: Slide shows, brochures, newsletter

MID-MICHIGAN ENVIRONMENTAL ACTION COUNCIL (MID-MEAC)

Street Address: 416 S. Cedar, Suite C
Lansing, MI 48912
Mailing Address: P.O. Box 17164
Lansing, MI 48901-7164
PH: (517) 485-9001
FX: (517) 485-9181
E-mail: mmeac@juno.com

Mid-MEAC will provide guidance and information to landowners on water quality, wetland protection, and other environmental issues. The organization also promotes public awareness through their Adopt-A-River program, workshops, presentations, and their bi-monthly newsletter, Mid-MEAC Environmental News.

Service Area: Mid-Michigan

Materials Available: Red Cedar River Watershed Riparian Handbook, Mid-Michigan's Red Cedar River Factsheet

NATIONAL WILDLIFE FEDERATION
GREAT LAKES NATURAL RESOURCE CENTER

213 W. Liberty, Suite 200
Ann Arbor, MI 48104
PH: (734) 769-3351
FX: (734) 769-1449
E-mail: greatlakes@nwf.org
Website: www.nwf.org/greatlakesoffice

The National Wildlife Federation's (NWF) Great Lakes Natural Resource Center's wetland protection activities include education, litigation, and legislative initiatives focused on water quality and biodiversity issues. NWF can provide expertise and information on wetland issues including local wetland management plans, implementation of federal and state wetland regulations, state assumption of federal wetland programs, educational materials on wetland functions, and biodiversity.

224

Service Area: Great Lakes wide

Materials Available: Guidebooks

THE NATURAL AREAS ASSOCIATION

P.O. Box 154
Okemos, MI 48805
PH: (517) 485-0710

The Natural Areas Association is a charitable trust which supports conservation of the natural environmental heritage through increased public awareness, education, and acquisition of public and private natural areas.

Service Area: Mid-Michigan

Materials Available: Brochures

NORTHERN MICHIGAN ENVIRONMENTAL ACTION COUNCIL (NMEAC)

P.O. Box 1166
Traverse City, MI 49685-1166
PH: (231) 947-6931
FX: (231) 947-5734
E-mail: nmeac@traverse.com

NMEAC is a volunteer citizen advocacy group that serves as a watchdog for the Greater Grand Traverse Region on land use issues. NMEAC has been actively addressing highway construction and urban sprawl which threatens hundreds of acres of wetlands in our area as well as the ongoing issue of the proposed golf course construction at the Homestead Resort on the Crystal River.

Service Area: Grand Traverse, Leelanau, Benzie (with some work in Antrim), Kalkaska, Wexford Counties

Materials Available: Brochures, newsletter

NORTH OAKLAND HEADWATERS LAND CONSERVANCY

P.O. Box 285
Clarkston, MI 48347
PH: (248) 846-6547
FX: (248) 846-6548
E-mail: NOHLC@hotmail.com
Website: www.nohlc.org

The mission of the North Oakland Headwaters Land Conservancy is to protect the rural character and quality of life in Northwest Oakland County by conserving the woods, fields, streams, and other natural resources in the headwaters areas of the Clinton, Shiawassee, Huron, and Flint rivers.

Service Area: Northwest Oakland County

NORTHWOODS WILDERNESS RECOVERY

P.O. Box 122
Marquette, MI 49855-0122
PH: (906) 226-6649
E-mail: drcornet@up.net
Website: www.northwoodswild.org

Northwoods Wilderness Recovery is dedicated to protecting Michigan's three national forests. They accomplish this through on-the-ground forest monitoring, education and outreach, appeals, and strategic litigation.

Service Area: Statewide

Materials Available: Brochures, newsletter, slide show, maps

OAKLAND LAND CONSERVANCY

P.O. Box 80902
Rochester, MI 48308
PH: (248) 601-2816
FX: (248) 601-4582
E-mail: folland@wwnet.net
Website: www.oaklandlandconservancy.org

The mission of the Oakland Land Conservancy is to work toward the protection and preservation of natural areas throughout Oakland County. OLC accepts donations of land and conservation easements that meet their criteria.

Service Area: Oakland County

Materials Available: Brochures, natural areas registry, newsletter, model conservation easement form, conservancy holdings maps

PARTNERSHIP FOR THE SAGINAW BAY WATERSHED
SAGINAW BAY VISITORS CENTER

3582 State Park Drive
Bay City, MI 48706
PH: (989) 797-6804
FX: (989) 797-6809

The Partnership for the Saginaw Bay Watershed provides educational materials on wetlands and water resources to interested citizens and local officials. The Council sponsors an "Adopt-A-Stream" program, school river monitoring, and workshops on local zoning ordinances to protect water resources. The Partnership is located in the Visitors Center which is active in wetland education for students.

Service Area: 22 counties ranging from Livingston to Iosco Counties

Materials Available: Brochures, county soil surveys, guidebooks, model local ordinances, slide shows, textbooks, U.S.G.S. topographic maps, videotapes, watershed maps

PERE MARQUETTE WATERSHED COUNCIL, INC.
P.O. Box 212
Baldwin, MI 49304
PH: (231) 745-2583
FX: (231) 745-7692
E-mail: info@peremarquette.org
Website: www.peremarquette.org

PMWC's comprehensive watershed assessment has been completed and is available in hard copy and CD-ROM. It will serve as a baseline for the development of a long-range river management plan. As recipients of a 1998 Great Lakes Fisheries Trust grant, through a variety of novel habitat improvement techniques, it will demonstrate an increased recruitment of salmonids in the Big South Branch tributary.

Service Area: Pere Marquette watershed; Lake, Mason, Oceana, Newaygo Counties

Materials Available: Brochures, textbooks, videotapes, MIRIS maps, Mainstream newsletter

PHEASANTS FOREVER, INC.
4971 West Cutler Road
Dewitt, MI 48820
PH: (989) 668-1033

Pheasants Forever, Inc. is a non-profit organization dedicated to preserving, creating, and enhancing wildlife habitat in the United States. The Michigan chapters raise money and keep those funds locally to improve the land's carrying capacity for primarily the ring-necked pheasant, but also for other species that associate in these habitats. Pheasants Forever, Inc. assists landowners working to restore or enhance wetlands with advice, funding, seed sources, etc.

Service Area: Tawas to Traverse City and south

Materials Available: Brochures, guidebooks, videotapes, seeds (things for planting)

POTAWATOMI LAND TRUST (PLT)
1100 N. Main Street, Suite 203
Ann Arbor, MI 48104
PH: (734) 302-5263
FX: (734) 302-1804
E-mail: info@washtenawlandtrust.org
Website: www.washtenawlandtrust.org

The PLT works with private landowners to identify wetland habitats and protect them in perpetuity either by acquiring lands in fee simple for management, as nature preserves or by negotiating the donation of development rights through conservation easements.

Service Area: Primarily Washtenaw County

Materials Available: Brochures, guidebooks, videotapes

THE QUIET EARTH GROUP
416 Longshore Drive
Ann Arbor, MI 48105-1624
PH: (734) 996-8845
FX: (734) 996-8732
E-mail: quietearth@recycle.com

The Quiet Earth Group (QEG) is a program of the Center for Environmental Policy, Economics and Science. QEG's environmental management expertise facilitates a market-based system for preserving and enhancing the natural resource base. The team of ecologists, engineers, economists, attorneys, land planners and appraisers perform joint valuation of economic and ecological assets, assesses ecological burdens of products and processes, and consolidates real estate appraisal with ecological value assessment.

Service Area: Statewide

Materials Available: Incentive-based conservation implementation, model local ordinances

RAISIN VALLEY LAND TRUST
P.O. Box 419
Manchester, MI 48158
PH: (734) 456-4901
FX: (734) 482-0222
E-mail: info@rvlt.org
Website: www.rvlt.org

The mission of the Raisin Valley Land Trust (RVLT) is to preserve the natural, agricultural and historical character of the upper River Raisin watershed which encompasses the Upper River Raisin watershed, S.W. Washtenaw, N.W. Lenawee, and S.E. Jackson Counties. They publish quarterly the RVLT Newsletter. RVLT accepts donations of land and conservation easements that meet their criteria.

Service Area: River Raisin Watershed-upper portion, S.W. Washtenaw, S.E. Jackson and Lenawee Counties

Materials Available: Brochures, county soil surveys, guidebooks, U.S.G.S. topographic maps, videotapes, watershed maps

SAGINAW BAY ADVISORY COUNCIL
P.O. Box 643
Bay City, MI 48707
(989) 893-3782

The Saginaw Bay Advisory Council is made up of people from all around the Saginaw Bay area. Dredge and fill applications are thoroughly reviewed by members, and all applications are discussed at monthly meetings, where a decision is made regarding whether to advise acceptance or denial of the application.

Service Area: Saginaw Bay Watershed

Materials Available: U.S.G.S. topographic maps, watershed maps, brochures, guidebooks, and videotapes

225

SAGINAW COUNTY METROPOLITAN PLANNING COMMISSION
615 Court Street
Saginaw, MI 48602
PH: (989) 797-6800
FX: (989) 797-6809
E-mail: jreithel@saginawcounty.com

The Saginaw County Metropolitan Planning Commission is working towards restoring habitat and reducing erosion along riparian corridors in Saginaw County. The Planning Commission has many maps and aerial photographs available for review within the office that may be utilized by citizens involved with wetland protection.

Service Area: Saginaw County

Materials Available: Guidebooks, MIRIS maps, national wetlands inventory maps, U.S.G.S. topographic maps, watershed maps

SARETT NATURE CENTER
2300 Benton Center Road
Benton Harbor, MI 49022
PH: (269) 927-4832
FX: (269) 927-2742
E-mail: sarett@sarett.com
Website: www.sarett.com

Sarett Nature Center teaches 25,000 school children each year about the value and importance of wetlands. The center is comprised of 800 acres of wetlands throughout as the trail system has been constructed through the floodplains of the Paw Paw River. Four graduate courses for teachers (Western Mich. Univ. credit) are also taught here. The Center has two 35' long voyageur canoes from which wetland and river natural science are taught.

Service Area: Southwest Michigan

Materials Available: Slide shows, videotapes

SEVEN PONDS NATURE CENTER
3854 Crawford Road
Dryden, MI 48428
PH: (810) 796-3200
E-mail: spnc@tir.com
Website: www.geocities.com/sevenponds

Seven Ponds Nature Center is a 323-acre nature sanctuary and environmental education center containing lakes, ponds, swamps, marshes and streams. Its mission is to raise the environmental awareness of its constituency.

Service Area: Southeastern Michigan

Materials Available: Slide shows, brochures, textbooks, videotapes

SIERRA CLUB, MACKINAC CHAPTER
109 East Grand River
Lansing, MI 48906
PH: (517) 484-2372
FX: (517) 484-3108
E-mail: mackinac.chapter@sierraclub.org
Website: www.michigan.sierraclub.org

Local Sierra groups around the state advocate for protection of wetlands in their region. The statewide chapter advocates for wetlands protection in the state legislature and with state agencies.

Service Area: Statewide

Materials Available: Brochures, videotapes

SOUTHEAST MICHIGAN LAND CONSERVANCY (SMLC)
1100 N. Main Street, Suite 212
Ann Arbor, MI 48104
PH: (734) 997-0942
E-mail: smlcaa@ameritech.net
Website: www.smlc.net

226

The Southeast Michigan Land Conservancy (SMLC) will help public and private landowners protect their wetlands using perpetual conservation easements. SMLC acquires key wetland and other habitats and assists local communities in acquiring land through the Michigan Natural Resources Trust Fund. SMLC especially promotes the preservation of riparian wetlands and is involved in wetland restoration on Conservancy-owned property.

Service Area: Seven county Southeast Michigan region: Livingston, Macomb, Monroe, Oakland, St.Clair, Washtenaw, Wayne Counties

Materials Available: Brochures, county soil surveys, slide shows, watershed maps

SOUTHWEST MICHIGAN LAND CONSERVANCY (SWMLC)
6851 South Sprinkle Road
Portage, MI 49002
PH: (269) 324-1600
FX: (269) 324-9760
E-mail: conserveland@swmlc.org
Website: www.swmlc.org

The Southwest Michigan Land Conservancy (SWMLC) protects the natural diversity and beauty of southwest Michigan by preserving significant land and scenic areas and fostering appreciation for and understanding of the environment. SWMLC accepts donations/bargain sales of land and donations of conservation easements that meet their criteria.

Service Area: Allegan, Barry, Berrien, Branch, Calhoun, Cass, Kalamazoo, St. Joseph, and Van Buren counties

Materials Available: Brochures, county soil surveys, national wetlands inventory maps, newsletter, slide shows, U.S.G.S. topographic maps, videotapes

SUPERIOR LAND CONSERVANCY (SLC)
(Committee of Southeast Michigan Land Conservancy)
P.O. Box 981024
Ypsilanti, MI 48198-1024
PH: (734) 997-0942
E-mail: smlc@voyager.net
Website: www.bendor.org/slc.shtml

The SLC primarily works to preserve the integrity of natural features, open space, and clear waters amidst the rapidly developing frontier between Detroit and Ann Arbor. In addition to establishing preserves, the organization works closely with township and county officials, other environmental groups and the public at large to create land use policy consistent with its mission. They have been instrumental in the enactment of Superior Township's wetlands ordinance.

Service Area: Superior Charter Township, Eastern Washtenaw County

Materials Available: Brochures, county soil surveys, guidebooks, locally produced wetland maps, slide shows, U.S.G.S. topographic maps, videotapes, natural features inventory published by SLC in 1992, historical features inventory and intensive historical study published by SLC in 1993 and 1996

SUPERIOR WILDERNESS ACTION NETWORK (SWAN)
P.O. Box 677
Sandstone, MN 55072
PH: (320) 245-6800
FX: (320) 245-6807
E-mail: swan@superiorwild.org
Website: www.superiorwild.org

SWAN's mission is to create public awareness of and gain support for the northwoods biodiversity reserve concept, to educate and mobilize citizens in the region, and to continue to gather information and data to incorporate into their superior wildlands map.

Service Area: Michigan's Upper Peninsula, Northern Wisconsin, and Northern Minnesota

Materials Available: Newsletter, maps

THE NATURE CONSERVANCY, MICHIGAN CHAPTER (TNC)
101 E. Grand River
Lansing, MI 48906
PH: (517) 316-0300
FX: (517) 316-9886
E-mail: michigan@tnc.org

The Nature Conservancy acquires, preserves, protects and manages wetlands that provide habitat for more species and functioning natural communities, and are representative of the landscape in Michigan.

Service Area: Statewide

Materials Available: Brochures, slide shows, videotapes

THE WATERSHED CENTER GRAND TRAVERSE BAY
232 East Front Street
Traverse City, MI 49684
PH: (231) 935-1514
FX: (231) 935-3829
E-mail: info@gtbay.org

The Watershed Center Grand Traverse Bay is a long-term watershed management program based on local partnership agreements. The Watershed Center refers landowners to partner organizations that have wetland expertise.

Service Area: Antrim, Charlevoix, Grand Traverse, Kalkaska, Leelanau Counties

Materials Available: U.S.G.S. topographic maps, locally produced wetland maps, watershed maps, guidebooks, textbooks, videotapes, model local ordinances

THREE LAKES ASSOCIATION
P.O. Box 689
Bellaire, MI 49615
PH: (231) 533-4852
E-mail: 3lakes@torchlake.com

The Three Lakes Association monitors MDEQ permits for Three Lakes Association area. They supply information on preservation and protection and support preserves in the Grass River and Skegemog Lake area.

Materials Available: County soil survey maps, U.S.G.S. topographic maps

THUMB BIOREGIONAL ALLIANCE
P.O. Box 116
Yale, MI 48097
E-mail: ThumbBio@aol.com

The Thumb Bioregional Alliance promotes wetland protection through a web of communication within an interdependent membership. Local guided field trips foster the investigation of regional points of interest promoting education and thoughtful living. Member-funded participatory projects encourage the community to make pro-active responses as stewards of a sustainable and healthy ecosystem.

Service Area: Michigan's lower peninsula "Thumb Region", i.e. Bay City-Flint to Detroit; east of I-75

Materials Available: County soil surveys, National Wetlands Inventory maps, watershed maps, resource personnel, slide shows, textbooks, model local ordinances, newsletter

THUNDER BAY RIVER WATERSHED COUNCIL
P.O. Box 751
Alpena, MI 49707

The Thunder Bay River Watershed Council is a volunteer organization working to protect water resources in the Thunder Bay River watershed.

TIP OF THE MITT WATERSHED COUNCIL
426 Bay Street
Petoskey, MI 49770
PH: (231) 347-1181
FX: (231) 347-5928
E-mail: info@watershedcouncil.org
Website: www.watershedcouncil.org

Tip of the Mitt Watershed Council (TOMWC) has many programs that focus on wetland protection, including coordination of policy review and comment through the Michigan Wetland Action Coalition, a planning and zoning program to promote wetland and water quality protection with local governments, and a wetland delineation service on private properties. Staff design wetland restoration, enhancement, and creation projects. TOMWC also publishes Great Lakes Aquatic Habitat News, and coordinates the Great Lakes Aquatic Habitat Network and Fund.

Service Area: Watersheds of Antrim, Charlevoix, Cheboygan, Emmet Counties

Materials Available: Brochures, guidebooks, locally produced wetland maps, county soil surveys, model local ordinances, textbooks, slide shows, U.S.G.S. topographic maps, videotapes, watershed maps

TROUT UNLIMITED
7 Trowbridge, N.E.
Grand Rapids, MI 49503
PH: (616) 460-0477
E-mail: rbowman@mctu.org

The mission of the Michigan Council of Trout Unlimited is to conserve, protect and restore Michigan's watersheds which support wild trout and salmon. The Council is interested in wetlands protection because they are a vital part of a watershed.

Service Area: Statewide

Materials Available: Brochures

UPPER PENINSULA ENVIRONMENTAL COALITION (UPEC)
P.O. Box 673
Houghton, MI 49931
PH: (906) 485-5909
FX: (906) 485-4671
E-mail: upecmichigan@yahoo.com
Website: www.upenvironment.org

UPEC selectively monitors dredge and fill applications for the entire upper peninsula of Michigan and sometimes provides comments or refers them to appropriate agencies and individuals. UPEC also helps to coordinate and develop action strategies for particular wetland protection issues.

Service Area: Upper Peninsula

Materials Available: Brochures, newsletter, forestry handbook

WASHTENAW LAND TRUST
1100 N. Main Street, #203
Ann Arbor, MI 48104
PH: (734) 302-LAND
FX: (734) 302-1804
E-mail: info@washtenawlandtrust.org
Website: www.washtenawlandtrust.org

WLT works with private landowners to identify wetland habitats and protect them in perpetuity by acquiring lands in fee for management as nature preserves, or by negotiating the donation or sale of conservation easements.

Service Area: Washtenaw County, NE Jackson County, some outlying areas

Materials Available: County soil surveys, USGS toP.O. maps, slide show, brochures, guidebooks, videotapes

WATER AND AIR TEAM FOR CHARLEVOIX (WATCH) INC.
P.O. Box 615
Charlevoix, MI 49720
PH: (231) 547-5530

WATCH routinely comments on dredge and fill applications and assists citizens with their comments as much as possible. WATCH's "Adopt-A-Stream" program can be expanded to include wetlands, and they are available to help in litigation or contested case hearings.

Service Area: Charlevoix County

Materials Available: brochures, guidebooks, textbooks

227

WEST BLOOMFIELD LAND CONSERVANCY
7379 Edinborough Drive
West Bloomfield, MI 48322
PH: (248) 661-6162
FX: (248) 661-6184

The West Bloomfield Land Conservancy has assisted in protecting two major park sites that have extensive wetland areas. The Conservancy does not currently hold any easements or deeds to land, although it could if certain criteria were met. Work to date has consisted primarily of education and advocacy.

WEST MICHIGAN ENVIRONMENTAL ACTION COUNCIL (WMEAC)
1514 Wealthy Street, S.E., Suite 280
Grand Rapids, MI 49506
PH: (616) 451-3051
FX: (616) 451-3054
E-mail: info@wmeac.org
Website: www.wmeac.org

WMEAC provides information and onsite investigation assistance to citizens as well as working with citizens and the DEQ to ensure clear communication and responsive action. WMEAC also has model ordinance materials to assist decision makers, developers and others in arriving at progressive solutions. Staff is able to assist with wetland delineation and is certified in the Purple Loosestrife Project.

Service Area: Allegan, Kent, Muskegon, Ottawa Counties on most issues, broader on some issues and state issues, Grand Rapids metro area on many issues

Materials Available: Brochures, county soil survey maps, model local ordinances, textbooks, U.S.G.S. topographic maps, watershed maps

WETLANDS CONSERVATION ASSOCIATION
P.O. Box 133
Stevensville, MI 49127-0133
PH: (269) 429-1862

228

The Wetlands Conservation Association (WCA) provides educational assistance to the general public, including setting up and presenting school programs. Wetland protection advice is also provided to the general public. WCA is also involved in protecting and enhancing water quality and biodiversity of area.

Service Area: Berrien, Cass, and VanBuren Counties

Materials Available: Brochures, county soil surveys, guidebooks, hands-on displays, national wetlands inventory maps, slide shows, textbooks, videotapes

WITH THE GRAIN
P.O. Box 517
Mattawan, MI 49071-0517
PH: (269) 624-1140
FX: (269) 349-9076
E-mail: wtg@wtgrain.org
Website: www.wtgrain.org

With the Grain is a non-profit organization dedicated to educating people about their effect on the environment and motivating them to make informed, responsible decisions. With the Grain evaluates the thinking behind individual, business, and municipal decisions, advocates long-term planning for natural resource preservation, and encourages individual self-empowerment. Consulting is available on land use planning and zoning issues, along with internet research and web development projects.

Service Area: Consulting statewide; VanBuren and adjoining counties in particular

Materials Available: County soil survey maps, MIRIS maps, model local ordinances, national wetlands inventory maps, textbooks, U.S.G.S. topographic maps, watershed maps

YELLOW DOG WATERSHED PRESERVE, INC.
P.O. Box 5
Big Bay, MI 49808
PH:(906) 345-9223
FX:(906) 345-9473
E-mail: ydwp@yellowdogwatershed.org
Web-site: www.yellowdogwatershed.org

The Yellow Dog Watershed Preserve (YDWP) is a non-profit organization whose mission is to preserve the Yellow Dog Watershed in its most natural state for the use of the public, now and for the benefit of future generations.

Service Area: Northern Marquette County–the Yellow Dog Watershed

Materials Available: USGS toP.O. maps, watershed maps, waterfall maps, slide show, brochures

APPENDIX B: State and Federal Wetland Regulatory Agencies

STATE AGENCIES

MICHIGAN DEPARTMENT OF ENVIRONMENTAL QUALITY

The Michigan Department of Environmental Quality (MDEQ) administers several regulatory statutes that protect wetlands, including the following parts of P.A. 451 of 1994: Inland Lakes and Streams, the Great Lakes Submerged Lands, and Wetland Protection, among others. In addition, the MDEQ also administers programs such as the P.A. 116 easement program and Section 6217 of the Coastal Zone Act Reauthorization Amendments.

Geological and Land Management Division
P.O. Box 30458
Lansing, MI 48909-7756
phone: (517) 241-1515
fax: (517) 241-1601

Water Division
P.O. Box 30273
Lansing, MI 48909
phone: (517) 335-4176
fax: (517) 335-0889

<u>District and Field Offices:</u>

Upper Peninsula District Office
420 5th St.
Gwinn, MI 49841
phone: (906) 346-8300

Cadillac District Office
120 W. Chapin St.
Cadillac, MI 49601-2158
phone: (231) 775-3960
fax: (231) 775-1511 or
fax: (231) 775-4050 (second floor)

Gaylord Field Office
2100 West M-32
Gaylord, MI 49735-9282
phone: (989) 731-4920
fax: (989) 731-6181

MICHIGAN DEPARTMENT OF ENVIRONMENTAL QUALITY
Districts

229

MICHIGAN DEPARTMENT OF NATURAL RESOURCES

Saginaw Bay District Office
503 N. Euclid Ave., Ste. 1
Bay City, MI 48706-2965
phone: (989) 686-8025
fax: (989) 684-9799 or
fax: (989) 686-0727

Grand Rapids District Office
State Office Bldg.
350 Ottawa NW, Unit 10
Grand Rapids, MI 49503-2341
phone: (616) 356-0500
fax: (616) 356-0201

Kalamazoo District Office
7953 Adobe Rd.
Kalamazoo, MI 49009-5026
phone: (269) 567-3500
fax: (269) 567-9440

Lansing District Office
525 W. Allegan (Constitution Hall)
P.O. Box 30242
Lansing, MI 48909-7742
phone: (517) 335-6010
fax: (517) 241-3571

Jackson District Office
301 E. Louis Glick Hwy.
Jackson, MI 49201-1556
phone: (517) 780-7690
fax: (517) 780-7855

SE Michigan District Office
38980 Seven Mile Rd.
Livonia, MI 48152-1006
phone: (734) 953-8905
fax: (734) 953-0243 or
fax: (734) 953-1544

Detroit Field Office
Cadillac Place
3058 West Grand Boulevard,
Suite 2-300
Detroit, MI 48202-6058
phone: (313) 456-4700
2nd floor fax: (313) 456-4692
9th floor fax: (313) 456-4662

Fisheries Division
Mason Building, Eighth Floor
P.O. Box 30446
Lansing, MI 48909
phone: (517) 373-1280
fax: (517) 373-0381

The Fisheries Division manages fisheries resources in the Great Lakes, 11,000 lakes, and 36,000 miles of rivers and streams. Its mission is to protect and enhance fish environments, habitat, populations and other forms of aquatic life and promote optimum use of these resources for the benefit of the people of Michigan. Fisheries biologists are often very helpful in providing comments on wetland permits regarding impacts to fisheries.

Forest Management Division
Mason Building, Fifth Floor
P.O. Box 30452
Lansing, MI 48909-7952
phone: (517) 373-1275
fax: (517) 373-2443

The Michigan Department of Natural Resources (MDNR) Forest Management Division administers the federally funded Forest Stewardship Program and the Stewardship Incentive Program.

Wildlife Division
Mason Building, 4th Floor
P.O. Box 30444
Lansing, MI 48909-7944
phone: (517) 373-1263

The Michigan Department of Natural Resources (MDNR) Wildlife Division is responsible for managing Michigan's wildlife resources. The Wildlife Division has restored or created thousands of acres of wetlands, administers Michigan's Endangered Species Protection Law and the Nongame Wildlife Fund Grants, and coordinates an amphibian monitoring program.

Field Headquarters and Management Unit Offices

Upper Peninsula Field Headquarters
1990 US-41 South
Marquette, MI 49855
phone: (906) 228-6561

Lower Peninsula Field Headquarters
P.O. Box 128
8717 N. Roscommon
Roscommon, MI 48653
phone: (989) 275-5151

Western U.P. Management Unit Office
1420 Highway US-2 West
Crystal Falls, MI 49920
phone: (906) 875-6622

Eastern U.P. Management Unit Office, Newberry Operations Service Center
5100 State Highway M123
Newberry, MI 49868
phone: (906) 293-5131

Northeastern Management Unit Office, Gaylord Operations Service Center
1732 M-32 West
Gaylord, MI 49735
phone: (989) 732-3541

Northwestern Management Unit Office, Cadillac Operations Service Center
8015 Mackinaw Trail
Cadillac, MI 49601
phone: (231) 775-9727

Saginaw Bay Management Unit Office, Bay City Operations Service Center
503 N. Euclid Ave.
Bay City, MI 48706
phone: (989) 684-9141

Southeastern Management Unit Office, Livonia Operations Service Center
38980 Seven Mile Rd.
Livonia, MI 48152
phone: (734) 953-0241

South Central Management Unit Office
10650 S. Bennett Rd.
Morrice, MI 48857
phone: (517) 625-4600

Southwestern Management Unit Office, Plainwell Operations Service Center
621 N. 10th St.
Plainwell, MI 49080
phone: (269) 685-6851

MICHIGAN DEPARTMENT OF NATURAL RESOURCES
Wildlife Management Unit Offices

LEGEND

⊗ Division Office

★ Offices

231

FEDERAL AGENCIES

U.S. ARMY CORPS OF ENGINEERS

Under Section 404 of the Clean Water Act and pursuant regulations, the U.S. Army Corps of Engineers is authorized to issue permits for the discharge of dredged or fill material in waters of the United States, including wetlands. Upon request, the Corps will send public notices of projects to interested landowners. Michigan is part of the Detroit District in the Great Lakes and Ohio River Division.

Detroit District Headquarters

477 Michigan Ave.
Detroit, MI 48226
toll free: 1-888-694-8313 or
(313) 226-6413

Detroit Area Office

6309 W. Jefferson, Bldg. 414
Detroit, MI 48209
phone: (313) 554-0753

Saginaw Field Office

2445 Weadock Rd.
Essexville, MI 48732
phone: (989) 894-4951

Grand Haven Area Office

307 South Harbor St.
Grand Haven, MI 49417
phone: (616) 842-5510

South Bend Sub-Office

2422 Viridian Dr., Ste. 101
South Bend, IN 46628
phone: (574) 232-1952

Marquette Field Office

1030 Wright St.
U.S. Forest Service Building
Marquette, MI 49855
phone: (906) 228-2833

Soo Area Office

St. Marys Falls Canal
Sault Ste. Marie, MI 49783
phone: (906) 632-3311

U.S. ENVIRONMENTAL PROTECTION AGENCY, REGION 5

Water Division (W-15J)
US EPA Region 5
77 W. Jackson Blvd.
Chicago, IL 60604-3590
phone: (312) 886-6115
fax: (312) 886-0168

The U.S. Environmental Protection Agency (US EPA) is a regulatory agency with a role in state planning, wetland inventory activities, law enforcement, and preparation and distribution of educational materials. The US EPA has oversight of the Clean Water Act Section 404 wetlands program and establishes regional wetlands policies. The Agency works to protect the chemical, physical, and biological integrity of waters of the United States, including wetlands. Their Wetland Protection State Development Grant Program funds many valuable wetland protection and management activities in Michigan, including this guidebook.

U.S. FISH AND WILDLIFE SERVICE

East Lansing Field Office
2651 Coolidge Rd.
East Lansing, MI 48823-6316
phone: (517) 351-2555
fax: (517) 351-1443

The U.S. Fish and Wildlife Service's mission is to conserve, protect, and enhance fish, wildlife, and their habitats (including wetlands) for the continuing benefit of people. The Service works with federal, state, and local governments, as well as private interests, to restore, enhance, and protect wetlands. It provides technical assistance and consultation on wetland restorations, federal endangered and threatened species, and environmental contaminant issues to other governments and private landowners.

USDA MICHIGAN FARM SERVICES AGENCY

3001 Coolidge Rd., Ste. 100
East Lansing, MI 48823-6321
phone: (517) 324-5110
fax: (517) 324-5120

The Farm Services Agency of the USDA administers the financial components of conservation provisions of the Farm Bill, including the Agricultural Conservation Program, the Conservation Reserve Program, and the Debt Cancellation Conservation Easements Program.

USDA NATURAL RESOURCES CONSERVATION SERVICE

3001 Coolidge Rd., Ste. 250
East Lansing, MI 48823-6123
phone: (517) 324-5270
fax: (517) 324-5171

The USDA Natural Resources Conservation Service (NRCS) is a technical agency that provides assistance to people to help conserve, improve, and sustain our resources and environment. The NRCS is responsible for identifying and delineating wetlands for purposes of the Wetland Provisions of the Farm Bills and Section 404 of the Clean Water Act on agricultural properties.

232

NATURAL RESOURCES AND ENVIRONMENTAL PROTECTION ACT
Act 451 of 1994

AN ACT to protect the environment and natural resources of the state; to codify, revise, consolidate, and classify laws relating to the environment and natural resources of the state; to regulate the discharge of certain substances into the environment; to regulate the use of certain lands, waters, and other natural resources of the state; to prescribe the powers and duties of certain state and local agencies and officials; to provide for certain charges, fees, and assessments; to provide certain appropriations; to prescribe penalties and provide remedies; to repeal certain parts of this act on a specific date; and to repeal certain acts and parts of acts.

History: 1994, Act 451, Eff. Mar. 30, 1995;–1996, Act 434, Imd. Eff. Dec. 2, 1996.

The people of the State of Michigan enact:

ARTICLE I GENERAL PROVISIONS

PART 1 SHORT TITLE AND SAVINGS CLAUSE

324.101 Short title.
Sec. 101. This act shall be known and may be cited as the "natural resources and environmental protection act".

History: 1994, Act 451, Eff. Mar. 30, 1995.

324.102 Repeal of statute; effect.
Sec. 102. The repeal of any statute by this act does not relinquish penalty, forfeiture, or liability, whether criminal or civil in nature, and such statute shall be treated as still remaining in force as necessary for the purpose of instituting or sustaining any proper action or prosecution for the enforcement of the penalty, forfeiture, or liability.

History: 1994, Act 451, Eff. Mar. 30, 1995.

324.103 Heading or title; effect.
Sec. 103. A heading or title of an article, chapter, part, or subpart of this act shall not be considered as a part of this act or be used to construe the act more broadly or narrowly than the text of the sections of the act would indicate, but shall be considered as inserted for the convenience of the users of this act.

History: 1994, Act 451, Eff. Mar. 30, 1995.

324.104 Members of predecessor agency; powers.
Sec. 104. When a board, commission, committee, council, or other agency created by or pursuant to this act was preceded by an agency with the same or similar name and functions, members of the predecessor agency shall continue in office for the duration of the terms of office for which they were appointed and with the new members appointed shall constitute the new agency. Members shall be appointed under this act only as terms of the former members expire or vacancies occur. Members of the predecessor agency may be appointed to the new agency to succeed themselves subject to the limits for the total period of service set forth in this act.

History: 1994, Act 451, Eff. Mar. 30, 1995.

324.105 Existing rules; effect.
Sec. 105. When the department or other agency is directed to promulgate rules by this act and rules exist on the date the requirement to promulgate rules takes effect, which rules the department or agency believes adequately cover the matter, the department or agency determine that new rules are not required or may delay the promulgation of new rules until the department or agency considers it advisable.

History: 1994, Act 451, Eff. Mar. 30, 1995.

324.106 Orders; effect.
Sec. 106. Except as otherwise provided by law, this act does not repeal or alter the content or effect of orders that were issued pursuant to an act that is repealed by this act and codified as a part of this act.

History: 1994, Act 451, Eff. Mar. 30, 1995.

324.107 Editorial changes; effect; intent.
Sec. 107. It is the intention of the legislature that editorial changes in the language of statutes codified as parts within this act not be construed as changes to the meanings of those statutes.

History: Add. 1995, Act 60, Imd. Eff. May 24, 1995.

PART 3
DEFINITIONS

324.301 Definitions.
Sec. 301. Except as otherwise defined in this act, as used in this act:

(a) "Commission" means the commission of natural resources.

(b) "Department" means the director of the department of natural resources or his or her designee to whom the director delegates a power or duty by written instrument.

(c) "Department of natural resources" means the principal state department created in section 501.

(d) "Director" means the director of the department of natural resources.

(e) "Local unit of government" means a municipality or county.

(f) "Municipality" means a city, village, or township.

(g) "Person" means an individual, partnership, corporation, association, governmental entity, or other legal entity.

(h) "Public domain" means all land owned by the state or land deeded to the state under state law.

(i) "Rule" means a rule promulgated pursuant to the administrative procedures act of 1969, Act No. 306 of the Public Acts of 1969, being sections 24.201 to 24.328 of the Michigan Compiled Laws.

History: 1994, Act 451, Eff. Mar. 30, 1995.

234

PART 303
WETLANDS PROTECTION

324.30301 Definitions.
Sec. 30301. As used in this part:

(a) "Fill material" means soil, rocks, sand, waste of any kind, or any other material that displaces soil or water or reduces water retention potential.

(b) "Minor drainage" includes ditching and tiling for the removal of excess soil moisture incidental to the planting, cultivating, protecting, or harvesting of crops or improving the productivity of land in established use for agriculture, horticulture, silviculture, or lumbering.

(c) "Person" means an individual, sole proprietorship, partnership, corporation, association, municipality, this state, and instrumentality or agency of this state, the federal government, or an instrumentality or agency of the federal government, or other legal entity.

(d) "Wetland" means land characterized by the presence of water at a frequency and duration sufficient to support, and that under normal circumstances does support, wetland vegetation or aquatic life, and is commonly referred to as a bog, swamp, or marsh and which is any of the following:

> (i) Contiguous to the Great Lakes or Lake St. Clair, an inland lake or pond, or a river or stream.

> (ii) Not contiguous to the Great Lakes, an inland lake or pond, or a river or stream; and more than 5 acres in size; except this sub paragraph shall not be of effect, except for the purpose of inventorying, in counties of less than 100,000 population until the department certifies to the commission it has substantially completed its inventory of wetlands in that county.

> (iii) Not contiguous to the Great Lakes, an inland lake or pond, or a river or stream; and 5 acres or less in size if the department determines that protection of the area is essential to the preservation of the natural resources of the state from pollution, impairment, or destruction and the department has so notified the owner; except this subparagraph may be utilized regardless of wetland size in a county in which subparagraph (ii) is of no effect; except for the purpose of inventorying, at the time.

History: Add. 1995, Act 59, Imd. Eff. May 24, 1995.

324.30302 Legislative findings; criteria to be considered in administration of part.
Sec. 30302.

(1) The legislature finds that:

> (a) Wetland conservation is a matter of state concern since a wetland of 1 county may be affected by acts on a river, lake, stream, or wetland of other counties.

(b) A loss of a wetland may deprive the people of the state of some or all of the following benefits to be derived from the wetland:

(i) Flood and storm control by the hydrologic absorption and storage capacity of the wetland.

(ii) Wildlife habitat by providing breeding, nesting, and feeding grounds and cover for many forms of wildlife, waterfowl, including migratory waterfowl, and rare, threatened, or endangered wildlife species.

(iii) Protection of subsurface water resources and provision of valuable watersheds and recharging ground water supplies.

(iv) Pollution treatment by serving as a biological and chemical oxidation basin.

(v) Erosion control by serving as a sedimentation area and filtering basin, absorbing silt and organic matter.

(vi) Sources of nutrients in water food cycles and nursery grounds and sanctuaries for fish.

(c) Wetlands are valuable as an agricultural resource for the production of food and fiber, including certain crops which may only be grown on sites developed from wetland.

(d) That the extraction and processing of nonfuel minerals may necessitate the use of wetland, if it is determined pursuant to section 30311 that the proposed activity is dependent upon being located in the wetland and that a prudent and feasible alternative does not exist.

(2) In the administration of this part, the department shall consider the criteria provided in subsection (1).

History: Add. 1995, Act 59, Imd. Eff. May 24, 1995.

324.30303 Studies regarding wetland resources; contracts; study as public record for distribution at cost.

Sec. 30303. The department may enter into an agreement to make contracts with the federal government, other state agencies, local units of government, private agencies, or persons for the purposes of making studies for the efficient preservation, management, protection, and use of wetland resources. A study shall be available as a public record for distribution at cost as provided in section 4 of the freedom of information act, Act No. 442 of the Public Acts of 1976, being section 15.234 of the Michigan Compiled Laws.

History: Add. 1995, Act 59, Imd. Eff. May 24, 1995.

324.30304 Prohibited activities.

Sec. 30304. Except as otherwise provided by this part or by a permit obtained from the department under sections 30306 to 30314, a person shall not do any of the following:

(a) Deposit or permit the placing of fill material in a wetland.

(b) Dredge, remove, or permit the removal of soil or minerals from a wetland.

(c) Construct, operate, or maintain any use or development in a wetland.

(d) Drain surface water from a wetland.

History: Add. 1995, Act 59, Imd. Eff. May 24, 1995.

324.30305 Activities not requiring permit under part; uses not requiring permit; farming operation in wetland not requiring permit; incidental creation of wetland.

Sec. 30305.

(1) Activities that require a permit under part 325 or part 301 or a discharge that is authorized by a discharge permit under section 3112 or 3113 do not require a permit under this part.

(2) The following uses are allowed in a wetland without a permit subject to other laws of this state and the owner's regulation:

(a) Fishing, trapping, or hunting.

(b) Swimming or boating.

(c) Hiking.

(d) Grazing of animals.

(e) Farming, horticulture, silviculture, lumbering, and ranching activities, including plowing, irrigation, irrigation ditching, seeding, cultivating, minor drainage, harvesting for the production of food, fiber, and forest products, or upland soil and water conservation practices. Wetland altered under this subdivision shall not be used for a purpose other than a purpose described in this subsection without a permit from the department.

(f) Maintenance or operation of serviceable structures in existence on October 1, 1980 or constructed pursuant to this part or former Act No. 203 of the Public Acts of 1979.

(g) Construction or maintenance of farm or stock ponds.

(h) Maintenance, operation, or improvement which includes straightening, widening, or deepening of the following which is necessary for the production or harvesting of agricultural products:

(i) An existing private agricultural drain.

(ii) That portion of a drain legally established pursuant to the drain code of 1956, Act No. 40 of the Public Acts of 1956, being sections 280.1 to 280.630 of the Michigan Compiled Laws, which has been constructed or improved for drainage purposes.

(iii) A drain constructed pursuant to other provisions of this part or former Act No. 203 of the Public Acts of 1979.

(i) Construction or maintenance of farm roads, forest roads, or temporary roads for moving mining or forestry equipment, if the roads are constructed and maintained in a manner to assure that any adverse effect on the wetland will be otherwise minimized.

(j) Drainage necessary for the production and harvesting of agricultural products if the wetland is owned by a person who is engaged in commercial farming and the land is to be used for the production and harvesting of agricultural products. Except as otherwise provided in this part, wetland improved under this subdivision after October 1, 1980 shall not be used for nonfarming purposes without a permit from the department. This subdivision shall not apply to a wetland which is contiguous to a lake or stream, or to a tributary of a lake or stream, or to a wetland that the department has determined by clear and convincing evidence to be a wetland that is necessary to be preserved for the public interest, in which case a permit is required.

(k) Maintenance or improvement of public streets, highways, or roads, within the right-of-way and in such a manner as to assure that any adverse effect on the wetland will be otherwise minimized. Maintenance or improvement does not include adding extra lanes, increasing the right-of-way, or deviating from the existing location of the street, highway, or road.

(l) Maintenance, repair, or operation of gas or oil pipelines and construction of gas or oil pipelines having a diameter of 6 inches or less, if the pipelines are constructed, maintained, or repaired in a manner to assure that any adverse effect on the wetland will be otherwise minimized.

(m) Maintenance, repair, or operation of electric transmission and distribution power lines and construction of distribution power lines, if the distribution power lines are constructed, maintained, or repaired in a manner to assure that any adverse effect on the wetland will be otherwise minimized.

(n) Operation or maintenance, including reconstruction of recently damaged parts, of serviceable dikes and levees in existence on October 1, 1980 or constructed pursuant to this part or former Act No. 203 of the Public Acts of 1979.

(o) Construction of iron and copper mining tailings basins and water storage areas.

236

(3) An activity in a wetland that was effectively drained for farming before October 1, 1980 and that on and after October 1, 1980 has continued to be effectively drained as part of an ongoing farming operation is not subject to regulation under this part.

(4) A wetland that is incidentally created as a result of 1 or more of the following activities is not subject to regulation under this part:

(a) Excavation for mineral or sand mining, if the area was not a wetland before excavation. This exemption does not include a wetland on or adjacent to a water body of 1 acre or more in size.

(b) Construction and operation of a water treatment pond or lagoon in compliance with the requirements of state or federal water pollution control regulations.

(c) A diked area associated with a landfill if the landfill complies with the terms of the landfill construction permit and if the diked area was not a wetland before diking.

History: Add. 1995, Act 59, Imd. Eff. May 24, 1995;—Am. 1996, Act 550, Imd. Eff. Jan. 15, 1997.

324.30306 Permit for use or development listed in section 324.30304; filing, form, and contents of application; proposed use or development as single permit application; fee; work done in violation of permit requirement; fee refund.
Sec. 30306.

(1) Except as provided in section 30307(6), to obtain a permit for a use or development listed in section 30304, a person shall file an application with the department on a form provided by the department. The application shall include all of the following:

(a) The person's name and address.

(b) The location of the wetland.

(c) A description of the wetland on which the use or development is to be made.

(d) A statement and appropriate drawings describing the proposed use or development.

(e) The wetland owner's name and address.

(f) An environmental assessment of the proposed use or development if requested by the department, which assessment shall include the effects upon wetland benefits and the effects upon the water quality, flow, and levels, and the wildlife, fish, and vegetation within a contiguous lake, river, or stream.

(2) For the purposes of subsection (1), a proposed use or development of a wetland shall be considered as a single permit application under this part if the scope, extent, and purpose of a use or development are made known at the time of the application for the permit.(3) Except as provided in subsections (4) and (5), an application for a permit submitted under subsection (1) shall be accompanied by the following fee:

(a) For a project in a category of activities for which a general permit is issued under section 30312, a fee of $100.00.

(b) For a major project, including any of the following, a fee of $2,000.00:

(i) Filling or draining of 1 acre or more of coastal or inland wetland.

(ii) 10,000 cubic yards or more of wetland fill.

(iii) A new golf course impacting wetland.

(iv) A subdivision impacting wetland.

(v) A condominium impacting wetland.

(c) For all other projects, a fee of $500.00.

(4) A project that requires review and approval under this part and 1 or more of the following is subject to only the single highest permit fee required under this part or the following:

(a) Section 3104.

(b) Part 301.

(c) Part 323.

(d) Part 325.

(e) Section 117 of the land division act, 1967 PA 288, MCL 560.117.

(5) If work has been done in violation of a permit requirement under this part and restoration is not ordered by the department, the department may accept an application for a permit if the application is accompanied by a fee equal to twice the permit fee required under this section.

(6) If the department determines that a permit is not required under this part, the department shall promptly refund the fee paid under this section.

History: Add. 1995, Act 59, Imd. Eff. May 24, 1995;–Am. 1998, Act 228, Imd. Eff. July 3, 1998.

324.30307 Hearing; location; notice; approval or disapproval of permit application; notice of and reasons for denial or modifications; conditions; appeal; legal action; request and fee for notification of pending permit applications; biweekly list of applications; effect of ordinance regulating wetlands; review of permit application by local unit of government; effect of failure to approve or disapprove within time period; recommendations; notice of permit issuance.
Sec. 30307.

(1) Within 60 days after receipt of the completed application and fee, the department may hold a hearing. If a hearing is held, it shall be held in the county where the wetland to which the permit is to apply is located. Notice of the hearing shall be made in the same manner as for the promulgation of rules under the administrative procedures act of 1969, 1969 PA 306, MCL 24.201 to 24.328. The department may approve or disapprove a permit application without a public hearing unless a person requests a hearing in writing within 20 days after the mailing of notification of the permit application as required by subsection (3) or unless the department determines that the permit application is of significant impact to warrant a public hearing.

(2) If a hearing is not held, the department shall approve or disapprove the permit application within 90 days after the completed permit application is filed with the department. If a hearing is held, the department shall approve or disapprove the permit application within 90 days after the conclusion of the hearing. The department may approve a permit application, request modifications in the application, or deny the permit application. If the department approves the permit application, the department shall prepare and send the permit to the applicant. If the department denies, or requests a modification of, the permit application, the department shall send notice of the denial or modification request and the reasons for the denial or the modifications requested to the applicant. Department approval may include the issuance of a permit containing conditions necessary for compliance with this part. If the department does not approve or disapprove the permit application within the time provided by this subsection, the permit application shall be considered approved, and the department shall be considered to have made the determinations required by section 30311. The action taken by the department may be appealed pursuant to the administrative procedures act of 1969, 1969 PA 306, MCL 24.201 to 24.328. A property owner may, after exhaustion of administrative remedies, bring appropriate legal action in a court of competent jurisdiction.

(3) A person who desires notification of pending permit applications may make a written request to the department accompanied by an annual fee of $25.00, which shall be credited to the general fund of the state. The department shall prepare a biweekly list of the applications made during the previous 2 weeks and shall promptly mail copies of the list for the remainder of the calendar year to the persons who requested notice. The biweekly list shall state the name and address of each applicant, the location of the wetland in the proposed use or development, including the size of both the proposed use or development and of the wetland affected, and a summary statement of the purpose of the use or development.

(4) A local unit of government may regulate wetland within its boundaries, by ordinance, only as provided under this part. This subsection is supplemental to the existing authority of a local unit of government. An ordinance adopted by a local unit of government pursuant to this subsection shall comply with all of the following:

    (a) The ordinance shall not provide a different definition of wetland than is provided in this part, except that a wetland ordinance may regulate wetland of less than 5 acres in size.

    (b) If the ordinance regulates wetland that is smaller than 2 acres in size, the ordinance shall comply with section 30309.

    (c) The ordinance shall comply with sections 30308 and 30310.

    (d) The ordinance shall not require a permit for uses that are authorized without a permit under section 30305, and shall otherwise comply with this part.

(5) Each local unit of government that adopts an ordinance regulating wetlands under subsection (4) shall notify the department.

(6) A local unit of government that adopts an ordinance regulating wetlands shall use an application form supplied by the department, and each person applying for a permit shall make application directly to the local unit of government. Upon receipt, the local unit of government shall forward a copy of each application along with any state fees that may have been submitted under section 30306 to the department. The department shall begin reviewing the application as provided in this part. The local unit of government shall review the application pursuant to its ordinance and shall modify, approve, or deny the application within 90 days after receipt. If a municipality does not approve or disapprove the permit application within the time period provided by this subsection, the permit application shall be considered approved, and the municipality shall be considered to have made the determinations as listed in section 30311. The denial of a permit shall be accompanied by a written statement of all reasons for denial. The failure to supply complete information with a permit application may be reason for denial of a permit. The department shall inform any interested person whether or not a local unit of government has an ordinance regulating wetlands. If the department receives an application with respect to a wetland which is located in a local unit of government which has an ordinance regulating wetlands, the department immediately shall forward the application to the local unit of government, which shall modify, deny, or approve the application under this subsection. The local unit of government shall notify the department of its decision. The department shall proceed as provided in this part.

(7) If a local unit of government does not have an ordinance regulating wetlands, the department shall promptly send a copy of the permit application to the local unit of government where the wetland is located. The local unit of government may review the application; may hold a hearing on the application; and may recommend approval, modification, or denial of the application to the department. The recommendations of the local unit of government shall be made and returned to the department within 45 days after the local unit of government's receipt of the permit application. The department shall approve, modify, or deny the application as provided in this part.

(8) In addition to the requirements of subsection (7), the department shall notify the local unit of government that the department has issued a permit under this part within the jurisdiction of that local unit of government within 15 days of issuance of the permit. The department shall enclose a copy of the permit with the notice.

238

History: Add. 1995, Act 59, Imd. Eff. May 24, 1995;–Am. 1995, Act 103, Imd. Eff. June 23, 1995;–Am. 1998, Act 228, Imd. Eff. July 3, 1998.

324.30308 Adoption of wetlands ordinance by local unit of government; availability of wetland inventory; completion of inventory map; notice; enforceable presumptions not created; processing wetland use applications.
Sec. 30308.

(1) Prior to the effective date of an ordinance authorized under section 30307(4), a local unit of government that wishes to adopt such an ordinance shall complete and make available to the public at a reasonable cost an inventory of all wetland within the local unit of government, except that a local unit of government located in a county that has a population of less than 100,000 is not required to include public lands on its map. A local unit of government shall make a draft of the inventory map available to the public, shall provide for public notice and comment opportunity prior to finalizing the inventory map, and shall respond in writing to written comments received by the local unit of government regarding the contents of the inventory. A local unit of government that has a wetland ordinance on December 18, 1992 has until June 18, 1994 to complete an inventory map and to otherwise comply with this part, or the local unit of government shall not continue to enforce that ordinance. Upon completion of an inventory map or upon a subsequent amendment of an inventory map, the local unit of government shall notify each record owner of property on the property tax roll of the local unit of government that the inventory maps exist or have been amended, where the maps may be reviewed, that the owner's property may be designated as a wetland on the inventory map, and that the local unit of government has an ordinance regulating wetland. The notice shall also inform the property owner that the inventory map does not necessarily include all of the wetlands within the local unit of government that may be subject to the wetland ordinance. The notice may be given by including the required information with the annual notice of the property owner's property tax assessment. A wetland inventory map does not create any legally enforceable presumptions regarding whether property that is or is not included on the inventory map is or is not a wetland.

(2) A local unit of government that adopts a wetland ordinance shall process wetland use applications in a manner that ensures that the same entity makes decisions on site plans, plats, and related matters, and wetland determinations, and that the applicant is not required to submit to a hearing on the application before more than 1 local unit of government decision making body. This requirement does not apply to either of the following:

    (a) A preliminary review by a planning department, planning consultant, or planning commission, prior to submittal to the decision making body if required by an ordinance.

    (b) An appeal process that is provided for appeal to the legislative body or other body designated to hear appeals.

History: Add. 1995, Act 59, Imd. Eff. May 24, 1995.

324.30309 Regulation by local unit of government of wetland less than 2 acres; permit application; determination.

Sec. 30309. A local unit of government that has adopted an ordinance under section 30307(4) that regulates wetland within its jurisdiction that is less than 2 acres in size shall comply with this section. Upon application for a wetland use permit in a wetland that is less than 2 acres in size, the local unit of government shall approve the permit unless the local unit of government determines that the wetland is essential to the preservation of the natural resources of the local unit of government and provides these findings, in writing, to the permit applicant stating the reasons for this determination. In making this determination, the local unit of government must find that 1 or more of the following exist at the particular site:

(a) The site supports state or federal endangered or threatened plants, fish, or wildlife appearing on a list specified in section 36505.

(b) The site represents what is identified as a locally rare or unique ecosystem.

(c) The site supports plants or animals of an identified local importance.

(d) The site provides groundwater recharge documented by a public agency.

(e) The site provides flood and storm control by the hydrologic absorption and storage capacity of the wetland.

(f) The site provides wildlife habitat by providing breeding, nesting, or feeding grounds or cover for forms of wildlife, waterfowl, including migratory waterfowl, and rare, threatened, or endangered wildlife species.

(g) The site provides protection of subsurface water resources and provision of valuable watersheds and recharging groundwater supplies.

(h) The site provides pollution treatment by serving as a biological and chemical oxidation basin.

(i) The site provides erosion control by serving as a sedimentation area and filtering basin, absorbing silt and organic matter.

(j) The site provides sources of nutrients in water food cycles and nursery grounds and sanctuaries for fish.

History: Add. 1995, Act 59, Imd. Eff. May 24, 1995.

324.30310 Regulation by local unit of government of wetland less than 2 acres; revaluation for assessment purposes; protest and appeal; judicial review; right to initiate proceedings not limited by section.

Sec. 30310.

239

(1) A local unit of government that adopts an ordinance authorized under section 30307(4) shall include in the ordinance a provision that allows a landowner to request a revaluation of the affected property for assessment purposes to determine its fair market value under the use restriction if a permit is denied by a local unit of government for a proposed wetland use. A landowner who is aggrieved by a determination, action, or inaction under this subsection may protest and appeal that determination, action, or inaction pursuant to the general property tax act, Act No. 206 of the Public Acts of 1893, being sections 211.1 to 211.157 of the Michigan Compiled Laws.

(2) If a permit applicant is aggrieved by a determination, action, or inaction by the local unit of government regarding the issuance of a permit, that person may seek judicial review in the same manner as provided in the administrative procedures act of 1969, Act No. 306 of the Public Acts of 1969, being sections 24.201 to 24.328 of the Michigan Compiled Laws.

(3) This section does not limit the right of a wetland owner to institute proceedings in any circuit of the circuit court of the state against any person when necessary to protect the wetland owner's rights.

History: Add. 1995, Act 59, Imd. Eff. May 24, 1995.

324.30311 Permit for activity listed in § 324.30304; approval conditioned on certain determinations; criteria; findings of necessity; criteria for determining unacceptable disruption to aquatic resources; additional showing.

Sec. 30311.

(1) A permit for an activity listed in section 30304 shall not be approved unless the department determines that the issuance of a permit is in the public interest, that the permit is necessary to realize the benefits derived from the activity, and that the activity is otherwise lawful.

(2) In determining whether the activity is in the public interest, the benefit which reasonably may be expected to accrue from the proposal shall be balanced against the reasonably foreseeable detriments of the activity. The decision shall reflect the national and state concern for the protection of natural resources from pollution, impairment, and destruction. The following general criteria shall be considered:

(a) The relative extent of the public and private need for the proposed activity.

(b) The availability of feasible and prudent alternative locations and methods to accomplish the expected benefits from the activity.

(c) The extent and permanence of the beneficial or detrimental effects that the proposed activity may have on the public and private uses to which the area is suited, including the benefits the wetland provides.

(d) The probable impact of each proposal in relation to the cumulative effect created by other existing and anticipated activities in the watershed.

(e) The probable impact on recognized historic, cultural, scenic, ecological, or recreational values and on the public health or fish or wildlife.

(f) The size of the wetland being considered.

(g) The amount of remaining wetland in the general area.

(h) Proximity to any waterway.

(i) Economic value, both public and private, of the proposed land change to the general area.

(3) In considering a permit application, the department shall give serious consideration to findings of necessity for the proposed activity which have been made by other state agencies.

(4) A permit shall not be issued unless it is shown that an unacceptable disruption will not result to the aquatic resources. In determining whether a disruption to the aquatic resources is unacceptable, the criteria set forth in section 30302 and subsection (2) shall be considered. A permit shall not be issued unless the applicant also shows either of the following:

(a) The proposed activity is primarily dependent upon being located in the wetland.

(b) A feasible and prudent alternative does not exist.

History: Add. 1995, Act 59, Imd. Eff. May 24, 1995.

324.30312 General permit for category of activities; notice and public hearing; determinations; requirements and standards; conditions; time for completion or termination of construction, development, or use; duration of general permit.
Sec. 30312.

(1) The department, after notice and opportunity for a public hearing, may issue general permits on a state or county basis for a category of activities if the department determines that the activities are similar in nature, will cause only minimal adverse environmental effects when performed separately, and will have only minimal cumulative adverse effect on the environment. A general permit issued under this subsection shall be based on the requirements of this part and the rules promulgated under this part, and shall set forth the requirements and standards that shall apply to an activity authorized by the general permit.

(2) The department may impose conditions on a permit for a use or development if the conditions are designed to remove an impairment to the wetland benefits, to mitigate the impact of a discharge of fill material, or to otherwise improve the water quality.

240

(3) The department may establish a reasonable time when the construction, development, or use is to be completed or terminated. A general permit shall not be valid for more than 5 years.

History: Add. 1995, Act 59, Imd. Eff. May 24, 1995.

324.30313 Grounds for revocation or modification of general permit; grounds for termination or modification for cause of general permit.
Sec. 30313.

(1) A general permit may be revoked or modified if, after opportunity for a public hearing or a contested case hearing under the administrative procedures act of 1969, Act No. 306 of the Public Acts of 1969, being sections 24.201 to 24.328 of the Michigan Compiled Laws, the department determines that the activities authorized by the general permit have an adverse impact on the environment or the activities would be more appropriately authorized by an individual permit.

(2) A permit may be terminated or modified for cause, including:

(a) A violation of a condition of the permit.

(b) Obtaining a permit by misrepresentation or failure to fully disclose relevant facts.

(c) A change in a condition that requires a temporary or permanent change in the activity.

History: Add. 1995, Act 59, Imd. Eff. May 24, 1995.

324.30314 Information required to obtain compliance with part; entering on premises.
Sec. 30314.

(1) The department shall require the holder of a permit to provide information the department reasonably requires to obtain compliance with this part.

(2) Upon reasonable cause or obtaining a search warrant, the department may enter on, upon, or through the premises on which an activity listed in section 30304 is located or on which information required to be maintained under subsection (1) is located.

History: Add. 1995, Act 59, Imd. Eff. May 24, 1995.

324.30315 Violation; order requiring compliance; civil action.
Sec. 30315.

(1) If, on the basis of information available to the department, the department finds that a person is in violation of this part or a condition set forth in a permit issued under section 30311 or 30312, the department shall issue an order requiring the person to comply with the prohibitions or conditions or the department shall request the attorney general to bring a civil action under section 30316(1).

(2) An order issued under subsection (1) shall state with reasonable specificity the nature of the violation and shall specify a time for compliance, not to exceed 30 days, which the department determines is reasonable, taking into account the seriousness of the violation and good faith efforts to comply with applicable requirements.

History: Add. 1995, Act 59, Imd. Eff. May 24, 1995.

324.30316 Civil action; commencement; request; venue; jurisdiction; violations; penalties; restoration of wetland.
Sec. 30316.

(1) The attorney general may commence a civil action for appropriate relief, including injunctive relief upon request of the department under section 30315(1). An action under this subsection may be brought in the circuit court for the county of Ingham or for a county in which the defendant is located, resides, or is doing business. The court has jurisdiction to restrain the violation and to require compliance with this part. In addition to any other relief granted under this section, the court may impose a civil fine of not more than $10,000.00 per day of violation. A person who violates an order of the court is subject to a civil fine not to exceed $10,000.00 for each day of violation.

(2) A person who violates this part is guilty of a misdemeanor, punishable by a fine of not more than $2,500.00.

(3) A person who willfully or recklessly violates a condition or limitation in a permit issued by the department under this part, or a corporate officer who has knowledge of or is responsible for a violation, is guilty of a misdemeanor, punishable by a fine of not less than $2,500.00 nor more than $25,000.00 per day of violation, or by imprisonment for not more than 1 year, or both. A person who violates this section a second or subsequent time is guilty of a felony, punishable by a fine of not more than $50,000.00 for each day of violation, or by imprisonment for not more than 2 years, or both.

(4) In addition to the penalties provided under subsections (1), (2), and (3), the court may order a person who violates this part to restore as nearly as possible the wetland that was affected by the violation to its original condition immediately before the violation. The restoration may include the removal of fill material deposited in the wetland or the replacement of soil, sand, or minerals.

History: Add. 1995, Act 59, Imd. Eff. May 24, 1995.

324.30317 Disposition of fees and civil fines; expenditures; report.
Sec. 30317. The civil fines collected under this part shall be forwarded to the state treasurer for deposit in the general fund of the state. The fees collected under this part shall be deposited in the land and water management permit fee fund created in section 30113. Subject to section 30113, the department shall expend money from the land and water management permit fee fund, upon appropriation, to support guidance for property owners and applicants, permit processing, compliance inspections, and enforcement activities under this part. Not more than 90 days after the end of each state fiscal year ending after 1997, the department shall prepare a report describing how money from the land and water management permit fee fund was expended during that fiscal year and an evaluation of the current statutory and department rules, bulletins, and letters definition of a wetland and any appropriate changes to that definition in the first report submitted to the legislature under this section and shall submit the report to the standing committees of the house of representatives and the senate that primarily address issues pertaining to the protection of natural resources and the environment, and the appropriations committees in the house of representatives and the senate. Other than civil fines and costs, the disposition of which is governed by section 8379 of the revised judicature act of 1961, 1961 PA 236, MCL 600.8379, or criminal fines, funds collected by a local unit of government under an ordinance authorized under section 30307(4) shall be deposited in the general fund of the local unit of government.

History: Add. 1995, Act 59, Imd. Eff. May 24, 1995;–Am. 1996, Act 530, Imd. Eff. Jan. 13, 1997;–Am. 1998, Act 228, Imd. Eff. July 3, 1998.

324.30318 Revaluation of property for assessment purposes.
Sec. 30318. If a permit is denied for a proposed wetland activity, the landowner may request a revaluation of the affected property for assessment purposes to determine its fair market value under the use restriction.

History: Add. 1995, Act 59, Imd. Eff. May 24, 1995.

324.30319 Rules; hearing; judicial review; proceedings to protect wetland owner's rights.
Sec. 30319.

(1) The department shall promulgate and enforce rules to implement this part.

(2) If a person is aggrieved by any action or inaction of the department, the person may request a formal hearing on the matter involved. The hearing shall be conducted by the department pursuant to the administrative procedures act of 1969, Act No. 306 of the Public Acts of 1969, being sections 24.201 to 24.328 of the Michigan Compiled Laws.

(3) A determination, action, or inaction by the department following the hearing is subject to judicial review as provided in Act No. 306 of the Public Acts of 1969.

(4) This section does not limit the right of a wetland owner to institute proceedings in any circuit of the circuit court of the state against any person when necessary to protect the wetland owner's rights.

History: Add. 1995, Act 59, Imd. Eff. May 24, 1995.

324.30320 Inventories of wetland; use; updating; maps, ground surveys, and descriptions as public documents; availability and cost of aerial photographs and satellite telemetry data reproduction to county register of deeds.

Sec. 30320.

(1) As inventories of wetland are completed, the inventories shall be used as one of the criteria by the department in issuing permits. The inventories shall be periodically updated. The maps, ground surveys, and descriptions of wetlands included in the inventories shall be submitted to the respective county register of deeds and shall become a public document available to review by any member of the public.

(2) Aerial photographs and satellite telemetry data reproductions shall be made available to the respective county register of deeds for cost as determined by the department.

History: Add. 1995, Act 59, Imd. Eff. May 24, 1995.

324.30321 Basis and filing of preliminary inventory of wetland; hearing in state planning and development region; notice; issuance and distribution of final inventory; legislators to receive inventories; assessment of property; report; reassessment; fee.

Sec. 30321.

(1) The department shall make or cause to be made a preliminary inventory of all wetland in this state on a county by county basis and file the inventory with the agricultural extension office, register of deeds, and county clerk.

(2) At least 2 hearings shall be held in each state planning and development region created by Executive Directive No. 1973-1. The hearing shall be held by the department after publication and due notice so that interested parties may comment on the inventory. After the hearings, the department shall issue a final inventory which shall be sent and kept by the agricultural extension office, register of deeds, and county clerk. Legislators shall receive an inventory of a county or regional classification for their districts including both preliminary and final inventories unless the legislators request not to receive the materials.

(3) Before an inventory is made of a county, a person who owns or leases a parcel of property located in that county may request that the department of environmental quality assess whether the parcel of property or a portion of the parcel is wetland. The request shall satisfy all of the following requirements:

(a) Be made on a form provided by the department.

242

(b) Be signed by the person who owns or leases the property.

(c) Contain a legal description of the parcel and, if only a portion of the parcel is to be assessed, a description of the portion to be assessed.

(d) Include a map showing the location of the parcel.

(e) Grant the department or its agent permission to enter on the parcel for the purpose of conducting the assessment.

(4) The department shall assess the parcel within a reasonable time after the request is made. The department may enter upon the parcel to conduct the assessment. Upon completion of the assessment, the department shall provide the person with a written assessment report. The assessment report shall do all of the following:

(a) Identify in detail the location of any wetland in the area assessed.

(b) If wetland is present in the area assessed, describe the types of activities that require a permit under this part.

(c) If the assessment report determines that the area assessed or part of the area assessed is not wetland, state that the department lacks jurisdiction under this part as to the area that the report determines is not wetland and that this determination is binding on the department for 3 years from the date of the assessment.

(d) Contain the date of the assessment.

(e) Advise that the person may request the department to reassess the parcel or any part of the parcel that the person believes was erroneously determined to be wetland if the request is accompanied by evidence pertaining to wetland vegetation, soils, or hydrology that is different from or in addition to the information relied upon by the department.

(f) Advise that the assessment report does not constitute a determination of wetland that may be regulated under local ordinance or wetland areas that may be regulated under federal law and advise how a determination of wetland areas regulated under federal law may be obtained.

(g) List regulatory programs that may limit land use activities on the parcel, advise that the list is not exhaustive, and advise that the assessment report does not constitute a determination of jurisdiction under those programs. The regulatory programs listed shall be those under the following parts:

    (i) Part 31, with respect to floodplains and floodways.

    (ii) Part 91.

    (iii) Part 301.

    (iv) Part 323.

    (v) Part 325.

    (vi) Part 353.

(5) A person may request the department to reassess any area assessed under subsections (3) and (4) that the person believes the department erroneously determined to be wetland. The requirements of subsections (3) and (4) apply to the request, assessment, and assessment report. However, the request shall be accompanied by evidence pertaining to wetland vegetation, soils, or hydrology that is different from or in addition to the information relied upon by the department. The assessment report shall not contain the information required by subsection (4)(e).

(6) If an assessment report determines that the area assessed or part of the area assessed is not a wetland regulated by the department under this part, then the area determined by the assessment report not to be a wetland is not a wetland regulated by the department under this part for a period of 3 years after the date of the assessment.

(7) The department may charge a fee for an assessment requested under subsection (3) based upon the cost to the department of conducting an assessment. History: Add. 1995, Act 59, Imd. Eff. May 24, 1995;–Am. 1996, Act 530, Imd. Eff. Jan. 13, 1997.

324.30322 Notice to owners of record of change in status of property.

Sec. 30322. As wetland inventories are completed as specified in section 30321, owners of record as identified by the current property tax roll shall be notified of the possible change in the status of their property. Notification shall be printed on the next property tax bill mailed to property owners in the county. It shall contain information specifying that a wetland inventory has been completed and is on file with the agricultural extension office, register of deeds, and county clerk, and that property owners may be subject to regulation under this part.

History: Add. 1995, Act 59, Imd. Eff. May 24, 1995.

324.30323 Legal rights or authority not abrogated; action to determine if property taken without just compensation; court order; limitation on value of property.

243

Sec. 30323.

(1) This part shall not be construed to abrogate rights or authority otherwise provided by law.

(2) For the purposes of determining if there has been a taking of property without just compensation under state law, an owner of property who has sought and been denied a permit from the state or from a local unit of government that adopts an ordinance pursuant to section 30307(4), who has been made subject to modifications or conditions in the permit under this part, or who has been made subject to the action or inaction of the department pursuant to this part or the action or inaction of a local unit of government that adopts an ordinance pursuant to section 30307(4) may file an action in a court of competent jurisdiction.

(3) If the court determines that an action of the department or a local unit of government pursuant to this part or an ordinance authorized pursuant to section 30307(4) constitutes a taking of the property of a person, then the court shall order the department or the local unit of government, at the department's or the local unit of government's option, as applicable, to do one or more of the following:

    (a) Compensate the property owner for the full amount of the lost value.

    (b) Purchase the property in the public interest as determined before its value was affected by this part or the local ordinance authorized under section 30307(4) or the action or inaction of the department pursuant to this part or the local unit of government pursuant to its ordinance.

    (c) Modify its action or inaction with respect to the property so as to minimize the detrimental affect to the property's value.

(4) For the purposes of this section, the value of the property may not exceed that share of the state equalized valuation of the total parcel that the area in dispute occupies of the total parcel of land, multiplied by 2, as determined by an inspection of the most recent assessment roll of the township or city in which the parcel is located.

History: Add. 1995, Act 59, Imd. Eff. May 24, 1995.

Note to readers: updated versions of this document can be found at www.michigan.gov./deq

Issued June 14, 2002
Issued Under Part 303, Wetlands Protection, of the Natural Resources and
Environmental Protection Act, 1994 PA 451, as amended, being Sections 324.30301
to 324.30323 of the Michigan Compiled Laws, Annotated

BACKGROUND INFORMATION

PURPOSE

Part 303, Wetlands Protection, of the Natural Resources and Environmental Protection Act, 1994 PA 451, as amended (NREPA), authorizes the Michigan Department of Environmental Quality (MDEQ), Land and Water Management Division (LWMD) to define types of regulated activities that would be expected to have only a minor impact on wetlands and that can, therefore, be reviewed through an expedited permit application process. This General Permit (GP) defines those activities that the LWMD has determined to be minor and also defines the legal authority and limitations for use of this process.

The purpose of this GP is to allow the LWMD to evaluate applications for permits for many minor activities in wetlands without the delays of unnecessary public noticing. The objective of this GP is to reduce the inconvenience and cost of the permit process for applicants proposing minor activities and to reduce the costs of administering the program while protecting the wetland resource.

Please note that this GP does not define projects that will be permitted, but only those that may be considered for expedited processing. Issuance of a permit will follow only if it is determined that the proposed activity is otherwise in accordance with the criteria and requirements of Part 303 and other applicable statutes.

GENERAL PERMIT PROCEDURES

A person seeking authorization under this GP must submit a permit application on a form supplied by the LWMD. A preliminary determination of whether an application may be processed under this GP is made by LWMD staff when the application is received. Applications processed under GP procedures are reviewed without issuance of a public notice. The preliminary determination must be confirmed by a site inspection. If at any time in the review process it is determined that an application for a specific project does not meet all the general and specific GP criteria, or that the project should be subjected to public review, the applicant will be notified and the application will be returned to Lansing for processing as an individual permit application, including the issuance of a public notice. The processing as an individual permit application may require the applicant to provide additional information and an additional application fee. The LWMD may deny the individual permit if warranted.

REGULATORY AUTHORITY

The LWMD, in accordance with Section 30312(1) of the NREPA, being Sections 324.30301 to 324.30323 of the Michigan Compiled Laws, Annotated; and the Administrative Rules for Wetlands Protection being R281.921 to R281.925, has determined that the activities listed in this GP meet the requirements given in Part 303 and the rules and, therefore, initially qualify for incorporation into this GP.

Section 30312(1) of the NREPA states, in part, "The department … may issue general permits … or a category of activities if the department determines that the activities are similar in nature, will cause only minimal adverse environmental effects when performed separately, and will have only minimal cumulative adverse effects on the environment."

Rule 281.923(1) of the Part 303 Administrative Rules indicates that:

An application for a proposed activity which is within a general permit category may be processed and issued by the department without the noticing or hearings specified under section 30307 of the act. The department may process, by public notice, an application which would normally qualify under a general permit category to allow more opportunity for public review and comment. Categories of minor activities will be established in the general permit in accordance with section 30312 of the act. The factors set forth in sections 30302 and 30311 of the act shall be considered in determining whether such a permit is in the best interest of the public.

GENERAL CRITERIA FOR PERMIT ISSUANCE

Section 30311 of the NREPA specifies the criteria that must be met before a permit may be issued. These general criteria, as well as the specific criteria detailed later in this GP, must be met before the LWMD can issue a permit under this GP.

Subsection (1) states that "A permit for an activity . . . shall not be approved unless the department determines that the issuance of the permit is in the public interest, that the permit is necessary to realize the benefits derived from the activity, and that the activity is otherwise lawful."

Subsection (4) states that "A permit shall not be issued unless it is shown that an unacceptable disruption will not result to the aquatic resources . . . .. A permit shall not be issued unless the applicant also shows either of the following:

    (a) The proposed activity is primarily dependent upon being located in the wetland.
    (b) A feasible and prudent alternative does not exist."

LIMITATIONS

The types of activities described in this document can typically be processed as minor actions. However, some activities will not qualify for this type of processing even if the listed criteria are met. Applications will not qualify for consideration under these categories if:

A) It is determined that the proposed project would constitute a "major discharge" subject to Federal review under any State-Federal memorandum of agreement;

B) The wetland is associated with sensitive natural resource areas including:

  1. a Federally designated wild and scenic river,
  2. a State designated natural river,
  3. a State or Federally designated wilderness or environmental area,
  4. a riverine floodway,
  5. a State or Federally listed or proposed threatened or endangered species,
  6. an identified historic or archeological area,
  7. an identified recharge area for drinking water aquifers,
  8. an identified rare or unique ecological type;

C) The LWMD determines that the decision making process would benefit from public review of the application;

D) The LWMD determines that a specific activity that would generally qualify as minor would, due to the proximity of other projects and the characteristics of the wetland, likely lead to adverse cumulative impacts;

E) The project also requires a permit under Parts 31, 301, or 325 but does not meet one of the minor categories under those Parts; or

F) The project also requires a permit under Parts 315, 323, or 353.

NEED FOR OTHER PERMITS
Issuance of a permit pursuant to GP procedures does not remove the need for other applicable local, State, or Federal permits.

GENERAL PERMIT CATEGORIES

The following activities are incorporated into this list of GP categories.

A) Small ponds and Shallow Water Development for Wildlife.
In addition to the General Criteria and Limitations outlined above, the proposed activity must meet the following specific criteria.

Construction or maintenance of water bodies less than one acre in size providing that dredge spoils including organic and inorganic soils, vegetation and debris shall be placed at an upland site, leveled and stabilized with sod, or seeded and mulched in such a manner as not to erode into any waterbody or wetland, and not be located in a floodway or harmfully interfere with flood flows. Direct connection to an existing inland lake or stream will not qualify for consideration under GP categories.

B) Simple Elevated or Floating Structures.
In addition to the General Criteria and Limitations outlined above, the proposed activity must meet the following specific criteria.

245

1. Boardwalks. Open pile or floating boardwalks on steel or timber posts not to exceed 6 feet in width except for widening to allow passage of wheel chairs, etc., at 150 foot intervals and with a maximum cumulative length through wetlands of 500 feet.

2. Platforms. Open pile or floating platforms on steel or timber posts not to exceed 120 square feet of surface area.

3. Safety Fences. Residential open wire safety fences elevated above the wetland on poles, placed to prevent children, pets, etc., from entering the wetland, and limited to 4 feet in height and 150 feet in total length through wetland.

C) Walkways.
In addition to the General Criteria and Limitations outlined above, the proposed activity must meet the following specific criteria.

Filling for walkways or footpaths not to exceed 6 feet in base width and 200 feet in length where boardwalks or elevated walkways are not feasible or practical. Culverts will be required where necessary to provide for the free flow of surface water. If in a floodplain, the grade elevation change shall not exceed six inches.

D) Driveways.
In addition to the General Criteria and Limitations outlined above, the proposed activity must meet the following specific criteria.

Construction of new driveways or the widening of existing driveways, provided that:

1. Any upland on the property or other alternatives, such as obtaining a permanent easement for access from adjacent upland if available or shared driveway, is utilized to the greatest degree possible;

2. The location of the driveway is at the least damaging place on the property (e.g., as close to any upland edge as possible) and the driveway crosses the shortest wetland area or area of least impact;

3. The portion or portions of the driveway that pass through wetland are restricted to a total of 16 feet in base width (includes the width of any existing drive and associated fill) and a total of 200 linear feet. The driveway may be wider than 16 feet at the intersection with the public road if the applicant provides proof that the additional width is a requirement of a public transportation agency. No ditches may be placed in the wetland in association with the driveway.

4. The driveway must terminate at a buildable upland site.

Culverts shall be placed as necessary to provide for the free flow of surface water and the movement of organisms. Fill shall be placed on filter fabric, or equivalent material if warranted by soil conditions. If in a floodplain, the grade elevation change shall not exceed six inches.

E) Utilities.
In addition to the General Criteria and Limitations outlined above, the proposed activity must meet the following specific criteria.
The placement of utilities through wetland, including activities such as,

Sewer and water line construction;
Electric transmission and telephone poles and lines;
Underground utility lines; or
Oil/gas pipelines with outside diameter larger than six inches;

provided that the following conditions are met:

1. Crossing sites shall be selected so as to minimize the impact on the wetland.

2. Construction shall be completed using construction methods, equipment, and materials that will minimize the impact on the wetland;

3. If excavated material is contaminated based on sediment leachate data, it may not be used as backfill and it shall be removed from the wetland and placed in a licensed landfill;

4. Project design features shall assure that backfill used in an excavated trench will not result in drainage of the wetland;

5, A minimum of 30 inches of cover shall be maintained between the top of the cable, pipe, encasement, etc., to the existing grade of the wetland;

6. The outside diameter of the pipe, cable, encasement, etc., shall not exceed 20 inches;

7. The top 6 inches to 12 inches of the trench shall be backfilled with topsoil from the trench. If material is contaminated, it shall be handled as indicated under 3. above, and uncontaminated, clean topsoil shall be brought in to fill the trench;

8. Excavated material sidecast or stockpiled in the wetland shall not remain for over 30 days and must be utilized as backfill or removed before completion of the project;

9. Excess excavated material must be removed from the wetland and disposed of at an upland site and stabilized to prevent erosion; and,

10. The applicant shall restore the disturbed area to preconstruction contours and conditions within 30 days of the completion of the project and revegetate the disturbed area.

F) Oil, Gas, and Mineral Well Access Roads.
In addition to the General Criteria and Limitations outlined above, the proposed activity must meet the following specific criteria.

246

Access roads for oil/gas drilling or mineral well drilling activities where angle drilling from upland is not feasible and where the activity is of minor impact, on both an individual and cumulative basis, to the wetland. Access roads shall not exceed 20 feet in base width on filter fabric or equivalent material. Culverts will be required, where necessary, to provide for the free flow of surface water or to avoid restricting low flows and the movement of aquatic organisms. Immediately upon plugging the well, all fill material shall be removed, the original wetland contours restored, and the site stabilized with a wetland seed source and mulched if necessary.

G) Stormwater Outfalls.
In addition to the General Criteria and Limitations outlined above, the proposed activity must meet the following specific criteria.

Stormwater outfalls provided that the outlet is riprapped or otherwise stabilized to prevent soil erosion and that the stormwater will be pretreated by incorporating permanent Best Management Practices or otherwise meet State water quality standards and applicable discharge permit requirements.

H) Culverts.
In addition to the General Criteria and Limitations outlined above, the proposed activity must meet the following specific criteria.

Culverts, if installed for water level equalization, i.e., to provide for the free flow of surface water between portions of a wetland system, and to equalize the static water pressure.

I) Emergency Drain Maintenance.
In addition to the General Criteria and Limitations outlined above, the proposed activity must meet the following specific criteria.

Projects not otherwise exempt under Section 30305(2)(h) involving maintenance, repair, or operation of an existing drain where necessary to alleviate flooding on an emergency basis, providing that:

1. The activity does not otherwise require a permit under Part 301, Inland Lakes and Streams, of the NREPA;

2. The area and extent of current wetlands will not be diminished; and

3. The activity is limited to restoring the drain to depths and widths that do not exceed historic dimensions as defined by the original permit issued under Parts 301 and/or 303, or by the original engineering design in the instance of a drain constructed prior to the effective date of Part 301.

J) Septic System Replacement.
In addition to the General Criteria and Limitations outlined above, the proposed activity must meet the following specific criteria.

Replacement of a failed on-site septic tank and/or drain field system providing that it is required by and meets design standards of the local health department. When possible the replacement tank and field system must be in the same location as the original system. Where the option is available, pump-back systems to upland will be required in place of mounded systems in order to qualify for construction under this GP category. A copy of the local health department permit or permission must be submitted to the LWMD at the time of application.

K) Repairs to Serviceable Structures.
In addition to the General Criteria and Limitations outlined above, the proposed activity must meet the following specific criteria.

Repairs to a serviceable structure that is not otherwise exempt from permits under Part 303 provided that the structure or fill is not to be put to uses differing from those uses specified or contemplated in the original design. This category applies to structures in existence on October 1, 1980, or constructed pursuant to Part 303. Minor deviations in the structure's configuration or filled area, including those due to changes in materials, construction techniques, current construction codes, or safety standards, that are necessary to make repairs may still be considered under this category providing that the environmental impacts resulting from the entire repair are minimal. Serviceable means useable as is or with minor repair, but not so degraded as to essentially require reconstruction. Serviceable structures damaged by storms, floods, fire, or other discrete events are included under this category provided that the repairs are commenced or under contract to commence within one year of the date of the damage.

This GP category cannot be used to authorize any alteration of drains, which are not considered "serviceable structures" for purposes of these regulations.

L) Completed Enforcement Actions.
In addition to the General Criteria and Limitations outlined above, the proposed activity must meet the following specific criteria.

Any structure, work, or discharge of dredged or fill material undertaken in accordance with, or remaining in place in compliance with, the terms of a final court decision, consent decree, or formal written settlement agreement resolving a violation of Part 303, provided that:

1. No more than five acres of wetland are impacted, and;

2. Resolution of the violation will provide environmental benefits equal to or greater than the environmental detriments caused by the violation.

The use of this GP does not preclude the requirement for mitigation or creation of a conservation easement in the decision, decree, or agreement.

M) Emergency Spill Cleanup.
In addition to the General Criteria and Limitations outlined above, the proposed activity must meet the following specific criteria.

Activities required for the emergency containment and cleanup of oil and hazardous substances provided that:

1. The work is done in accordance with State or Federal contingency plans;

2. The MDEQ division or Federal agency responsible for requiring the spill cleanup concurs with the proposed containment and cleanup actions, and the applicant provides some proof of this concurrence with the application; and

247

3. The wetland will be fully restored to its original condition prior to the discharge or spill.

N) Cleanup of Hazardous Substances and Hazardous and Toxic Waste.
In addition to the General Criteria and Limitations outlined above, the proposed activity must meet the following specific criteria.

Specific activities required to affect the containment, stabilization, or removal of hazardous substances or hazardous or toxic waste materials that are performed, ordered, or sponsored by the U.S. Environmental Protection Agency or the MDEQ provided that the plan prevents, to the extent feasible, any impacts to water or wetlands. The application must include a delineation of the affected wetland and a letter from the agency requiring the cleanup confirming the need for and explaining the scope of the cleanup. Court-ordered remedial action plans or related settlements also qualify under this category. This category does not include the establishment of new disposal sites, nor does it include improvements or expansions of existing sites, such as caps, leachate collection ponds, access roads, etc., that are used for the disposal of hazardous or toxic wastes, all of which will be processed as individual permit applications.

O) Maintenance Dredging of Man-made Stormwater and Wastewater Treatment Ponds and Lagoons.
In addition to the General Criteria and Limitations outlined above, the proposed activity must meet the following specific criteria.

Excavation and removal of accumulated sediment for maintenance of functional, active, and legally constructed stormwater detention or detention basins, sediment basins, treatment ponds and lagoons, or other man-made water treatment or retention areas created for those sole purposes, provided that the dredged material is placed in an upland site outside of regulated floodplains and stabilized with sod, or seeded, mulched, or riprapped, as necessary, to prevent soil erosion into any inland lake, stream, or wetland, or dredged material that is placed in a licensed landfill based on sediment leachate analysis of the material. The applicant shall submit the analytical results and sampling locations with the application. The upland disposal sites or licensed landfill must be identified in the plans.

P) Public Road Projects.
In addition to the General Criteria and Limitations outlined above, the proposed activity must meet the following specific criteria.

Public road projects contained within the existing right-of-way where all practical means have been used to minimize the wetland impact, and all components of the project will impact no more than two acres of wetland. This category shall be further restricted to the following:

1. **Safety Improvements.** The following projects which, after a finding of necessity by the public transportation agency, are determined to be required for safety reasons and for which the wetland fill will not exceed one-third acre per wetland.

    a) Flattening of road slopes to meet the minimum safety standard.
    b) Construction of standard shoulder widths.
    c) Installation of guardrail flares.
    d) Intersection improvements.
    e) Elimination of roadside obstacles, such as sign platforms and utility poles.
    f) Addition of a lane for safety reasons.

2. **Roadside Ditch Maintenance.** Re-establishment of existing roadside ditches to the original size, shape, and location where the draining of adjacent wetlands will not occur. Excavated materials must be disposed of and stabilized on upland, except when a berm is needed along the ditch to minimize adjacent wetland drainage.

3. **Equalizer Culverts.** Replacement, extension, or maintenance of an existing equalizer culvert that is required to maintain a hydraulic connection and static water pressure between parts of a wetland severed by an existing roadway where the extension will not exceed the toe of slope on either side of the fill.

4. **Temporary Work Pads.** Temporary work pads where the site will be restored to its preconstruction condition within one year.

Q) **Minor Fills.**
In addition to the General Criteria and Limitations outlined above, the proposed activity must meet the following specific criteria.

Minor fills for the construction or expansion of single family residences with the total fill area in wetlands not exceeding one-quarter acre for all phases of the residential construction, including driveways (this GP category cannot be used in conjunction with Category D. Driveways) garages, small storage sheds (not to exceed 100 square feet), and all waste treatment facilities, provided that:

1. No fill shall be placed in any part of a wetland that is inundated by water and provides fish and/or wildlife habitat functions at any time.

2. All upland on the property shall be utilized to the greatest degree possible.

3. The proposed fill in wetlands shall be at the least damaging location on the property.

4. All necessary actions shall be taken to minimize on-site and off-site impacts including sewage treatment systems that pump back to uplands where feasible.

5. The filled area surrounding building foundations will not be greater than 15 feet from the edge of the foundation to the toe of the slope. Fill slopes shall not be flatter than 1 vertical to 4 horizontal. Additional fill for purposes such as landscaping or recreational facilities will not qualify under this category.

6. The ownership of the parcel of land shall have been maintained within the immediate family (the original owners or their children) since October 1, 1980.

Note: This minor fill GP can be used only once on a parcel of land that existed prior to October 1, 1980, and only one permit can be granted to a family. It cannot be used on parcels established on or after October 1, 1980. Only one permit under this minor fill provision of the GP may be granted to a person.

248

R) **Restoration of Altered Wetland Areas.**
In addition to the General Criteria and Limitations outlined above, the proposed activity must meet the following specific criteria.

This category applies only to projects that serve to restore or enhance wetland hydrology, vegetation, and functions of altered wetlands. Altered wetlands include areas that have been partially or fully drained, or where other land use conversions have resulted in significant alteration of the original character of the site. This category does not include the conversion of unaltered wetlands or other stable beneficial wetland ecosystems to another aquatic use, such as the creation of a pond or impoundment where a wet meadow, fen, or forested wetland exists. Projects under this category are limited to the restoration of altered wetlands by State, Federal, and nonprofit conservation agencies and organizations.

Such activities include:

1. Installation and maintenance of small water control structures, dikes, and berms;

2. Removal or blocking of existing drainage structures; and,

3. Construction of small nesting islands.

Wetland fill for dikes, nesting islands, and other structures shall not exceed two acres. The purpose of such fill shall be to increase the functions and value of wetland resources and shall not result in a net loss of wetland acreage or function.

The following activities cannot be authorized under this General Permit category; individual permits are required:

1. Construction of a dike or berm that is six feet of more in height and that impounds an area of five acres or more during a design flood; such activity requires authorization under Part 315, Dam Safety of the NREPA.

2. Any encroachment of a floodplain, floodway, or stream channel that drains over two square miles except for those activities meeting the minor project categories listed the State's Floodplain Regulatory Authority found in Part 31, Water Resources Protection, of the NREPA.

3. Any alteration of a lake or stream requiring approval under Part 301, Inland Lakes and Streams, of the NREPA, except those activities meeting minor project categories listed in the Administrative Rules for Part 301.

4. Any alteration of Great Lakes submerged bottomlands requiring approval under Part 325, Submerged Lands, of the NREPA, except those activities meeting the minor project categories listed in Part 325.

5. Projects that require a permit under Part 323, Shorelands Protection and Management of the NREPA.

6. Projects that require a permit under Part 353, Sand Dune Protection and Management, of the NREPA.

This GP modifies and replaces the June 18, 1997 General Permit Categories for Minor Activities in Wetlands in the State of Michigan and shall expire on June 14, 2007, unless revoked or modified before that date.

WETLAND PROTECTION

[By authority conferred on the department of environmental quality by section 30319 of Act No. 451 of the Public Acts of 1994, as amended, being §324.30319 of the Michigan Compiled Laws]

R 281.921 Definitions.

Rule 1.

(1) As used in these rules:

    (a) "Act" means Act No. 203 of the Public Acts of 1979, being S281.701 et seq. of the Michigan Compiled Laws.

    (b) "Contiguous" means any of the following:
        (i) A permanent surface water connection or other direct physical contact with an inland lake or pond, a river or stream, one of the Great Lakes, or Lake St. Clair.
        (ii) A seasonal or intermittent direct surface water connection to an inland lake or pond, a river or stream, one of the Great Lakes, or Lake St. Clair.
        (iii) A wetland is partially or entirely located within 500 feet of the ordinary high watermark of an inland lake or pond or a river or stream or is within 1,000 feet of the ordinary high watermark of one of the Great Lakes or Lake St. Clair, unless it is determined by the department, pursuant to R 281.924(4), that there is no surface water or groundwater connection to these waters.
        (iv) Two or more areas of wetland separated only by barriers, such as dikes, roads, berms, or other similar features, but with any of the wetland areas contiguous under the criteria described in paragraph (i), (ii), or (iii) of this subdivision. The connecting waters of the Great Lakes, including the St. Marys, St. Clair, and Detroit rivers, shall be considered part of the Great Lakes for purposes of this definition.

    (c) "General permit" means a permit which, as authorized by section 10 of the act, is issued for categories of minor activities, as defined in subdivision (f) of this subrule.

    (d) "Individual permit" means a permit which, as authorized by sections 7, 8, and 9 of the act, is issued for categories of activities that are not classified as minor.

    (e) "Inland lake or pond, a river or stream" means any of the following:
        (i) A river or stream which has definite banks, a bed, and visible evidence of a continued flow or continued occurrence of water.
        (ii) A natural or permanent artificial inland lake or impoundment that has definite banks, a bed, visible evidence of a continued occurrence of water, and a surface area of water that is more than 5 acres. This does not include lakes constructed by excavating or diking dry land and maintained for the sole purpose of cooling or storing water and does not include lagoons used for treating polluted water.
        (iii) A natural or permanent artificial pond that has permanent open water with a surface area that is more than 1 acre, but less than 5 acres. This does not include ponds constructed by excavating or diking dry land and maintained for the sole purpose of cooling or storing water and does not include lagoons used for treating polluted water.

    (f) "Minor activities" means activities that are similar in nature, that will cause only minimal adverse environmental effects when performed separately, and that will have only minimal cumulative adverse effects on the environment.

    (g) "Wetland vegetation" means plants that exhibit adaptations to allow, under normal conditions, germination or propagation and to allow growth with at least their root systems in water or saturated soil.

(2) As used in the act:

    (a) "Electric distribution line" means underground lines below 30 kilovolts and lines supported by wood poles.

    (b) "Electric transmission line" means those conductors and their necessary supporting or containing structures located outside of buildings that are used for transmitting a supply of electric energy, except those lines defined in subdivision (a) of this subrule.

    (c) "Pipelines having a diameter of 6 inches or less" means a pipe which is equal to or less than what is commonly referred to as a 6-inch pipe and which has an actual measured outside diameter of less than 6.75 inches.

(3) Terms defined in the act have the same meanings when used in these rules.

History: 1988 MR 6, Eff. July 8, 1988.

R 281.922 Permit applications.

Rule 2.

(1) An application for a permit shall be made on a form prescribed and provided by the department.

(2) An application for a permit shall not be deemed as received or filed until the department has received all information requested on the application form, the application fee, and other information authorized by the act and necessary to reach a decision. The period for granting or denying an application begins as soon as all such information and the application fee are received by the department.

(3) Application fees shall be submitted to the department with the initial submittal of an application form. The fee shall be paid by check, money order, or draft made payable to: "State of Michigan."

(4) An application may be considered to be withdrawn and the file for the application may be closed if an applicant fails to respond to any written inquiry or request from the department for information requested as a part of the application form within 30 days of the request or such longer period of time as needed by the applicant to provide the information agreed to, in writing, between the applicant and the department.

(5) Upon request, the department shall provide any person with a copy of a permit application and supporting documents consistent with all provisions of Act No. 442 of the Public Acts of 1976, as amended, being S15.231 et seq. of the Michigan Compiled Laws.

(6) Decisions reached by the department which deny or modify an application for a permit shall be supported by written documentation to the applicant based upon the applicable criteria contained in section 9 of the act. The department shall create a form based on the criteria from section 9 of the act to be completed and placed into each application file. When a proposed activity involves a coordinated review by federal agencies as provided for under the act and section 404 of title IV of the clean water act of 1977, 33 U.S.C. S1344, the department shall prepare a fact sheet pursuant to 40 C.F.R. S124.8 (April 1, 1983) and 40 C.F.R. S233.39 (April 1, 1983) for inclusion in the application file.

History: 1988 MR 6, Eff. July 8, 1988.

R 281.922a Permit application review criteria.

Rule 2a.

(1) The department shall review a permit application to undertake an activity listed in section 30304 of the act according to the criteria in section 30311 of the act.

(2) As required by subsection 30311(4) of the act, a permit applicant shall bear the burden of demonstrating that an unacceptable disruption to aquatic resources will not occur as a result of the proposed activity and demonstrating either of the following:
    (a) The proposed activity is primarily dependent upon being located in the wetland.

    (b) There are no feasible and prudent alternatives to the proposed activity.

(3) A permit applicant shall provide adequate information, including documentation as required by the department, to support the demonstrations required by section 30311 of the act. The department shall independently evaluate the information provided by the applicant to determine if the applicant has made the required demonstrations.

250

(4) A permit applicant shall completely define the purpose for which the permit is sought, including all associated activities. An applicant shall not so narrowly define the purpose as to limit a complete analysis of whether an activity is primarily dependent upon being located in the wetland and of feasible and prudent alternatives. The department shall independently evaluate and determine if the project purpose has been appropriately and adequately defined by the applicant, and shall process the application based on that determination.

(5) The department shall consider a proposed activity as primarily dependent upon being located in the wetland only if the activity is the type that requires a location within the wetland and wetland conditions to fulfill its basic purpose; that is, it is wetland-dependent. Any activity that can be undertaken in a non-wetland location is not primarily dependent upon being located in the wetland.

(6) An alternative is feasible and prudent if both of the following provisions apply:

    (a) The alternative is available and capable of being done after taking into consideration cost, existing technology, and logistics.

    (b) The alternative would have less adverse impact on aquatic resources. A feasible and prudent alternative may include any or all of the following:
        (i) Use of a location other than the proposed location.
        (ii) A different configuration.
        (iii) Size.
        (iv) Method that will accomplish the basic project purpose. The applicant shall demonstrate that, given all pertinent information, there are no feasible and prudent alternatives that have less impact on aquatic resources. In making this demonstration, the applicant may provide information regarding factors such as alternative construction technologies; alternative project layout and design; local land use regulations and infrastructure; and pertinent environmental and resource issues. This list of factors is not exhaustive and no particular factor will necessarily be dispositive in any given case.

(7) If an activity is not primarily dependent upon being located in the wetland, it is presumed that a feasible and prudent alternative exists unless an applicant clearly demonstrates that a feasible and prudent alternative does not exist.

(8) Unless an applicant clearly demonstrates otherwise, it is presumed that a feasible and prudent alternative involving a non-wetland location will have less adverse impact on aquatic resources than an alternative involving a wetland location.

(9) An area not presently owned by the permit applicant that could reasonably be obtained, utilized, expanded, or managed in order to fulfill the basic purpose of the proposed activity is a feasible and prudent alternative location.

(10) An alternative may be considered feasible and prudent even if it does not accommodate components of a proposed activity that are incidental to or severable from the basic purpose of the proposed activity.

(11) An alternative may be considered feasible and prudent even if it entails higher costs or reduced profit. However, the department shall consider the reasonableness of the higher costs or reduced profit in making its determination.

(12) The department may offer a permit for a modification of an activity proposed in an application if the proposed activity cannot be permitted under the criteria listed in section 30311 of the act and if the modification makes that activity consistent with the criteria listed in section 30311 of the act.

> (a) The applicant may accept the permit for the modification of the proposed activity by signing it and returning it to the department within 30 days of the date of the offer. The permit shall be considered issued upon countersignature by the department.

> (b) The permit application is considered denied if the applicant does not sign and return the permit for the modification of the proposed activity to the department within thirty days of the date of the offer. The permit applicant may then appeal the denial pursuant to sections 30307(2) and 30319(2) of the act.

> (c) The date on which the modification is offered shall be considered the date of the department's approval or disapproval of the application pursuant to section 30307(2) of the act.

History: 2000 MR 6, Eff. Apr. 27, 2000.

R 281.923 Permits.

Rule 3.
(1) An application for a proposed activity which is within a general permit category may be processed and issued by the department without the noticing or hearings specified under sections 7, 8, and 9 of the act. The department may process, by public notice, an application which would normally qualify under a general permit category to allow more opportunity for public review and comment. Categories of minor activities will be established in the general permit in accordance with section 10 of the act. The factors set forth in sections 3 and 9 of the act shall be considered in determining whether such a permit is in the best interest of the public.

(2) Applications for activities that are not classified as minor shall be reviewed through the process prescribed under sections 7, 8, and 9 of the act. The department may issue an individual permit 21 days after the mailing of notification of the permit application if comments of nonobjection have been received from the municipality, if a public hearing has not been requested, and if the proposed activities are otherwise in accordance with the act.

(3) If the department does not approve or disapprove the permit application within the time provided by section 8(2) of the act, the permit application shall be considered approved and the department shall be considered to have made the determination required by section 9 of the act.

(4) When a project involves activities regulated under Act No. 247 of the Public Acts of 1955, as amended, being S322.701 et seq. of the Michigan Compiled Laws, or Act No. 346 of the Public Acts of 1972, as amended, being S281.951 et seq. of the Michigan Compiled Laws, or the act, the applicant shall submit 1 application for all activities regulated under these acts. Only 1 permit for these activities will be issued or denied by applying the criteria of the appropriate acts. If a permit is issued, conditions shall reflect the requirements of all appropriate acts.

(5) A permit may be issued for a period extending until the end of the following calendar year. A permit may be issued for a longer period of time if agreed to, in writing, between the applicant and the department. Before a permit expires, extensions of time may be granted by the department upon receipt of a written request from the permit holder explaining why such an extension is needed to complete the project. Up to two 12-month extensions shall be granted if there is no change in the activity for which the permit was originally issued. Administrative fees shall not be required for such extensions.

(6) Any permit issued under the act does not obviate the necessity of receiving, when applicable, approval from other federal, state, and local government agencies.

(7) Any permit issued by the department under the act may be revoked or suspended, after notice and an opportunity for a hearing, for any of the following causes:

> (a) A violation of a condition of the permit.

> (b) Obtaining a permit by misrepresentation or failure to fully disclose relevant facts in the application.

> (c) A change in a condition that requires a temporary or permanent change in the activity.

History: 1988 MR 6, Eff. July 8, 1988.

R 281.924 Wetland Assessments.

Rule 4.
(1) When performing wetland assessments, as required by section 30321 of Act No. 451 of The Public Acts of 1994, as amended, being §324.30321 of the Michigan Compiled Laws, the department shall utilize criteria consistent with the definition of "wetland" provided in section 30301(d) of Act No. 451 of the Public Acts of 1994, as amended, being §324.30321(d) of the Michigan Compiled Laws, and shall provide a written wetland assessment report to the person who owns or leases the property or his or her agent within 30 days of the on-site evaluation, whether the parcel contains wetland or nonwetland, or both, and the basis for the determination. The department shall assess a parcel or any portion of a parcel as identified by the person making the request.

(2) When performing wetland assessments, the department shall rely on visible evidence that the normal seasonal frequency and duration of water is above, at, or near the surface of the area to verify the existence of a wetland. Under normal circumstances, the frequency and duration of water that is necessary to determine an area to be a wetland will be reflected in the vegetation or aquatic life present within the area being considered. A wetland that has not been recently or severely disturbed will contain a predominance, not just an occurrence, of wetland vegetation or aquatic life. If there is a predominance of wetland vegetation, and if there is no direct visible evidence that water is, or has been, at or above the surface, then the department shall use the following characteristics of the soils or substrate to verify the existence of a wetland:

    (a) The presence of a soil that is saturated, flooded, or ponded long enough during the growing season to develop anaerobic conditions in the upper part of the soil that favor the growth and regeneration of wetland vegetation.

    (b) Physical or chemical characteristics of a soil column that provide evidence of the current and recent degree of saturation or inundation. Characteristics, such as a gleyed or low chroma matrix, mottling, or chemically demonstrated anaerobic conditions, can beutilized to identify the current and recent depth and fluctuation of the water table or inundation.

(3) If the department makes a determination that a wetland otherwise outside of the jurisdiction of the act is essential to the preservation of the natural resources of the state under section 30301(d)(iii) of Act No. 451 of the Public Acts of 1994, as amended, being §324.30321(d)(iii) of the Michigan Compiled Laws, the department shall provide the findings, in writing, to the legal landowner or lessee stating the reasons for the determination. In making the determination, the department must find that 1 or more of the following functions apply to a particular site:

    (a) It supports state or federal endangered or threatened plants, fish, or wildlife specified in section 36501 of Act No. 457 of the Public Acts of 1994, as amended, being §324.36501 of the Michigan Compiled Laws.

    (b) It represents what the state has identified as a rare or unique ecosystem.

    (c) It supports plants or animals of an identified regional importance.

    (d) It provides groundwater recharge documented by a public agency.

(4) Upon the request of a person who owns or leases a parcel of property or his or her agent, the department shall determine if there is no surface or groundwater connection that meets the definition of "contiguous" under R281.921(l)(b)(iii). The department shall make the determination in writing and shall provide the determination to the person making the request within a reasonable period of time after receipt of the request.

(5)   (1) A person who requests a wetland assessment shall submit a form provided by the department. The form shall contain all information required under section 30321(3) of Act No. 451 of the Public Acts of 1994, as amended, being §324.30321(3) of the Michigan Compiled Laws, and shall be accompanied by a check for the appropriate fee as set forth in this rule.

    (2) All fees are nonrefundable.

    (3) A person who owns or leases a parcel of property or his or her agent may request any of the following 3 levels of wetland assessment with corresponding levels of fees:

    (a) For a fee of $50.00, the department will provide copies of wetland information immediately available for an identified area, including state and federal maps on file with the department that show the approximate location of wetlands on the parcel. In addition, information specified by section 30321(e), (f), and (g) of Act No. 451 of the Public Acts of 1994, as amended, being §324.30321(e), (f), and (g) of the Michigan Compiled Laws, regarding regulatory processes, limitations, and appeals will be provided to a person who makes a request. Since the information and maps provided will not be based upon an on-site review, they will be useful for planning purposes, but the department will not certify where wetlands are and are not specifically located on the given parcel.

    (b) For a fee of $200.00 for 1 acre or less, the department will perform an on-site assessment of a parcel or portion of a parcel that has its boundaries marked by the person who makes the request, to identify and describe areas that are and are not wetland on the site, unless identification and description are not possible under the conditions of the site, as outlined under (4), below. The fee for the service will increase by $50.00 per acre for an assessment area larger than 1 acre. If the assessment report determines that the area assessed or part of the area assessed is not wetland, then the report will state that the department lacks jurisdiction over the area that is not wetland, if any, and that the determination that an area is not wetland is binding on the department for 3 years from the date of the assessment.

    (c) For a fee of $150.00 for 1 acre or less, the department will perform an on-site review of a mapped, flagged, and other wise identifiable area to confirm specific boundaries established by a professional wetland consultant between wetlands and areas that are not wetlands. The fee for the service will increase by $15.00 per acre for larger parcels. The wetland and nonwetland boundaries delineated must be flagged by a wetland consultant representing the person who made the request. The boundaries must have been established utilizing methods and procedures consistent with Act No. 451 of the Public Acts of 1994, as amended, being §324.30319 et seq. of the Michigan Compiled Laws and these rules. If the department finds substantial errors during the confirmation process and the person making the request wishes to proceed, then the department will require that a new delineation by a consultant representing the person who made the request be completed and that new fees in the amount of 1/2 of the original fee be submitted for the on-site confirmation of the new delineation and the assessment report. If the assessment report determines that the area assessed or part of the area assessed is not wetland, then the report will state that the department lacks jurisdiction over the area that is not wetland and that the determination that an area is not wetland is binding on the department for 3 years from the date of the assessment. If documentation of the specific boundary is desired, then the person who is making the request will provide, for department approval, an acceptable and reproducible survey of the agreed upon boundaries.

(4) If recent severe disturbances of the site have occurred, for example, removal of native vegetation, disturbance of soils, or diversion of drainage, making it impossible during a routine site visit to determine whether or not the area requested for assessment contains or has contained wetland or nonwetland, then the department will provide the person who made the request with a report that specifies the reasons for its inability to make a determination. The department will include with the report a description of the necessary technical information to be provided by the person who made the request in order for the department to make a final assessment or confirm a delineated boundary.

History: 1988 MR 6, Eff. July 8, 1988; 1998 MR 7, Eff. July 18, 1998.

R 281.925 Mitigation.
Rule 5.
(1) As authorized by section 30312(2) of the act, the department may impose conditions on a permit for a use or development if the conditions are designed to remove an impairment to the wetland benefits, to mitigate the impact of a discharge of fill material, or to otherwise improve the water quality.

(2) The department shall consider mitigation only after all of the following conditions are met:

(a) The wetland impacts are otherwise permittable under sections 30302 and 30311 of the act.

(b) No feasible and prudent alternative to avoid wetland impacts exists.

(c) An applicant has used all practical means to minimize impacts to wetlands. This may include the permanent protection of wetlands on the site not directly impacted by the proposed activity.

(3) The department shall require mitigation as a condition of a wetland permit issued under part 303 of the act, except as follows:

(a) The department may waive the mitigation condition if either of the following provisions applies:
(i) The permitted wetland impact is less than 1/3 of an acre and no reasonable opportunity for mitigation exists.
(ii) The basic purpose of the permitted activity is to create or restore wetlands or to increase wetland habitat.

(b) If an activity is authorized and permitted under the authority of a general permit issued under section 30312(1) of the act, then the department shall not require mitigation. Public transportation agencies may provide mitigation for projects authorized under a general permit at sites approved by the department under a memorandum of understanding between the department and public transportation agencies.

(4) The department shall require mitigation to compensate for unavoidable wetland impacts permitted under part 303 of the act utilizing one or more of the following methods:

253

(a) The restoration of previously existing wetlands.

(b) The creation of new wetlands.

(c) The acquisition of approved credits from a wetland mitigation bank established under R 281.951 et seq.

(d) In certain circumstances, the preservation of existing wetlands. The preservation of existing wetlands may be considered as mitigation only if the department determines that all of the following conditions are met:
(i) The wetlands to be preserved perform exceptional physical or biological functions that are essential to the preservation of the natural resources of the state or the preserved wetlands are an ecological type that is rare or endangered.
(ii) The wetlands to be preserved are under a demonstrable threat of loss or substantial degradation due to human activities that are not under the control of the applicant and that are not otherwise restricted by state law.
(iii) The preservation of the wetlands as mitigation will ensure the permanent protection of the wetlands that would otherwise be lost or substantially degraded.

(5) The restoration of previously existing wetlands is preferred over the creation of new wetlands where none previously existed. Enhancement of existing wetlands is not considered mitigation. For purposes of this rule, wetland restoration means the reestablishment of wetland characteristics and functions at a site where they have ceased to exist through the replacement of wetland hydrology, vegetation, or soils.

(6) An applicant shall submit a mitigation plan when requested by the department. The department may incorporate all or part of the proposed mitigation plan as permit conditions. The mitigation plan shall include all of the following elements:

(a) A statement of mitigation goals and objectives, including the wetland types to be restored, created, or preserved.

(b) Information regarding the mitigation site location and ownership.

(c) A site development plan.

(d) A description of baseline conditions at the proposed mitigation site, including a vicinity map showing all existing rivers, lakes, and streams, and a delineation of existing surface waters and wetlands within the proposed mitigation area.

(e) Performance standards to evaluate the mitigation.

(f) A monitoring plan.

(g) A schedule for completion of the mitigation.

(h) Provisions for the management and long-term protection of the site. The department shall, when requested by the applicant, meet with the applicant to review the applicant's mitigation plan.

(7) An applicant shall provide mitigation to assure that, upon completion, there will be no net loss of wetlands. The mitigation shall meet the following criteria as determined by the department:

(a) Mitigation shall be provided on-site where it is practical to mitigate on site and where beneficial to the wetland resources.

(b) If subdivision (a) of this subrule does not apply, then an applicant shall provide mitigation in the immediate vicinity of the permitted activity if practical and beneficial to the wetland resources. "Immediate vicinity" means within the same watershed as the location of the proposed project. For purposes of this rule, a watershed refers to a drainage area in which the permitted activity occurs where it may be possible to restore certain wetland functions, including hydrologic, water quality, and aquatic habitat functions. Watershed boundaries are shown in Figure 1 in R 281.951.

(c) Mitigation shall be on-site or in the immediate vicinity of the permitted activity unless the department determines that subdivisions (a) and (b) of this subrule are infeasible and impractical.

(d) The department shall require that mitigation be of a similar ecological type as the impacted wetland where feasible and practical.

(e) If the replacement wetland is of a similar ecological type as the impacted wetland, then the department shall require that the ratio of acres of wetland mitigation provided for each acre of permitted wetland loss shall be as follows:
    (i) Restoration or creation of 5.0 acres of mitigation for 1.0 acre of permitted impact on wetland types that are rare or imperiled on a statewide basis.
    (ii) Restoration or creation of 2.0 acres of mitigation for 1.0 acre of permitted impact on forested wetland types, coastal wetlands not included under (i) of this subdivision, and wetlands that border upon inland lakes.
    (iii) Restoration or creation of 1.5 acres of mitigation for 1.0 acre of permitted impact on all other wetland types.
    (iv) 10 acres of mitigation for 1.0 acre of impact in situations where the mitigation is in the form of preservation of existing wetland as defined in subrule (4) of this rule.

(f) The department may adjust the ratios prescribed by this rule as follows:
    (i) The ratio may be increased if the replacement wetland is of a different ecological type than the impacted wetland.
    (ii) If the department determines that an adjustment would be beneficial to the wetland resources due to factors specific to the mitigation site or the site of the proposed activity, then the department may increase or decrease the number of acres of mitigation to be provided by no more than 20 percent. This shall not limit the amount which a ratio may be increased under subdivision (f)(i) of this subrule.

254

(g) The mitigation shall give consideration to replacement of the predominant wetland benefits lost within the impacted wetland.

(h) The department shall double the required ratios if a permit is issued for an application accepted under section 30306(5) of the act.

(i) The department shall determine mitigation ratios for wetland dependent activities on a site-specific basis.

(8) Except where mitigation is to occur on state or federally owned property or where the mitigation is to occur in the same municipality where the project is proposed, the department shall give notice to the municipality where the proposed mitigation site is located and shall provide an opportunity to comment in writing to the department on the proposed mitigation plan before a mitigation plan is approved by the department.

(9) An applicant shall complete mitigation activities before initiating other permitted activities, unless a concurrent schedule is agreed upon between the department and the applicant, and an adequate financial assurance mechanism is provided by the applicant.

(10) The department may require financial assurances to ensure that mitigation is accomplished as specified.

(11) An applicant shall protect the mitigation area by a permanent conservation easement or similar instrument that provides for the permanent protection of the natural resource functions and values of the mitigation site, unless the department determines that such controls are impractical to impose in conjunction with mitigation that was undertaken as part of state funded response activity under Act No. 451 of the Public Acts of 1994, as amended.

(12) An applicant, with the approval of the department, may provide all or a portion of the mitigation through the acquisition of approved credits from a wetland mitigation bank established under R 281.951 et seq. One credit shall be utilized for each acre of mitigation required under subrule (7) of this rule.

History: 1988 MR 6, Eff. July 8, 1988; 2000 MR 6, Eff. Apr. 27, 2000.

Note to readers: updated versions of this document can be found at http://www.michigan.gov/deq

APPENDIX F: Federal 404 (b)(1) Guidelines

PART 230 SECTION 404(b)(1) GUIDELINES FOR
SPECIFICATION OF DISPOSAL SITES FOR DREDGED OR FILL MATERIAL
SUBPART A. GENERAL

230.1 Purpose and policy.
230.2 Applicability.
230.3 Definitions.
230.4 Organization.
230.5 General procedures to be followed.
230.6 Adaptability.
230.7 General permits.

230.1 Purpose and policy.
(a) The purpose of these Guidelines is to restore and maintain the chemical, physical, and biological integrity of waters of the United States through the control of discharges of dredged or fill material.

(b) Congress has expressed a number of policies in the Clean Water Act. These Guidelines are intended to be consistent with and to implement those policies.

(c) Fundamental to these Guidelines is the precept that dredged or fill material should not be discharged into the aquatic ecosystem, unless it can be demonstrated that such a discharge will not have an unacceptable adverse impact either individually or in combination with known and/or probable impacts of other activities affecting the ecosystems of concern.

(d) From a national perspective, the degradation or destruction of special aquatic sites, such as filling operations in wetlands, is considered to be among the most severe environmental impacts covered by these Guidelines. The guiding principle should be that degradation or destruction of special sites may represent an irreversible loss of valuable aquatic resources.

255

230.2 Applicability.
(a) These Guidelines have been developed by the Administrator of the Environmental Protection Agency in conjunction with the Secretary of the Army acting through the Chief of Engineers under section 404(b)(1) of the Clean Water Act (33 U.S.C. 1344). The Guidelines are applicable to the specification of disposal sites for discharges of dredged or fill material into waters of the United States. Sites may be specified through:

> (1) The regulatory program of the U.S. Army Corps of Engineers under sections 404(a) and (e) of the Act (see 33 CFR Parts 320, 323 and 325);

> (2) The civil works program of the U.S. Army Corps of Engineers (see 33 CFR 209.145 and section 150 of Pub. L. 94-587, Water Resources Development Act of 1976);

> (3) Permit programs of States approved by the Administrator of the Environmental Protection Agency in accordance with section 404(g) and (h) of the Act (see 40 CFR parts 122, 123 and 124);

> (4) Statewide dredged or fill material regulatory programs with best management practices approved under section 208(b)(4)(B) and (C) of the Act (see 40 CFR 35.1560);

> (5) Federal construction projects which meet criteria specified in section 404(r) of the Act.

(b) These Guidelines will be applied in the review of proposed discharges of dredged or fill material into navigable waters which lie inside the baseline from which the territorial sea is measured, and the discharge of fill material into the territorial sea, pursuant to the procedures referred to in paragraphs (a)(1) and (2) of this section. The discharge of dredged material into the territorial sea is governed by the Marine Protection, Research, and Sanctuaries Act of 1972, Pub. L. 92-532, and regulations and criteria issued pursuant thereto (40 CFR parts 220 through 228).

(c) Guidance on interpreting and implementing these Guidelines may be prepared jointly by EPA and the Corps at the national or regional level from time to time. No modifications to the basic application, meaning, or intent of these Guidelines will be made without rulemaking by the Administrator under the Administrative Procedure Act (5 U.S.C. 551 et seq.).

230.3 Definitions.
For purposes of this part, the following terms shall have the meanings indicated:

(a) The term *Act* means the Clean Water Act (also known as the Federal Water Pollution Control Act or FWPCA) Pub. L. 92-500, as amended by Pub. L. 95-217, 33 U.S.C. 1251, et seq.

(b) The term *adjacent* means bordering, contiguous, or neighboring. Wetlands separated from other waters of the United States by man-made dikes or barriers, natural river berms, beach dunes, and the like are "adjacent wetlands."

(c) The terms *aquatic environment* and *aquatic ecosystem* mean waters of the United States, including wetlands, that serve as habitat for interrelated and interacting communities and populations of plants and animals.

(d) The term *carrier of contaminant* means dredged or fill material that contains contaminants.

(e) The term *contaminant* means a chemical or biological substance in a form that can be incorporated into, onto or be ingested by and that harms aquatic organisms, consumers of aquatic organisms, or users of the aquatic environment, and includes but is not limited to the substances on the 307(a)(1) list of toxic pollutants promulgated on January 31, 1978 (43 FR 4109).

(f) [Reserved]

(g) [Reserved]

(h) The term *discharge point* means the point within the disposal site at which the dredged or fill material is released.

(i) The term *disposal site* means that portion of the "waters of the United States" where specific disposal activities are permitted and consist of a bottom surface area and any overlying volume of water. In the case of wetlands on which surface water is not present, the disposal site consists of the wetland surface area.

(j) [Reserved]

(k) The term *extraction site* means the place from which the dredged or fill material proposed for discharge is to be removed.

(l) [Reserved]

(m) The term *mixing zone* means a limited volume of water serving as a zone of initial dilution in the immediate vicinity of a discharge point where receiving water quality may not meet quality standards or other requirements otherwise applicable to the receiving water. The mixing zone should be considered as a place where wastes and water mix and not as a place where effluents are treated.

(n) The term *permitting authority* means the District Engineer of the U.S. Army Corps of Engineers or such other individual as may be designated by the Secretary of the Army to issue or deny permits under section 404 of the Act; or the State Director of a permit program approved by EPA under section 404(g) and section 404(h) or his delegated representative.

(o) The term *pollutant* means dredged spoil, solid waste, incinerator residue, sewage, garbage, sewage sludge, munitions, chemical wastes, biological materials, radioactive materials not covered by the Atomic Energy Act, heat, wrecked or discarded equipment, rock, sand, cellar dirt, and industrial, municipal, and agricultural waste discharged into water. The legislative history of the Act reflects that "radioactive materials" as included within the definition of "pollutant" in section 502 of the Act means only radioactive materials which are not encompassed in the definition of source, byproduct, or special nuclear materials as defined by the Atomic Energy Act of 1954, as amended, and regulated under the Atomic Energy Act. Examples of radioactive materials not covered by the Atomic Energy Act and, therefore, included within the term "pollutant", are radium and accelerator produced isotopes. See Train v. Colorado Public Interest Research Group, Inc., 426 U.S. 1 (1976).

256

(p) The term *pollution* means the man-made or man-induced alteration of the chemical, physical, biological or radiological integrity of an aquatic ecosystem.

(q) The term *practicable* means available and capable of being done after taking into consideration cost, existing technology, and logistics in light of overall project purposes.

(q-1) *Special aquatic sites* means those sites identified in subpart E. They are geographic areas, large or small, possessing special ecological characteristics of productivity, habitat, wildlife protection, or other important and easily disrupted ecological values. These areas are generally recognized as significantly influencing or positively contributing to the general overall environmental health or vitality of the entire ecosystem of a region. (See section 230.10(a)(3))

(r) The term *territorial sea* means the belt of the sea measured from the baseline as determined in accordance with the Convention on the Territorial Sea and the Contiguous Zone and extending seaward a distance of three miles.

(s) The term *waters of the United States* means:

(1) All waters which are currently used, or were used in the past, or may be susceptible to use in interstate or foreign commerce, including all waters which are subject to the ebb and flow of the tide;

(2) All interstate waters including interstate wetlands;

(3) All other waters such as intrastate lakes, rivers, streams (including intermittent streams), mudflats, sandflats, wetlands, sloughs, prairie potholes, wet meadows, playa lakes, or natural ponds, the use, degradation or destruction of which could affect interstate or foreign commerce including any such waters:

(i) Which are or could be used by interstate or foreign travelers for recreational or other purposes; or

(ii) From which fish or shellfish are or could be taken and sold in interstate or foreign commerce; or

(iii) Which are used or could be used for industrial purposes by industries in interstate commerce;

(4) All impoundments of waters otherwise defined as waters of the United States under this definition;

(5) Tributaries of waters identified in paragraphs (s)(1) through (4) of this section;

(6) The territorial sea;

(7) Wetlands adjacent to waters (other than waters that are themselves wetlands) identified in paragraphs (s)(1) through (6) of this section; waste treatment systems, including treatment ponds or lagoons designed to meet the requirements of CWA (other than cooling ponds as defined in 40 CFR 423.11(m) which also meet the criteria of this definition) are not waters of the United States. Waters of the United States do not include prior converted cropland. Notwithstanding the determination of an area's status as prior converted cropland by any other federal agency, for the purposes of the Clean Water Act, the final authority regarding Clean Water Act jurisdiction remains with EPA.

(t) The term *wetlands* means those areas that are inundated or saturated by surface or ground water at a frequency and duration sufficient to support, and that under normal circumstances do support, a prevalence of vegetation typically adapted for life in saturated soil conditions. Wetlands generally include swamps, marshes, bogs and similar areas.

[45 FR 85344, Dec. 24, 1980, as amended at 58 FR 45037, Aug. 25, 1993]

230.4 Organization.
The Guidelines are divided into eight subparts. Subpart A presents those provisions of general applicability, such as purpose and definitions. Subpart B establishes the four conditions which must be satisfied in order to make a finding that a proposed discharge of dredged or fill material complies with the Guidelines. Section 230.11 of subpart B, sets forth factual determinations which are to be considered in determining whether or not a proposed discharge satisfies the subpart B conditions of compliance. Subpart C describes the physical and chemical components of a site and provides guidance as to how proposed discharges of dredged or fill material may affect these components. Subparts D through F detail the special characteristics of particular aquatic ecosystems in terms of their values, and the possible loss of these values due to discharges of dredged or fill material. Subpart G prescribes a number of physical, chemical, and biological evaluations and testing procedures to be used in reaching the required factual determinations. Subpart H details the means to prevent or mimimize adverse effects. Subpart I concerns advanced identification of disposal areas.

230.5 General procedures to be followed.
In evaluating whether a particular discharge site may be specified, the permitting authority should use these Guidelines in the following sequence:

(a) In order to obtain an overview of the principal regulatory provisions of the Guidelines, review the restrictions on discharge in section 230.10(a) through (d), the measures to mimimize adverse impact of subpart H, and the required factual determinations of section 230.11.

(b) Determine if a General permit (section 230.7) is applicable; if so, the applicant needs merely to comply with its terms, and no further action by the permitting authority is necessary. Special conditions for evaluation of proposed General permits are contained in section 230.7. If the discharge is not covered by a General permit:

(c) Examine practicable alternatives to the proposed discharge, that is, not discharging into the waters of the U.S. or discharging into an alternative aquatic site with potentially less damaging consequences (section 230.10(a)).

257

(d) Delineate the candidate disposal site consistent with the criteria and evaluations of section 230.11(f).

(e) Evaluate the various physical and chemical components which characterize the non-living environment of the candidate site, the substrate and the water including its dynamic characteristics (subpart C).

(f) Identify and evaluate any special or critical characteristics of the candidate disposal site, and surrounding areas which might be affected by use of such site, related to their living communities or human uses (subparts D, E, and F).

(g) Review Factual Determinations in section 230.11 to determine whether the information in the project file is sufficient to provide the documentation required by section 230.11 or to perform the pre-testing evaluation described in section 230.60, or other information is necessary.

(h) Evaluate the material to be discharged to determine the possibility of chemical contamination or physical incompatibility of the material to be discharged (section 230.60).

(i) If there is a reasonable probability of chemical contamination, conduct the appropriate tests according to the section on Evaluation and Testing (section 230.61).

(j) Identify appropriate and practicable changes to the project plan to minimize the environmental impact of the discharge, based upon the specialized methods of minimization of impacts in subpart H.

(k) Make and document Factual Determinations in section 230.11.

(l) Make and document Findings of Compliance (section 230.12) by comparing Factual Determinations with the requirements for discharge of section 230.10.

This outline of the steps to follow in using the Guidelines is simplified for purposes of illustration. The actual process followed may be iterative, with the results of one step leading to a reexamination of previous steps. The permitting authority must address all of the relevant provisions of the Guidelines in reaching a Finding of Compliance in an individual case.

230.6 Adaptability.
(a) The manner in which these Guidelines are used depends on the physical, biological, and chemical nature of the proposed extraction site, the material to be discharged, and the candidate disposal site, including any other important components of the ecosystem being evaluated. Documentation to demonstrate knowledge about the extraction site, materials to be extracted, and the candidate disposal site is an essential component of guideline application. These Guidelines allow evaluation and documentation for a variety of activities, ranging from those with large, complex impacts on the aquatic environment to those for which the impact is likely to be innocuous. It is unlikely that the Guidelines will apply in their entirety to any one activity, no matter how complex. It is anticipated that substantial numbers of permit applications will be for minor, routine activities that have little, if any, potential for significant degradation of the aquatic environment. It generally is not intended or expected that extensive testing, evaluation or analysis will be needed to make findings of compliance in such routine cases.

Where the conditions for General permits are met, and where numerous applications for similar activities are likely, the use of General permits will eliminate repetitive evaluation and documentation for individual discharges.

(b) The Guidelines user, including the agency or agencies responsible for implementing the Guidelines, must recognize the different levels of effort that should be associated with varying degrees of impact and require or prepare commensurate documentation. The level of documentation should reflect the significance and complexity of the discharge activity.

(c) An essential part of the evaluation process involves making determinations as to the relevance of any portion(s) of the Guidelines and conducting further evaluation only as needed. However, where portions of the Guidelines review procedure are "short form" evaluations, there still must be sufficient information (including consideration of both individual and cumulative impacts) to support the decision of whether to specify the site for disposal of dredged or fill material and to support the decision to curtail or abbreviate the evaluation process. The presumption against the discharge in 230.1 applies to this decision-making.

(d) In the case of activities covered by General permits or section 208(b)(4)(B) and (C) Best Management Practices, the analysis and documentation required by the Guidelines will be performed at the time of General permit issuance or section 208(b)(4)(B) and (C) Best Management Practices promulgation and will not be repeated when activities are conducted under a General permit or section 208(b)(4)(B) and (C) Best Management Practices control. These Guidelines do not require reporting or formal written communication at the time individual activities are initiated under a General permit or section 208(b)(4)(B) and (C) Best Management Practices. However, a particular General permit may require appropriate reporting.

230.7 General permits.
(a) *Conditions for the issuance of General permits.* A General permit for a category of activities involving the discharge of dredged or fill material complies with the Guidelines if it meets the applicable restrictions on the discharge in section 230.10 and if the permitting authority determines that:

(1) The activities in such category are similar in nature and similar in their impact upon water quality and the aquatic environment;

(2) The activities in such category will have only minimal adverse effects when performed separately; and

(3) The activities in such category will have only minimal cumulative adverse effects on water quality and the aquatic environment.

(b) *Evaluation process.* To reach the determinations required in paragraph (a) of this section, the permitting authority shall set forth in writing an evaluation of the potential individual and cumulative impacts of the category of activities to be regulated under the General permit. While some of the information necessary for this evaluation can be obtained from potential permittees and others through the proposal of General permits for public review, the evaluation must be completed before any General permit is issued, and the results must be published with the final permit.

(1) This evaluation shall be based upon consideration of the prohibitions listed in section 230.10(b) and the factors listed in section 230.10(c), and shall include documented information supporting each factual determination in section 230.11 of the Guidelines (consideration of alternatives in section 230.10(a) are not directly applicable to General permits);

(2) The evaluation shall include a precise description of the activities to be permitted under the General permit, explaining why they are sufficiently similar in nature and in environmental impact to warrant regulation under a single General permit based on subparts C through F of the Guidelines. Allowable differences between activities which will be regulated under the same General permit shall be specified. Activities otherwise similar in nature may differ in environmental impact due to their location in or near ecologically sensitive areas, areas with unique chemical or physical characteristics, areas containing concentrations of toxic substances, or areas regulated for specific human uses or by specific land or water management plans (e.g., areas regulated under an approved Coastal Zone Management Plan). If there are specific geographic areas within the purview of a proposed General permit (called a draft General permit under a State 404 program), which are more appropriately regulated by individual permit due to the considerations cited in this paragraph, they shall be clearly delineated in the evaluation and excluded from the permit. In addition, the permitting authority may require an individual permit for any proposed activity under a General permit where the nature or location of the activity makes an individual permit more appropriate.

(3) To predict cumulative effects, the evaluation shall include the number of individual discharge activities likely to be regulated under a General permit until its expiration, including repetitions of individual discharge activities at a single location.

SUBPART B. COMPLIANCE WITH THE GUIDELINES

230.10 Restrictions on discharge.
230.11 Factual determinations.
230.12 Findings of compliance or non-compliance with the restrictions on discharge.

230.10 Restrictions on discharge.
Note: Because other laws may apply to particular discharges and because the Corps of Engineers or State 404 agency may have additional procedural and substantive requirements, a discharge complying with the requirement of these Guidelines will not automatically receive a permit.

Although all requirements in section 230.10 must be met, the compliance evaluation procedures will vary to reflect the seriousness of the potential for adverse impacts on the aquatic ecosystems posed by specific dredged or fill material discharge activities.

(a) Except as provided under section 404(b)(2), no discharge of dredged or fill material shall be permitted if there is a practicable alternative to the proposed discharge which would have less adverse impact on the aquatic ecosystem, so long as the alternative does not have other significant adverse environmental consequences.

(1) For the purpose of this requirement, practicable alternatives include, but are not limited to:

(i) Activities which do not involve a discharge of dredged or fill material into the waters of the United States or ocean waters;

(ii) Discharges of dredged or fill material at other locations in waters of the United States or ocean waters;

(2) An alternative is practicable if it is available and capable of being done after taking into consideration cost, existing technology, and logistics in light of overall project purposes. If it is otherwise a practicable alternative, an area not presently owned by the applicant which could reasonably be obtained, utilized, expanded or managed in order to fulfill the basic purpose of the proposed activity may be considered.

(3) Where the activity associated with a discharge which is proposed for a special aquatic site (as defined in subpart E) does not require access or proximity to or siting within the special aquatic site in question to fulfill its basic purpose (i.e., is not "water dependent"), practicable alternatives that do not involve special aquatic sites are presumed to be available, unless clearly demonstrated otherwise. In addition, where a discharge is proposed for a special aquatic site, all practicable alternatives to the proposed discharge which do not involve a discharge into a special aquatic site are presumed to have less adverse impact on the aquatic ecosystem, unless clearly demonstrated otherwise.

(4) For actions subject to NEPA, where the Corps of Engineers is the permitting agency, the analysis of alternatives required for NEPA environmental documents, including supplemental Corps NEPA documents, will in most cases provide the information for the evaluation of alternatives under these Guidelines. On occasion, these NEPA documents may address a broader range of alternatives than required to be considered under this paragraph or may not have considered the alternatives in sufficient detail to respond to the requirements of these Guidelines. In the latter case, it may be necessary to supplement these NEPA documents with this additional information.

(5) To the extent that practicable alternatives have been identified and evaluated under a Coastal Zone Management program, a section 208 program, or other planning process, such evaluation shall be considered by the permitting authority as part of the consideration of alternatives under the Guidelines. Where such evaluation is less complete than that contemplated under this subsection, it must be supplemented accordingly.

(b) No discharge of dredged or fill material shall be permitted if it:

(1) Causes or contributes, after consideration of disposal site dilution and dispersion, to violations of any applicable State water quality standard;

(2) Violates any applicable toxic effluent standard or prohibition under section 307 of the Act;

(3) Jeopardizes the continued existence of species listed as endangered or threatened under the Endangered Species Act of 1973, as amended, or results in likelihood of the destruction or adverse modification of a habitat which is determined by the Secretary of Interior or Commerce, as appropriate, to be a critical habitat under the Endangered Species Act of 1973, as amended. If an exemption has been granted by the Endangered Species Committee, the terms of such exemption shall apply in lieu of this subparagraph;

259

(4) Violates any requirement imposed by the Secretary of Commerce to protect any marine sanctuary designated under title III of the Marine Protection, Research, and Sanctuaries Act of 1972.

(c) Except as provided under section 404(b)(2), no discharge of dredged or fill material shall be permitted which will cause or contribute to significant degradation of the waters of the United States. Findings of significant degradation related to the proposed discharge shall be based upon appropriate factual determinations, evaluations, and tests required by subparts B and G, after consideration of subparts C through F, with special emphasis on the persistence and permanence of the effects outlined in those subparts. Under these Guidelines, effects contributing to significant degradation considered individually or collectively, include:

(1) Significantly adverse effects of the discharge of pollutants on human health or welfare, including but not limited to effects on municipal water supplies, plankton, fish, shellfish, wildlife, and special aquatic sites;

(2) Significantly adverse effects of the discharge of pollutants on life stages of aquatic life and other wildlife dependent on aquatic ecosystems, including the transfer, concentration, and spread of pollutants or their byproducts outside of the disposal site through biological, physical, and chemical processes;

(3) Significantly adverse effects of the discharge of pollutants on aquatic ecosystem diversity, productivity, and stability. Such effects may include, but are not limited to, loss of fish and wildlife habitat or loss of the capacity of a wetland to assimilate nutrients, purify water, or reduce wave energy; or

(4) Significantly adverse effects of discharge of pollutants on recreational, aesthetic, and economic values.

(d) Except as provided under section 404(b)(2), no discharge of dredged or fill material shall be permitted unless appropriate and practicable steps have been taken which will minimize potential adverse impacts of the discharge on the aquatic ecosystem. Subpart H identifies such possible steps.

230.11 Factual determinations.

The permitting authority shall determine in writing the potential short-term or long-term effects of a proposed discharge of dredged or fill material on the physical, chemical, and biological components of the aquatic environment in light of subparts C through F. Such factual determinations shall be used in section 230.12 in making findings of compliance or non-compliance with the restrictions on discharge in section 230.10. The evaluation and testing procedures described in section 230.60 and section 230.61 of subpart G shall be used as necessary to make, and shall be described in, such determination. The determinations of effects of each proposed discharge shall include the following:

(a) *Physical substrate determinations.* Determine the nature and degree of effect that the proposed discharge will have, individually and cumulatively, on the characteristics of the substrate at the proposed disposal site. Consideration shall be given to the similarity in particle size, shape, and degree of compaction of the material proposed for discharge and the material constituting the substrate at the disposal site, and any potential changes in substrate elevation and bottom contours, including changes outside of the disposal site which may occur as a result of erosion, slumpage, or other movement of the discharged material. The duration and physical extent of substrate changes shall also be considered. The possible loss of environmental values (section 230.20) and actions to minimize impact (subpart H) shall also be considered in making these determinations. Potential changes in substrate elevation and bottom contours shall be predicted on the basis of the proposed method, volume, location, and rate of discharge, as well as on the individual and combined effects of current patterns, water circulation, wind and wave action, and other physical factors that may affect the movement of the discharged material.

(b) *Water circulation, fluctuation, and salinity determinations.* Determine the nature and degree of effect that the proposed discharge will have individually and cumulatively on water, current patterns, circulation including downstream flows, and normal water fluctuation. Consideration shall be given to water chemistry, salinity, clarity, color, odor, taste, dissolved gas levels, temperature, nutrients, and eutrophication plus other appropriate characteristics. Consideration shall also be given to the potential diversion or obstruction of flow, alterations of bottom contours, or other significant changes in the hydrologic regime. Additional consideration of the possible loss of environmental values (sections 230.23 through 230.25) and actions to minimize impacts (subpart H), shall be used in making these determinations. Potential significant effects on the current patterns, water circulation, normal water fluctuation and salinity shall be evaluated on the basis of the proposed method, volume, location, and rate of discharge.

(c) *Suspended particulate/turbidity determinations.* Determine the nature and degree of effect that the proposed discharge will have, individually and cumulatively, in terms of potential changes in the kinds and concentrations of suspended particulate/turbidity in the vicinity of the disposal site. Consideration shall be given to the grain size of the material proposed for discharge, the shape and size of the plume of suspended particulates, the duration of the discharge and resulting plume and whether or not the potential changes will cause violations of applicable water quality standards. Consideration should also be given to the possible loss of environmental values (section 230.21) and to actions for minimizing impacts (subpart H). Consideration shall include the proposed method, volume, location, and rate of discharge, as well as the individual and combined effects of current patterns, water circulation and fluctuations, wind and wave action, and other physical factors on the movement of suspended particulates.

(d) *Contaminant determinations.* Determine the degree to which the material proposed for discharge will introduce, relocate, or increase contaminants. This determination shall consider the material to be discharged, the aquatic environment at the proposed disposal site, and the availability of contaminants.

(e) *Aquatic ecosystem and organism determinations.* Determine the nature and degree of effect that the proposed discharge will have, both individually and cumulatively, on the structure and function of the aquatic ecosystem and organisms. Consideration shall be given to the effect at the proposed disposal site of potential changes in substrate characteristics and elevation, water or substrate chemistry, nutrients, currents, circulation, fluctuation, and salinity, on the recolonization and existence of indigenous aquatic organisms or communities. Possible loss of environmental values (section 230.31), and actions to minimize impacts (subpart H) shall be examined. Tests as described in section 230.61 (Evaluation and Testing), may be required to provide information on the effect of the discharge material on communities or populations of organisms expected to be exposed to it.

260

(f) *Proposed disposal site determinations.*

    (1) Each disposal site shall be specified through the application of these Guidelines. The mixing zone shall be confined to the smallest practicable zone within each specified disposal site that is consistent with the type of dispersion determined to be appropriate by the application of these Guidelines. In a few special cases under unique environmental conditions, where there is adequate justification to show that widespread dispersion by natural means will result in no significantly adverse environmental effects, the discharged material may be intended to be spread naturally in a very thin layer over a large area of the substrate rather than be contained within the disposal site.

    (2) The permitting authority and the Regional Administrator shall consider the following factors in determining the acceptability of a proposed mixing zone:

        (i) Depth of water at the disposal site;

        (ii) Current velocity, direction, and variability at the disposal site;

        (iii) Degree of turbulence;

        (iv) Stratification attributable to causes such as obstructions, salinity or density profiles at the disposal site;

        (v) Discharge vessel speed and direction, if appropriate;

        (vi) Rate of discharge;

        (vii) Ambient concentration of constituents of interest;

        (viii) Dredged material characteristics, particularly concentrations of constituents, amount of material, type of material (sand, silt, clay, etc.) and settling velocities;

        (ix) Number of discharge actions per unit of time;

        (x) Other factors of the disposal site that affect the rates and patterns of mixing.

(g) *Determination of cumulative effects on the aquatic ecosystem.*

(1) Cumulative impacts are the changes in an aquatic ecosystem that are attributable to the collective effect of a number of individual discharges of dredged or fill material. Although the impact of a particular discharge may constitute a minor change in itself, the cumulative effect of numerous such piecemeal changes can result in a major impairment of the water resources and interfere with the productivity and water quality of existing aquatic ecosystems.

(2) Cumulative effects attributable to the discharge of dredged or fill material in waters of the United States should be predicted to the extent reasonable and practical. The permitting authority shall collect information and solicit information from other sources about the cumulative impacts on the aquatic ecosystem. This information shall be documented and considered during the decision-making process concerning the evaluation of individual permit applications, the issuance of a General permit, and monitoring and enforcement of existing permits.

(h) *Determination of secondary effects on the aquatic ecosystem.*

(1) Secondary effects are effects on an aquatic ecosystem that are associated with a discharge of dredged or fill materials, but do not result from the actual placement of the dredged or fill material. Information about secondary effects on aquatic ecosystems shall be considered prior to the time final section 404 action is taken by permitting authorities.

(2) Some examples of secondary effects on an aquatic ecosystem are fluctuating water levels in an impoundment and downstream associated with the operation of a dam, septic tank leaching and surface runoff from residential or commercial developments on fill, and leachate and runoff from a sanitary landfill located in waters of the U.S. Activities to be conducted on fast land created by the discharge of dredged or fill material in waters of the United States may have secondary impacts within those waters which should be considered in evaluating the impact of creating those fast lands.

230.12 Findings of compliance or non-compliance with the restrictions on discharge.

(a) On the basis of these Guidelines (subparts C through G) the proposed disposal sites for the discharge of dredged or fill material must be:

(1) Specified as complying with the requirements of these Guidelines; or

(2) Specified as complying with the requirements of these Guidelines with the inclusion of appropriate and practicable discharge conditions (see subpart H) to minimize pollution or adverse effects to the affected aquatic ecosystems; or

(3) Specified as failing to comply with the requirements of these Guidelines where:

(i) There is a practicable alternative to the proposed discharge that would have less adverse effect on the aquatic ecosystem, so long as such alternative does not have other significant adverse environmental consequences; or

(ii) The proposed discharge will result in significant degradation of the aquatic ecosystem under section 230.10(b) or (c); or

261

(iii) The proposed discharge does not include all appropriate and practicable measures to minimize potential harm to the aquatic ecosystem; or

(iv) There does not exist sufficient information to make a reasonable judgment as to whether the proposed discharge will comply with these Guidelines.

(b) Findings under this section shall be set forth in writing by the permitting authority for each proposed discharge and made available to the permit applicant. These findings shall include the factual determinations required by section 230.11, and a brief explanation of any adaptation of these Guidelines to the activity under consideration. In the case of a General permit, such findings shall be prepared at the time of issuance of that permit rather than for each subsequent discharge under the authority of that permit.

SUBPART C. POTENTIAL IMPACTS ON PHYSICAL AND CHEMICAL CHARACTERISTICS OF THE AQUATIC ECOSYSTEM

230.20 Substrate.
230.21 Suspended particulates/turbidity.
230.22 Water.
230.23 Current patterns and water circulation.
230.24 Normal water fluctuations.
230.25 Salinity gradients.

Note: The effects described in this subpart should be considered in making the factual determinations and the findings of compliance or non-compliance in subpart B.

230.20 Substrate.

(a) The substrate of the aquatic ecosystem underlies open waters of the United States and constitutes the surface of wetlands. It consists of organic and inorganic solid materials and includes water and other liquids or gases that fill the spaces between solid particles.

(b) Possible loss of environmental characteristics and values: The discharge of dredged or fill material can result in varying degrees of change in the complex physical, chemical, and biological characteristics of the substrate. Discharges which alter substrate elevation or contours can result in changes in water circulation, depth, current pattern, water fluctuation and water temperature. Discharges may adversely affect bottom-dwelling organisms at the site by smothering immobile forms or forcing mobile forms to migrate. Benthic forms present prior to a discharge are unlikely to recolonize on the discharged material if it is very dissimilar from that of the discharge site. Erosion, slumping, or lateral displacement of surrounding bottom of such deposits can adversely affect areas of the substrate outside the perimeters of the disposal site by changing or destroying habitat. The bulk and composition of the discharged material and the location, method, and timing of discharges may all influence the degree of impact on the substrate.

230.21 Suspended particulates/turbidity.

(a) Suspended particulates in the aquatic ecosystem consist of fine-grained mineral particles, usually smaller than silt, and organic particles. Suspended particulates may enter water bodies as a result of land runoff, flooding, vegetative and planktonic breakdown, resuspension of bottom sediments, and man's activities including dredging and filling. Particulates may remain suspended in the water column for variable periods of time as a result of such factors as agitation of the water mass, particulate specific gravity, particle shape, and physical and chemical properties of particle surfaces.

(b) Possible loss of environmental characteristics and values: The discharge of dredged or fill material can result in greatly elevated levels of suspended particulates in the water column for varying lengths of time. These new levels may reduce light penetration and lower the rate of photosynthesis and the primary productivity of an aquatic area if they last long enough. Sight-dependent species may suffer reduced feeding ability leading to limited growth and lowered resistance to disease if high levels of suspended particulates persist. The biological and the chemical content of the suspended material may react with the dissolved oxygen in the water, which can result in oxygen depletion. Toxic metals and organics, pathogens, and viruses absorbed or adsorbed to fine-grained particulates in the material may become biologically available to organisms either in the water column or on the substrate. Significant increases in suspended particulate levels create turbid plumes which are highly visible and aesthetically displeasing. The extent and persistence of these adverse impacts caused by discharges depend upon the relative increase in suspended particulates above the amount occurring naturally, the duration of the higher levels, the current patterns, water level, and fluctuations present when such discharges occur, the volume, rate, and duration of the discharge, particulate deposition, and the seasonal timing of the discharge.

230.22 Water.

(a) Water is the part of the aquatic ecosystem in which organic and inorganic constituents are dissolved and suspended. It constitutes part of the liquid phase and is contained by the substrate. Water forms part of a dynamic aquatic life-supporting system. Water clarity, nutrients and chemical content, physical and biological content, dissolved gas levels, pH, and temperature contribute to its life-sustaining capabilities.

(b) Possible loss of environmental characteristics and values: The discharge of dredged or fill material can change the chemistry and the physical characteristics of the receiving water at a disposal site through the introduction of chemical constituents in suspended or dissolved form. Changes in the clarity, color, odor, and taste of water and the addition of contaminants can reduce or eliminate the suitability of water bodies for populations of aquatic organisms, and for human consumption, recreation, and aesthetics. The introduction of nutrients or organic material to the water column as a result of the discharge can lead to a high biochemical oxygen demand (BOD), which in turn can lead to reduced dissolved oxygen, thereby potentially affecting the survival of many aquatic organisms. Increases in nutrients can favor one group of organisms such as algae to the detriment of other more desirable types such as submerged aquatic vegetation, potentially causing adverse health effects, objectionable tastes and odors, and other problems.

230.23 Current patterns and water circulation.

(a) Current patterns and water circulation are the physical movements of water in the aquatic ecosystem. Currents and circulation respond to natural forces as modified by basin shape and cover, physical and chemical characteristics of water strata and masses, and energy dissipating factors.

(b) Possible loss of environmental characteristics and values: The discharge of dredged or fill material can modify current patterns and water circulation by obstructing flow, changing the direction or velocity of water flow, changing the direction or velocity of water flow and circulation, or otherwise changing the dimensions of a water body. As a result, adverse changes can occur in: Location, structure, and dynamics of aquatic communities; shoreline and substrate erosion and depositon rates; the deposition of suspended particulates; the rate and extent of mixing of dissolved and suspended components of the water body; and water stratification.

230.24 Normal water fluctuations.

(a) Normal water fluctuations in a natural aquatic system consist of daily, seasonal, and annual tidal and flood fluctuations in water level. Biological and physical components of such a system are either attuned to or characterized by these periodic water fluctuations.

(b) Possible loss of environmental characteristics and values: The discharge of dredged or fill material can alter the normal water-level fluctuation pattern of an area, resulting in prolonged periods of inundation, exaggerated extremes of high and low water, or a static, nonfluctuating water level. Such water level modifications may change salinity patterns, alter erosion or sedimentation rates, aggravate water temperature extremes, and upset the nutrient and dissolved oxygen balance of the aquatic ecosystem. In addition, these modifications can alter or destroy communities and populations of aquatic animals and vegetation, induce populations of nuisance organisms, modify habitat, reduce food supplies, restrict movement of aquatic fauna, destroy spawning areas, and change adjacent, upstream, and downstream areas.

230.25 Salinity gradients.

(a) Salinity gradients form where salt water from the ocean meets and mixes with fresh water from land.

(b) Possible loss of environmental characteristics and values: Obstructions which divert or restrict flow of either fresh or salt water may change existing salinity gradients. For example, partial blocking of the entrance to an estuary or river mouth that significantly restricts the movement of the salt water into and out of that area can effectively lower the volume of salt water available for mixing within that estuary. The downstream migration of the salinity gradient can occur, displacing the maximum sedimentation zone and requiring salinity-dependent aquatic biota to adjust to the new conditions, move to new locations if possible, or perish. In the freshwater zone, discharge operations in the upstream regions can have equally adverse impacts. A significant reduction in the volume of fresh water moving into an estuary below that which is considered normal can affect the location and type of mixing thereby changing the characteristic salinity patterns. The resulting changed circulation pattern can cause the upstream migration of the salinity gradient displacing the maximim sedimentation zone. This migration may affect those organisms that are adapted to freshwater environments. It may also affect municipal water supplies.

Note: Possible actions to minimize adverse impacts regarding site characteristics can be found in subpart H.

SUBPART D. POTENTIAL IMPACTS ON BIOLOGICAL CHARACTERISTICS OF THE AQUATIC ECOSYSTEM

230.30 Threatened and endangered species.
230.31 Fish, crustaceans, mollusks, and other aquatic organisms in the food web.
230.32 Other wildlife.

Note: The impacts described in this subpart should be considered in making the factual determinations and the findings of compliance or non-compliance in subpart B.

230.30 Threatened and endangered species.

(a) An endangered species is a plant or animal in danger of extinction throughout all or a significant portion of its range. A threatened species is one in danger of becoming an endangered species in the foreseeable future throughout all or a significant portion of its range. Listings of threatened and endangered species as well as critical habitats are maintained by some individual States and by the U.S. Fish and Wildlife Service of the Department of the Interior (codified annually at 50 CFR 17.11). The Department of Commerce has authority over some threatened and endangered marine mammals, fish and reptiles.

(b) Possible loss of values: The major potential impacts on threatened or endangered species from the discharge of dredged or fill material include:

    (1) Covering or otherwise directly killing species;

    (2) The impairment or destruction of habitat to which these species are limited. Elements of the aquatic habitat which are particularly crucial to the continued survival of some threatened or endangered species include adequate good quality water, spawning and maturation areas, nesting areas, protective cover, adequate and reliable food supply, and resting areas for migratory species. Each of these elements can be adversely affected by changes in either the normal water conditions for clarity, chemical content, nutrient balance, dissolved oxygen, pH, temperature, salinity, current patterns, circulation and fluctuation, or the physical removal of habitat; and

    (3) Facilitating incompatible activities.

(c) Where consultation with the Secretary of the Interior occurs under section 7 of the Endangered Species Act, the conclusions of the Secretary concerning the impact(s) of the discharge on threatened and endangered species and their habitat shall be considered final.

230.31 Fish, crustaceans, mollusks, and other aquatic organisms in the food web.

(a) Aquatic organisms in the food web include, but are not limited to, finfish, crustaceans, mollusks, insects, annelids, planktonic organisms, and the plants and animals on which they feed and depend upon for their needs. All forms and life stages of an organism, throughout its geographic range, are included in this category.

(b) Possible loss of values: The discharge of dredged or fill material can variously affect populations of fish, crustaceans, mollusks and other food web organisms through the release of contaminants which adversely affect adults, juveniles, larvae, or eggs, or result in the establishment or proliferation of an undesirable competitive species of plant or animal at the expense of the desired resident species. Suspended particulates settling on attached or buried eggs can smother the eggs by limiting or sealing off their exposure to oxygenated water. Discharge of dredged and fill material may result in the debilitation or death of sedentary organisms by smothering, exposure to chemical contaminants in dissolved or suspended form, exposure to high levels of suspended particulates, reduction in food supply, or alteration of the substrate upon which they are dependent. Mollusks are particularly sensitive to the discharge of material during periods of reproduction and growth and development due primarily to their limited mobility. They can be rendered unfit for human consumption by tainting, by production and accumulation of toxins, or by ingestion and retention of pathogenic organisms, viruses, heavy metals or persistent synthetic organic chemicals. The discharge of dredged or fill material can redirect, delay, or stop the reproductive and feeding movements of some species of fish and crustacea, thus preventing their aggregation in accustomed places such as spawning or nursery grounds and potentially leading to reduced populations. Reduction of detrital feeding species or other representatives of lower trophic levels can impair the flow of energy from primary consumers to higher trophic levels. The reduction or potential elimination of food chain organism populations decreases the overall productivity and nutrient export capability of the ecosystem.

230.32 Other wildlife.

(a) Wildlife associated with aquatic ecosystems are resident and transient mammals, birds, reptiles, and amphibians.

(b) Possible loss of values: The discharge of dredged or fill material can result in the loss or change of breeding and nesting areas, escape cover, travel corridors, and preferred food sources for resident and transient wildlife species associated with the aquatic ecosystem. These adverse impacts upon wildlife habitat may result from changes in water levels, water flow and circulation, salinity, chemical content, and substrate characteristics and elevation. Increased water turbidity can adversely affect wildlife species which rely upon sight to feed, and disrupt the respiration and feeding of certain aquatic wildlife and food chain organisms. The availability of contaminants from the discharge of dredged or fill material may lead to the bioaccumulation of such contaminants in wildlife. Changes in such physical and chemical factors of the environment may favor the introduction of undesirable plant and animal species at the expense of resident species and communities. In some aquatic environments lowering plant and animal species diversity may disrupt the normal functions of the ecosystem and lead to reductions in overall biological productivity.

Note: Possible actions to minimize adverse impacts regarding characteristics of biological components of the aquatic ecosystem can be found in subpart H.

263

SUBPART E. POTENTIAL IMPACTS ON SPECIAL AQUATIC SITES

230.40 Sanctuaries and refuges.
230.41 Wetlands.
230.42 Mud flats.
230.43 Vegetated shallows.
230.44 Coral reefs.
230.45 Riffle and pool complexes.

Note: The impacts described in this subpart should be considered in making the factual determinations and the findings of compliance or non-compliance in subpart B. The definition of special aquatic sites is found in section 230.3(q-1).

230.40 Sanctuaries and refuges.

(a) Sanctuaries and refuges consist of areas designated under State and Federal laws or local ordinances to be managed principally for the preservation and use of fish and wildlife resources.

(b) Possible loss of values: Sanctuaries and refuges may be affected by discharges of dredged or fill material which will:

(1) Disrupt the breeding, spawning, migratory movements or other critical life requirements of resident or transient fish and wildlife resources;

(2) Create unplanned, easy and incompatible human access to remote aquatic areas;

(3) Create the need for frequent maintenance activity;

(4) Result in the establishment of undesirable competitive species of plants and animals;

(5) Change the balance of water and land areas needed to provide cover, food, and other fish and wildlife habitat requirements in a way that modifies sanctuary or refuge management practices;

(6) Result in any of the other adverse impacts discussed in subparts C and D as they relate to a particular sanctuary or refuge.

230.41 Wetlands.

(a)

(1) Wetlands consist of areas that are inundated or saturated by surface or ground water at a frequency and duration sufficient to support, and that under normal circumstances do support, a prevalence of vegetation typically adapted for life in saturated soil conditions.

264

(2) Where wetlands are adjacent to open water, they generally constitute the transition to upland. The margin between wetland and open water can best be established by specialists familiar with the local environment, particularly where emergent vegetation merges with submerged vegetation over a broad area in such places as the lateral margins of open water, headwaters, rainwater catch basins, and groundwater seeps. The landward margin of wetlands also can best be identified by specialists familiar with the local environment when vegetation from the two regions merges over a broad area.

(3) Wetland vegetation consists of plants that require saturated soils to survive (obligate wetland plants) as well as plants, including certain trees, that gain a competitive advantage over others because they can tolerate prolonged wet soil conditions and their competitors cannot. In addition to plant populations and communities, wetlands are delimited by hydrological and physical characteristics of the environment. These characteristics should be considered when information about them is needed to supplement information available about vegetation, or where wetland vegetation has been removed or is dormant.

(b) Possible loss of values: The discharge of dredged or fill material in wetlands is likely to damage or destroy habitat and adversely affect the biological productivity of wetlands ecosystems by smothering, by dewatering, by permanently flooding, or by altering substrate elevation or periodicity of water movement. The addition of dredged or fill material may destroy wetland vegetation or result in advancement of succession to dry land species. It may reduce or eliminate nutrient exchange by a reduction of the system's productivity, or by altering current patterns and velocities. Disruption or elimination of the wetland system can degrade water quality by obstructing circulation patterns that flush large expanses of wetland systems, by interfering with the filtration function of wetlands, or by changing the aquifer recharge capability of a wetland. Discharges can also change the wetland habitat value for fish and wildlife as discussed in subpart D. When disruptions in flow and circulation patterns occur, apparently minor loss of wetland acreage may result in major losses through secondary impacts. Discharging fill material in wetlands as part of municipal, industrial or recreational development may modify the capacity of wetlands to retain and store floodwaters and to serve as a buffer zone shielding upland areas from wave actions, storm damage and erosion.

230.42 Mud flats.

(a) Mud flats are broad flat areas along the sea coast and in coastal rivers to the head of tidal influence and in inland lakes, ponds, and riverine systems. When mud flats are inundated, wind and wave action may resuspend bottom sediments. Coastal mud flats are exposed at extremely low tides and inundated at high tides with the water table at or near the surface of the substrate. The substrate of mud flats contains organic material and particles smaller in size than sand. They are either unvegetated or vegetated only by algal mats.

(b) Possible loss of values: The discharge of dredged or fill material can cause changes in water circulation patterns which may permanently flood or dewater the mud flat or disrupt periodic inundation, resulting in an increase in the rate of erosion or accretion. Such changes can deplete or eliminate mud flat biota, foraging areas, and nursery areas. Changes in inundation patterns can affect the chemical and biological exchange and decomposition process occurring on the mud flat and change the deposition of suspended material affecting the productivity of the area. Changes may reduce the mud flat's capacity to dissipate storm surge runoff.

230.43 Vegetated shallows.

(a) Vegetated shallows are permanently inundated areas that under normal circumstances support communities of rooted aquatic vegetation, such as turtle grass and eelgrass in estuarine or marine systems as well as a number of freshwater species in rivers and lakes.

(b) Possible loss of values: The discharge of dredged or fill material can smother vegetation and benthic organisms. It may also create unsuitable conditions for their continued vigor by: (1) Changing water circulation patterns; (2) releasing nutrients that increase undesirable algal populations; (3) releasing chemicals that adversely affect plants and animals; (4) increasing turbidity levels, thereby reducing light penetration and hence photosynthesis; and (5) changing the capacity of a vegetated shallow to stabilize bottom materials and decrease channel shoaling. The discharge of dredged or fill material may reduce the value of vegetated shallows as nesting, spawning, nursery, cover, and forage areas, as well as their value in protecting shorelines from erosion and wave actions. It may also encourage the growth of nuisance vegetation.

230.44 Coral reefs.

(a) Coral reefs consist of the skeletal deposit, usually of calcareous or silicaceous materials, produced by the vital activities of anthozoan polyps or other invertebrate organisms present in growing portions of the reef.

(b) Possible loss of values: The discharge of dredged or fill material can adversely affect colonies of reef building organisms by burying them, by releasing contaminants such as hydrocarbons into the water column, by reducing light penetration through the water, and by increasing the level of suspended particulates. Coral organisms are extremely sensitive to even slight reductions in light penetration or increases in suspended particulates. These adverse effects will cause a loss of productive colonies which in turn provide habitat for many species of highly specialized aquatic organisms.

230.45 Riffle and pool complexes.

(a) Steep gradient sections of streams are sometimes characterized by riffle and pool complexes. Such stream sections are recognizable by their hydraulic characteristics. The rapid movement of water over a coarse substrate in riffles results in a rough flow, a turbulent surface, and high dissolved oxygen levels in the water. Pools are deeper areas associated with riffles. Pools are characterized by a slower stream velocity, a steaming flow, a smooth surface, and a finer substrate. Riffle and pool complexes are particularly valuable habitat for fish and wildlife.

(b) Possible loss of values: Discharge of dredged or fill material can eliminate riffle and pool areas by displacement, hydrologic modification, or sedimentation. Activities which affect riffle and pool areas and especially riffle/pool ratios, may reduce the aeration and filtration capabilities at the discharge site and downstream, may reduce stream habitat diversity, and may retard repopulation of the disposal site and downstream waters through sedimentation and the creation of unsuitable habitat. The discharge of dredged or fill material which alters stream hydrology may cause scouring or sedimentation of riffles and pools. Sedimentation induced through hydrological modification or as a direct result of the deposition of unconsolidated dredged or fill material may clog riffle and pool areas, destroy habitats, and create anaerobic conditions. Eliminating pools and meanders by the discharge of dredged or fill material can reduce water holding capacity of streams and cause rapid runoff from a watershed. Rapid runoff can deliver large quantities of flood water in a short time to downstream areas resulting in the destruction of natural habitat, high property loss, and the need for further hydraulic modification.

Note: Possible actions to minimize adverse impacts on site or material characteristics can be found in subpart H.

265

SUBPART F. POTENTIAL EFFECTS ON HUMAN USE CHARACTERISTICS

230.50 Municipal and private water supplies.
230.51 Recreational and commercial fisheries.
230.52 Water-related recreation.
230.53 Aesthetics.
230.54 Parks, national and historical monuments, national seashores, wilderness areas, research sites and similar preserves.

Note: The effects described in this subpart should be considered in making the factual determinations and the findings of compliance or non-compliance in subpart B.

230.50 Municipal and private water supplies.

(a) Municipal and private water supplies consist of surface water or ground water which is directed to the intake of a municipal or private water supply system.

(b) Possible loss of values: Discharges can affect the quality of water supplies with respect to color, taste, odor, chemical content and suspended particulate concentration, in such a way as to reduce the fitness of the water for consumption. Water can be rendered unpalatable or unhealthy by the addition of suspended particulates, viruses and pathogenic organisms, and dissolved materials. The expense of removing such substances before the water is delivered for consumption can be high. Discharges may also affect the quantity of water available for municipal and private water supplies. In addition, certain commonly used water treatment chemicals have the potential for combining with some suspended or dissolved substances from dredged or fill material to form other products that can have a toxic effect on consumers.

230.51 Recreational and commercial fisheries.

(a) Recreational and commercial fisheries consist of harvestable fish, crustaceans, shellfish, and other aquatic organisms used by man.

(b) Possible loss of values: The discharge of dredged or fill materials can affect the suitability of recreational and commercial fishing grounds as habitat for populations of consumable aquatic organisms. Discharges can result in the chemical contamination of recreational or commercial fisheries. They may also interfere with the reproductive success of recreational and commercially important aquatic species through disruption of migration and spawning areas. The introduction of pollutants at critical times in their life cycle may directly reduce populations of commercially important aquatic organisms or indirectly reduce them by reducing organisms upon which they depend for food. Any of these impacts can be of short duration or prolonged, depending upon the physical and chemical impacts of the discharge and the biological availability of contaminants to aquatic organisms.

230.52 Water-related recreation.

(a) Water-related recreation encompasses activities undertaken for amusement and relaxation. Activities encompass two broad categories of use: consumptive, e.g., harvesting resources by hunting and fishing; and non-comsumptive, e.g. canoeing and sight-seeing.

(b) Possible loss of values: One of the more important direct impacts of dredged or fill disposal is to impair or destroy the resources which support recreation activities. The disposal of dredged or fill material may adversely modify or destroy water use for recreation by changing turbidity, suspended particulates, temperature, dissolved oxygen, dissolved materials, toxic materials, pathogenic organisms, quality of habitat, and the aesthetic qualities of sight, taste, odor, and color.

230.53 Aesthetics.

(a) Aesthetics associated with the aquatic ecosystem consist of the perception of beauty by one or a combination of the senses of sight, hearing, touch, and smell. Aesthetics of aquatic ecosystems apply to the quality of life enjoyed by the general public and property owners.

(b) Possible loss of values: The discharge of dredged or fill material can mar the beauty of natural aquatic ecosystems by degrading water quality, creating distracting disposal sites, inducing inappropriate development, encouraging unplanned and incompatible human access, and by destroying vital elements that contribute to the compositional harmony or unity, visual distinctiveness, or diversity of an area. The discharge of dredged or fill material can adversely affect the particular features, traits, or characteristics of an aquatic area which make it valuable to property owners. Activities which degrade water quality, disrupt natural substrate and vegetational characteristics, deny access to or visibility of the resource, or result in changes in odor, air quality, or noise levels may reduce the value of an aquatic area to private property owners.

230.54 Parks, national and historical monuments, national seashores, wilderness areas, research sites, and similar preserves.

(a) These preserves consist of areas designated under Federal and State laws or local ordinances to be managed for their aesthetic, educational, historical, recreational, or scientific value.

(b) Possible loss of values: The discharge of dredged or fill material into such areas may modify the aesthetic, educational, historical, recreational and/or scientific qualities there-by reducing or eliminating the uses for which such sites are set aside and managed.

SUBPART G. EVALUATION AND TESTING

230.60 General evaluation of dredged or fill material.
230.61 Chemical, biological, and physical evaluation and testing.

230.60 General evaluation of dredged or fill material.

The purpose of these evaluation procedures and the chemical and biological testing sequence outlined in section 230.61 is to provide information to reach the determinations required by section 230.11. Where the results of prior evaluations, chemical and biological tests, scientific research, and experience can provide information helpful in making a determination, these should be used. Such prior results may make new testing unnecessary. The information used shall be documented. Where the same information applies to more than one determination, it may be documented once and referenced in later determinations.

(a) If the evaluation under paragraph (b) indicates the dredged or fill material is not a carrier of contaminants, then the required determinations pertaining to the presence and effects of contaminants can be made without testing. Dredged or fill material is most likely to be free from chemical, biological, or other pollutants where it is composed primarily of sand, gravel, or other naturally occurring inert material. Dredged material so composed is generally found in areas of high current or wave energy such as streams with large bed loads or coastal areas with shifting bars and channels. However, when such material is discolored or contains other indications that contaminants may be present, further inquiry should be made.

(b) The extraction site shall be examined in order to assess whether it is sufficiently removed from sources of pollution to provide reasonable assurance that the proposed discharge material is not a carrier of contaminants. Factors to be considered include but are not limited to:

(1) Potential routes of contaminants or contaminated sediments to the extraction site, based on hydrographic or other maps, aerial photography, or other materials that show watercourses, surface relief, proximity to tidal movement, private and public roads, location of buildings, municipal and industrial areas, and agricultural or forest lands.

(2) Pertinent results from tests previously carried out on the material at the extraction site, or carried out on similar material for other permitted projects in the vicinity. Materials shall be considered similar if the sources of contamination, the physical configuration of the sites and the sediment composition of the materials are comparable, in light of water circulation and stratification, sediment accumulation and general sediment characteristics. Tests from other sites may be relied on only if no changes have occurred at the extraction sites to render the results irrelevant.

(3) Any potential for significant introduction of persistent pesticides from land runoff or percolation;

(4) Any records of spills or disposal of petroleum products or substances designated as hazardous under section 311 of the Clean Water Act (See 40 CFR part 116);

(5) Information in Federal, State and local records indicating significant introduction of pollutants from industries, municipalities, or other sources, including types and amounts of waste materials discharged along the potential routes of contaminants to the extraction site; and

(6) Any possibility of the presence of substantial natural deposits of minerals or other substances which could be released to the aquatic environment in harmful quantities by man-induced discharge activities.

(c) To reach the determinations in section 230.11 involving potential effects of the discharge on the characteristics of the disposal site, the narrative guidance in subparts C through F shall be used along with the general evaluation procedure in section 230.60 and, if necessary, the chemical and biological testing sequence in section 230.61. Where the discharge site is adjacent to the extraction site and subject to the same sources of contaminants, and materials at the two sites are substantially similar, the fact that the material to be discharged may be a carrier of contaminants is not likely to result in degradation of the disposal site. In such circumstances, when dissolved material and suspended particulates can be controlled to prevent carrying pollutants to less contaminated areas, testing will not be required.

(d) Even if the section 230.60(b) evaluation (previous tests, the presence of polluting industries and information about their discharge or runoff into waters of the U.S., bioinventories, etc.) leads to the conclusion that there is a high probability that the material proposed for discharge is a carrier of contaminants, testing may not be necessary if constraints are available to reduce contamination to acceptable levels within the disposal site and to prevent contaminants from being transported beyond the boundaries of the disposal site, if such constraints are acceptable to the permitting authority and the Regional Administrator, and if the potential discharger is willing and able to implement such constraints. However, even if tests are not performed, the permitting authority must still determine the probable impact of the operation on the receiving aquatic ecosystem. Any decision not to test must be explained in the determinations made under section 230.11.

230.61 Chemical, biological, and physical evaluation and testing.
Note: The Agency is today proposing revised testing guidelines. The evaluation and testing procedures in this section are based on the 1975 section 404(b)(1) interim final Guidelines and shall remain in effect until the revised testing guidelines are published as final regulations.

(a) No single test or approach can be applied in all cases to evaluate the effects of proposed discharges of dredged or fill materials. This section provides some guidance in determining which test and/or evaluation procedures are appropriate in a given case. Interim guidance to applicants concerning the applicability of specific approaches or procedures will be furnished by the permitting authority.

(b) *Chemical-biological interactive effects.* The principal concerns of discharge of dredged or fill material that contain contaminants are the potential effects on the water column and on communities of aquatic organisms.

(1) *Evaluation of chemical-biological interactive effects.* Dredged or fill material may be excluded from the evaluation procedures specified in paragraphs (b) (2) and (3) of this section if it is determined, on the basis of the evaluation in section 230.60, that the likelihood of contamination by contaminants is acceptably low, unless the permitting authority, after evaluating and considering any comments received from the Regional Administrator, determines that these procedures are necessary. The Regional Administrator may require, on a case-by-case basis, testing approaches and procedures by stating what additional information is needed through further analyses and how the results of the analyses will be of value in evaluating potential environmental effects. If the General Evaluation indicates the presence of a sufficiently large number of chemicals to render impractical the identification of all contaminants by chemical testing, information may be obtained from bioassays in lieu of chemical tests.

(2) *Water column effects.*

(i) Sediments normally contain constituents that exist in various chemical forms and in various concentrations in several locations within the sediment. An elutriate test may be used to predict the effect on water quality due to release of contaminants from the sediment to the water column. However, in the case of fill material originating on land which may be a carrier of contaminants, a water leachate test is appropriate.

(ii) Major constituents to be analyzed in the elutriate are those deemed critical by the permitting authority, after evaluating and considering any comments received from the Regional Administrator, and considering results of the evaluation in section 230.60. Elutriate concentrations should be compared to concentrations of the same constituents in water from the disposal site. Results should be evaluated in light of the volume and rate of the intended discharge, the type of discharge, the hydrodynamic regime at the disposal site, and other information relevant to the impact on water quality. The permitting authority should consider the mixing zone in evaluating water column effects. The permitting authority may specify bioassays when such procedures will be of value.

(3) *Effects on benthos.* The permitting authority may use an appropriate benthic bioassay (including bio-accumulation tests) when such procedures will be of value in assessing ecological effects and in establishing discharge conditions.

(c) *Procedure for comparison of sites.*

(1) When an inventory of the total concentration of contaminants would be of value in comparing sediment at the dredging site with sediment at the disposal site, the permitting authority may require a sediment chemical analysis. Markedly different concentrations of contaminants between the excavation and disposal sites may aid in making an environmental assessment of the proposed disposal operation. Such differences should be interpreted in terms of the potential for harm as supported by any pertinent scientific literature.

(2) When an analysis of biological community structure will be of value to assess the potential for adverse environmental impact at the proposed disposal site, a comparison of the biological characteristics between the excavation and disposal sites may be required by the permitting authority. Biological indicator species may be useful in evaluating the existing degree of stress at both sites. Sensitive species representing community components colonizing various substrate types within the sites should be identified as possible bioassay organisms if tests for toxicity are required. Community structure studies should be performed only when they will be of value in determining discharge conditions. This is particularly applicable to large quantities of dredged material known to contain adverse quantities of toxic materials. Community studies should include benthic organisms such as microbiota and harvestable shellfish and finfish. Abundance, diversity, and distribution should be documented and correlated with substrate type and other appropriate physical and chemical environmental characteristics.

(d) *Physical tests and evaluation.* The effect of a discharge of dredged or fill material on physical substrate characteristics at the disposal site, as well as on the water circulation, fluctuation, salinity, and suspended particulates content there, is important in making factual determinations in section 230.11. Where information on such effects is not otherwise available to make these factual determinations, the permitting authority shall require appropriate physical tests and evaluations as are justified and deemed necessary. Such tests may include sieve tests, settleability tests, compaction tests, mixing zone and suspended particulate plume determinations, and site assessments of water flow, circulation, and salinity characteristics.

267

SUBPART H. ACTIONS TO MINIMIZE ADVERSE EFFECTS

230.70 Actions concerning the location of the discharge.
230.71 Actions concerning the material to be discharged.
230.72 Actions controlling the material after discharge.
230.73 Actions affecting the method of dispersion.
230.74 Actions related to technology.
230.75 Actions affecting plant and animal populations.
230.76 Actions affecting human use.
230.77 Other actions.

Note: There are many actions which can be undertaken in response to 203.10(d) to minimize the adverse effects of discharges of dredged or fill material. Some of these, grouped by type of activity, are listed in this subpart.

230.70 Actions concerning the location of the discharge.
The effects of the discharge can be minimized by the choice of the disposal site. Some of the ways to accomplish this are by:

(a) Locating and confining the discharge to minimize smothering of organisms;

(b) Designing the discharge to avoid a disruption of periodic water inundation patterns;

(c) Selecting a disposal site that has been used previously for dredged material discharge;

(d) Selecting a disposal site at which the substrate is composed of material similar to that being discharged, such as discharging sand on sand or mud on mud;

(e) Selecting the disposal site, the discharge point, and the method of discharge to minimize the extent of any plume;

(f) Designing the discharge of dredged or fill material to minimize or prevent the creation of standing bodies of water in areas of normally fluctuating water levels, and minimize or prevent the drainage of areas subject to such fluctuations.

230.71 Actions concerning the material to be discharged.
The effects of a discharge can be minimized by treatment of, or limitations on the material itself, such as:

(a) Disposal of dredged material in such a manner that physiochemical conditions are maintained and the potency and availability of pollutants are reduced.

268

(b) Limiting the solid, liquid, and gaseous components of material to be discharged at a particular site;

(c) Adding treatment substances to the discharge material;

(d) Utilizing chemical flocculants to enhance the deposition of suspended particulates in diked disposal areas.

230.72 Actions controlling the material after discharge.
The effects of the dredged or fill material after discharge may be controlled by:

(a) Selecting discharge methods and disposal sites where the potential for erosion, slumping or leaching of materials into the surrounding aquatic ecosystem will be reduced. These sites or methods include, but are not limited to:

    (1) Using containment levees, sediment basins, and cover crops to reduce erosion;

    (2) Using lined containment areas to reduce leaching where leaching of chemical constituents from the discharged material is expected to be a problem;

(b) Capping in-place contaminated material with clean material or selectively discharging the most contaminated material first to be capped with the remaining material;

(c) Maintaining and containing discharged material properly to prevent point and nonpoint sources of pollution;

(d) Timing the discharge to minimize impact, for instance during periods of unusual high water flows, wind, wave, and tidal actions.

230.73 Actions affecting the method of dispersion.
The effects of a discharge can be minimized by the manner in which it is dispersed, such as:

(a) Where environmentally desirable, distributing the dredged material widely in a thin layer at the disposal site to maintain natural substrate contours and elevation;

(b) Orienting a dredged or fill material mound to minimize undesirable obstruction to the water current or circulation pattern, and utilizing natural bottom contours to minimize the size of the mound;

(c) Using silt screens or other appropriate methods to confine suspended particulate/turbidity to a small area where settling or removal can occur;

(d) Making use of currents and circulation patterns to mix, disperse and dilute the discharge;

(e) Minimizing water column turbidity by using a submerged diffuser system. A similar effect can be accomplished by submerging pipeline discharges or otherwise releasing materials near the bottom;

(f) Selecting sites or managing discharges to confine and minimize the release of suspended particulates to give decreased turbidity levels and to maintain light penetration for organisms;

(g) Setting limitations on the amount of material to be discharged per unit of time or volume of receiving water.

230.74 Actions related to technology.
Discharge technology should be adapted to the needs of each site. In determining whether the discharge operation sufficiently minimizes adverse environmental impacts, the applicant should consider:

(a) Using appropriate equipment or machinery, including protective devices, and the use of such equipment or machinery in activities related to the discharge of dredged or fill material;

(b) Employing appropriate maintenance and operation on equipment or machinery, including adequate training, staffing, and working procedures;

(c) Using machinery and techniques that are especially designed to reduce damage to wetlands. This may include machines equipped with devices that scatter rather than mound excavated materials, machines with specially designed wheels or tracks, and the use of mats under heavy machines to reduce wetland surface compaction and rutting;

(d) Designing access roads and channel spanning structures using culverts, open channels, and diversions that will pass both low and high water flows, accommodate fluctuating water levels, and maintain circulation and faunal movement;

(e) Employing appropriate machinery and methods of transport of the material for discharge.

230.75 Actions affecting plant and animal populations.
Minimization of adverse effects on populations of plants and animals can be achieved by:

(a) Avoiding changes in water current and circulation patterns which would interfere with the movement of animals;

(b) Selecting sites or managing discharges to prevent or avoid creating habitat conducive to the development of undesirable predators or species which have a competitive edge ecologically over indigenous plants or animals;

(c) Avoiding sites having unique habitat or other value, including habitat of threatened or endangered species;

269

(d) Using planning and construction practices to institute habitat development and restoration to produce a new or modified environmental state of higher ecological value by displacement of some or all of the existing environmental characteristics. Habitat development and restoration techniques can be used to minimize adverse impacts and to compensate for destroyed habitat. Use techniques that have been demonstrated to be effective in circumstances similar to those under consideration wherever possible. Where proposed development and restoration techniques have not yet advanced to the pilot demonstration stage, initiate their use on a small scale to allow corrective action if unanticipated adverse impacts occur;

(e) Timing discharge to avoid spawning or migration seasons and other biologically critical time periods;

(f) Avoiding the destruction of remnant natural sites within areas already affected by development.

230.76 Actions affecting human use.
Minimization of adverse effects on human use potential may be achieved by:

(a) Selecting discharge sites and following discharge procedures to prevent or minimize any potential damage to the aesthetically pleasing features of the aquatic site (e.g. viewscapes), particularly with respect to water quality;

(b) Selecting disposal sites which are not valuable as natural aquatic areas;

(c) Timing the discharge to avoid the seasons or periods when human recreational activity associated with the aquatic site is most important;

(d) Following discharge procedures which avoid or minimize the disturbance of aesthetic features of an aquatic site or ecosystem;

(e) Selecting sites that will not be detrimental or increase incompatible human activity, or require the need for frequent dredge or fill maintenance activity in remote fish and wildlife areas;

(f) Locating the disposal site outside of the vicinity of a public water supply intake.

230.77 Other actions.
(a) In the case of fills, controlling runoff and other discharges from activities to be conducted on the fill;

(b) In the case of dams, designing water releases to accommodate the needs of fish and wildlife;

(c) In dredging projects funded by Federal agencies other than the Corps of Engineers, maintain desired water quality of the return discharge through agreement with the Federal funding authority on scientifically defensible pollutant concentration levels in addition to any applicable water quality standards;

(d) When a significant ecological change in the aquatic environment is proposed by the discharge of dredged or fill material, the permitting authority should consider the ecosystem that will be lost as well as the environmental benefits of the new system.

SUBPART I: PLANNING TO SHORTEN PERMIT PROCESSING TIME

230.80 Advanced identification of disposal areas.

230.80 Advanced identification of disposal areas.

(a) Consistent with these Guidelines, EPA and the permitting authority, on their own initiative or at the request of any other party and after consultation with any affected State that is not the permitting authority, may identify sites which will be considered as:

(1) Possible future disposal sites, including existing disposal sites and non-sensitive areas; or

(2) Areas generally unsuitable for disposal site specification;

(b) The identification of any area as a possible future disposal site should not be deemed to constitute a permit for the discharge of dredged or fill material within such area or a specification of a disposal site. The identification of areas that generally will not be available for disposal site specification should not be deemed as prohibiting applications for permits to discharge dredged or fill material in such areas. Either type of identification constitutes information to facilitate individual or General permit application and processing;

(c) An appropriate public notice of the proposed identification of such areas shall be issued;

(d) To provide the basis for advanced identification of disposal areas, and areas unsuitable for disposal, EPA and the permitting authority shall consider the likelihood that use of the area in question for dredged or fill material disposal will comply with these Guidelines. To facilitate this analysis, EPA and the permitting authority should review available water resources management data including data available from the public, other Federal and State agencies, and information from approved Coastal Zone Management programs and River Basin Plans;

(e) The permitting authority should maintain a public record of the identified areas and a written statement of the basis for identification.

Note to readers: updated versions of this document can be found athttp://www.epa.gov/OWOW/wetlands/40cfr/part230.html

270

APPENDIX G: Municipalities with Local Wetland Ordinances

As of April 15, 2002

COUNTY	MUNICIPALITY
Allegan	Clyde Township
Antrim	County-wide
Antrim	Forest Home Township
Charlevoix	Hayes Township
Genesee	Argentine Township
Genesee	Fenton, City of
Genesee	Fenton Township
Grand Traverse	Whitewater Township
Huron	Caseville Township/Village
Ingham	Meridian, Charter Township of
Lapeer	Elba Township
Leelanau	Empire, Village of
Livingston	Brighton Township
Livingston	Genoa Township
Livingston	Pinckney, Village of
Mackinac	Clark Township
Manistee	Manistee Township
Monroe	LaSalle Township
Oakland	Addison Township
Oakland	Auburn Hills, City of
Oakland	Bloomfield Township
Oakland	Franklin, Village of
Oakland	Independence, Charter Township of
Oakland	Milford, Charter Township of
Oakland	Novi, City of
Oakland	Oakland, Charter Township of
Oakland	Orchard Lake Village
Oakland	Orion, Charter Township of
Oakland	Oxford, Charter Township of
Oakland	Rochester Hills, City of
Oakland	Southfield, City of
Oakland	Waterford, Charter Township of
Oakland	West Bloomfield, Charter Township of
Oakland	White Lake Township
Oakland	Wixom, City of
St. Joseph	Fabius, Township of
Washtenaw	Ann Arbor, City of
Washtenaw	Ann Arbor, Charter Township of
Washtenaw	Salem Township
Washtenaw	Superior, Charter Township of
Wayne	Grosse Ile, Township of

271

For citizen wetland protection advocates who are interested in receiving copies of the ordinances above for use as models, please contact the municipality directly. Many of the organizations listed in Appendix A have model local ordinances to distribute. In addition, organizations such as the Michigan Society of Planning Officials, the American Planning Association, and private consulting firms such as the Planning and Zoning Center, Inc. have local model wetlands protection ordinances available.

* Ordinances in this list vary from those which condition the issuance of a local permit on appropriate state and federal wetland permits to those which require a separate local wetlands review and permit.

In an effort to enhance readability, the text contains no direct citations or footnotes. However, there were many resources that provided valuable background information either directly or indirectly for the content of this book. These resources are included below. This list of resources can also serve as a bibliography for your further reading.

Alinsky, Saul D. *Rules for Radicals and Reveille for Radicals*, Random House, Inc., New York, NY 1989.

Auvine, Brian et. al. *A Manual for Group Facilitators*, The Center for Conflict Resolution, Madison, WI 1985.

Avery, Michael et. al. *Building United Judgment: A Handbook for Consensus Decision-Making*, The Center for Conflict Resolution, Madison, WI 1985.

Ballenger, Bruce and Adela Awner. *Membership Recruiting Manual*, Northern Rockies Action Group, Helena, MT 1981.

Barnes, B.V. and W.H. Wagner, Jr. *Michigan Trees: A Guide to the Trees of Michigan and the Great Lakes Region* University of Michigan, Ann Arbor, MI 1981.

Beamish, Richard. *Getting the Word Out in the Fight to Save the Earth*, The Johns Hopkins University Press, Baltimore, MD 1995.

Black, Henry Campbell, Joseph Nolan, and M.J. Connolly. *Black's Law Dictionary, Fifth Edition*, West Publishing Company, St. Paul, MN 1979.

Bobo, Kim et. al. Organizing for Social Change: *A Manual for Activists in the 1990s*, The Midwest Academy, Santa Ana, CA 1996.

Bortin, Virginia. *Publicity for Volunteers: A Handbook*, Walker and Company, New York, NY 1981.

Brooks, R.P., D.A. Devlin, and J. Hassinger. *Wetlands and Wildlife*, Pennsylvania State University, University Park, PA 1993.

Brown, Stephen. *Preserving Great Lakes Wetlands: An Environmental Agenda*, Tip of the Mitt Watershed Council, Petoskey, MI 1990.

Burke, David G. et. al. *Protecting Nontidal Wetlands*, American Planning Association, Washington, D.C. 1988.

Chabot, Amy. "Preliminary Results from the Marsh Monitoring Program in 1995" in V.7 N.1 *Great Lakes Wetlands* edited by Wilfred Cwikiel, Tip of the Mitt Watershed Council, Petoskey, MI 1996.

Coie, Perkins. *Non-Profit Organizations, Public Policy, and the Political Process: A Guide to the Internal Revenue Code and Federal Election Campaign Act*, Citizens Vote, Inc., New York, NY 1987.

Cold, Kenneth C. "Designation of Property as Wetlands Held Not a Taking" in *Michigan Environmental Law Letter* edited by Joseph M. Polito, Honigman, Miller, Schwartz, and Cohn, Detroit, November 1991.

Covin, Gregory L. ed. *Fiscal Sponsorship: Six Ways to Do it Right*, Study Center Press, San Francisco, CA 1993.

Cowardin, Lewis M. et. al. *Classification of Wetlands and Deepwater Habitats of the United States*, U.S. Department of Interior, U.S. Fish and Wildlife Services, Office of Biological Services, Washington, D.C. 1979.

CPAs for the Public Interest. *The Audit Process: A Guide for Not-for-Profit Organizations*, CPAs for the Public Interest, Chicago, IL 1989.

Cwikiel, Wilfred. *Living with Michigan's Wetlands: A Landowner's Guide (Third Printing)*, Tip of the Mitt Watershed Council, Petoskey, MI 1998

Cwikiel, Wilfred. *Michigan Wetlands: Yours to Protect (Second Edition)*, Tip of the Mitt Watershed Council, Petoskey, MI 1992.

Dahl, T.E. *Wetlands Losses in the United States 1780 to 1980's*, U.S. Department of the Interior, Fish and Wildlife Service, Washington, D.C. 1990.

Dean, Lillian F. *Protecting Wetlands at the Local Level: Options for Southeast Michigan Communities*, Rouge River Watershed Council, Detroit, MI 1991.

East Michigan Environmental Action Council. *A Guide to Michigan's Watercourse and Wetland Protection Laws*, Clinton River Watershed Council, Utica, MI 1981.

Environmental Defense Fund. *How Wet Is a Wetland? The Impacts of the Proposed Revisions to the Federal Wetlands Delineation Manual*, Environmental Defense Fund and the World Wildlife Fund, Washington, D.C. 1992.

Federal Interagency Committee for Wetland Delineation. *Federal Manual for Identifying and Delineating Jurisdictional Wetlands*, A cooperative technical publication by U.S. Army Corps of Engineers, U.S. Environmental Protection Agency, U.S. Fish and Wildlife Service, and U.S.D.A. Soil Conservation Service, Washington, D.C. 1989.

Flanagan, Joan. The Grass Roots Fundraising Book, Contemporary Books, Inc., Chicago, IL 1992.

Flanagan, Joan. *The Successful Volunteer Organization: Getting Started and Getting Results in Nonprofit, Charities, Grassroots, and Community Groups*, Contemporary Books, Inc., Chicago, IL 1984.

Fuller, Douglas. *Understanding, Living With, and Controlling Shoreline Erosion* Tip of the Mitt Watershed Council, Petoskey, MI 1995.

Goldman-Carter, Jan. *A Citizen's Guide to Protecting Wetlands*, National Wildlife Federation, Washington, D.C. 1989.

Gruenwald, Gail S. *Michigan Wetlands: Yours to Protect*, Tip of the Mitt Watershed Council, Petoskey, MI 1987.

Hammer, Donald. *Creating Freshwater Wetlands*, Lewis Publishers, Chelsea, MI 1992.

Hedemann, Ed ed. *War Resistors League Organizer's Manual*, War Resistors, New York, NY 1981.

Henderson, Carrol L. *Landscaping for Wildlife*, Minnesota Department of Natural Resources, St. Paul, MN 1981.

Henderson, John. "The Economics of Wetland Loss." in V.3 N.1 *Great Lakes Wetlands* edited by Wilfred Cwikiel, Tip of the Mitt Watershed Council, Petoskey, MI 1992.

Herman, K.D., L.A. Masters, M.R. Penskar, A.A. Reznicek, G.S. Wilhelm, and W.W. Brodowicz. *Floristic Quality Assessment With Wetland Categories and Computer Application Programs for the State of Michigan.* Michigan Department of Natural Resources, Lansing, MI 1996.

Klein, Kim. *Fundraising for Social Change*, Chardon Press, Berkeley, CA 1985.

Kusler, J.A. *Our National Wetland Heritage: A Protection Guidebook*, Environmental Law Institute, Washington, D.C. 1983.

Kusler, J.A. *Regulating Sensitive Lands*, Ballinger Publishing Company, Cambridge, MA 1980.

Kusler, J.A. and Mary E. Kentula. *Wetland Creation and Restoration: The Status of the Science*, Island Press, Washington, D.C. 1990.

Leopold, Aldo. *A Sand County Almanac*, Oxford University Press, Inc., 1949.

Marble, A.D. *A Guide to Wetland Functional Design*, Lewis Publishers, Chelsea, MI 1992.

Maryland Bar Association, ed. *Starting a Nonprofit Organization: A Practical Guide to Organizing, Incorporating, and Obtaining Tax Exempt Status*, The Community Law Center and The Maryland Association of Nonprofit Organizations, Baltimore, MD 1992.

Maryland Department of Natural Resources. *The Private Landowner's Wetlands Assistance Guide: Voluntary Options for Wetlands Stewardship in Maryland*, developed for workshops held in Eastern and Western Maryland, 1992.

Michaud, Joy P. *At Home With Wetlands: A Landowner's Guide*, Washington State Department of Ecology, Olympia, WA 1990.

Michigan Bar Association. "Real Property – Taking" in *Michigan Opinion Notes*, Michigan Bar Journal, June 1990.

Michigan Department of Environmental Quality. *MDEQ Wetland Delineation Manual: A Technical Manual for Identifying Wetlands in Michigan*, MDEQ, Land and Water Management Division, Lansing, MI 2001

Michigan Department of Natural Resources. *A Wetland Conservation Strategy for Michigan*, MDNR, Land and Water Management Division, Lansing, MI 1993.

Michigan Department of Natural Resources. *Wetland Determination Manual Draft for Field Testing, Volume 1*, MDNR, Land and Water Management Division, Lansing, MI 1989.

Michigan Department of Natural Resources. *Wetland Protection Guidebook*, MDNR, Land and Water Management Division, Lansing, MI 1988.

Michigan Society of Planning Officials. *Community Planning Handbook: Tools and Techniques for Guiding Community Change*, Michigan Society of Planning Officials, Rochester, MI 1991.

Mitchell, M.K. and W.B. Stapp. *Field Manual for Water Quality Monitoring (Eighth Edition)*, Thomson-Shore, Inc., Dexter, MI 1994.

Mitsch, William J. and James G. Gosselink. *Wetlands: Second Edition*, Van Nostrand Reinhold Company, Inc., New York, NY 1993.

Mitsch, William J. "Wetlands Ecological Engineering and Self Design" in V.3 N.1 *Great Lakes Wetlands* edited by Wilfred Cwikiel, Tip of the Mitt Watershed Council, Petoskey, MI 1992.

Mueller, Tara. "Federal Claims Court Awards Millions in Damages to Landowners for Regulatory Taking" in *The Back Forty*, October 1990.

National Audubon Society, Great Lakes Regional Office. *Saving Wetlands: A Citizens' Guide to Action in Michigan*, National Audubon Society, Columbus, OH 1991.

Paulson, Gerald A. *Wetlands and Water Quality: A Citizen's Handbook for Protecting Wetlands*, Lake Michigan Federation, Chicago, IL 1990.

Redmond, Ann. "How Successful is Mitigation?" in V.14 N.1 *National Wetlands Newsletter* edited by Steve Mattox. Environmental Law Institute, Washington, D.C. 1992.

273

Reed, Jr., Porter B. *National List of Plant Species that Occur in Wetlands* U.S. Fish and Wildlife Service, Washington, D.C. 1988.

Riexinger, Patricia. "Classification of Wetlands: A Perspective From New York," in V.2 N.4 *Great Lakes Wetlands* edited by Wilfred Cwikiel, Tip of the Mitt Watershed Council, Petoskey, MI 1991.

River Network. *Starting Up: A Handbook for New River and Watershed Organizations*, River Network.

Robinson, Andy. *Grassroots Grants: An Activist's Guide to Proposal Writing*, 1996.

Roth, E.M., R.D. Olsen, P.L. Snow, and R.R. Sumner. *Oregon Freshwater Wetland Assessment Methodology* edited by S.G. McCannell, Oregon Division of State Lands, Salem, OR 1993.

Scodari, Paul F. *Wetlands Protection: The Role of Economics*, Environmental Law Institute, Washington, D.C. 1990.

Smith, Helen V. *Michigan Wildflowers*, Cranbrook Institute of Science, Bloomfield Hill, MI 1966.

Small, Stephen J. *Preserving Family Lands: Essential Tax Strategies for the Landowner*, Landowner Planning Center, Boston, MI 1992.

Stone, W.A. and A.J.L. Stone. *Wetlands and Ground Water in the United States*, American Groundwater Trust, Dublin, OH 1994.

The Conservation Foundation. *Protecting America's Wetlands: An Action Agenda*, The Conservation Foundation, Washington, D.C. 1988.

The Natural Lands Trust, Inc. *A Handbook for the Landowner: The Use and Protection of Privately Held Natural Lands*, The Natural Lands Trust, Inc., Philadelphia, PA 1982.

The Water Pollution Control Federation. *The Clean Water Act of 1987*, The Water Pollution Control Federation, Alexandria, VA 1987.

Thunhorst, G.A. *Wetland Planting Guide for the Northeastern United States* Environmental Concern, Inc., St Michaels, MD 1993.

Tiner, Ralph. "How Wet is a Wetland?" in V.2 N.3 *Great Lakes Wetlands* edited by Wilfred Cwikiel. Tip of the Mitt Watershed Council, Petoskey, MI 1991.

Trister, Michael B. *An Advocate's Guide to Lobbying and Political Activity for Nonprofits*, Children's Defense Fund, Washington, D.C. 1991.

Twolan-Strutt, Lisa. *Wetlands and Woodlots* Issues Paper, No. 1995-1, North American Wetlands Conservation Council (Canada), Ottawa, ONT 1995.

U.S.D.A. Natural Resources Conservation Service. *Better Wetlands: More than a dozen ideas to improve restored wetlands for wildlife and personal enjoyment*, USDA, Washington, D.C. 1995.

U.S.D.A. Soil Conservation Service. "Ponds: Planning, Design, and Construction," *Agriculture Handbook 590*, Washington D.C. 1971.

U.S.D.A. Soil Conservation Service. *Engineering Field Handbook*, Chapter 13: "Wetland Restoration, Enhancement, or Creation," Washington, D.C. 1992.

U.S. Environmental Protection Agency, Region I. T*he Federal Wetlands Protection Program in New England: A Guide to Section 404 for Citizens and States*, U.S. EPA, Boston, MA 1991.

U.S. Environmental Protection Agency, Office of Wetlands, Oceans, and Watersheds. *Natural Wetlands and Urban Stormwater: Potential Impacts and Management*, U.S. EPA Washington, D.C. 1991.

U.S. Environmental Protection Agency, Office of Wetlands, Oceans, and Watersheds. *Proposed Revisions to the Federal Manual for Delineating Wetlands*, U.S. EPA, Washington, D.C. 1991.

Voss, Edward. *Michigan Flora Part I: Gymnosperms and Monocots*, Cranbrook Institute of Science and University of Michigan Herbarium, Bloomfield Hills and Ann Arbor, MI 1972.

Voss, Edward. *Michigan Flora Part 2: Dicots*, Cranbrook Institute of Science and University of Michigan Herbarium, Bloomfield Hills and Ann Arbor, MI 1985.

Voss, Edward. *Michigan Flora Part 3: Dicots, Concluded* Cranbrook Institute of Science and University of Michigan Herbarium, Bloomfield Hills and Ann Arbor, MI 1996

APPENDIX I: Glossary

Acid - A substance that yields positively charged Hydrogen ions when in solution.

Acidic - Solutions (including soil moisture and water vapor) which have a pH value less than 7 (neutral).

Acidophilic vegetation (acidophile) - Vegetation adapted to living in acidic conditions.

Activism - The doctrine or policy of taking positive, direct action to achieve an end, especially a political or social end.

Adjacent wetlands - Wetlands that border, are contiguous to, or neighbor another body of water and have a hydrological connection to that body of water.

Advocacy - The act of advocating, or speaking, or writing in support of something.

Aerobic - A condition in which molecular oxygen is a part of the environment and freely available to organisms.

Alkali (Base) - A substance which yields negatively charged hydroxide or carbonate ions when in solution.

Alkaline (Basic) - Solutions (including soil moisture and water vapor) which have a pH value greater than 7 (neutral).

Alluvium - Alluvium, or alluvial soil, is soil composed primarily of eroded material, such as sand, silt, or clay, that has been deposited on the bottom of water bodies or on land by rivers and streams overflowing their banks. For example, an alluvial river swamp is a depressional area along the floodplain of a river or creek that is continuously or almost continuously flooded.

Anaerobic - A condition in which molecular oxygen is absent (or effectively so) from the environment.

Aquifer - A geologic formation that is capable of yielding a significant amount of ground water to a well or spring.

Benthic - Being in or on substrate, usually refers to bottom-dwelling organisms in lakes.

Biodiversity - The sum of all species of plants and animals. An ecosystem is considered healthy when it supports the most diverse numbers and types of species it is capable of supporting.

275

Bog - A peatland which is for all practical purposes isolated from ground or surface water (only significant water inputs are directly from rain) and dominated by mosses (*Sphagnum* spp.), sedges, shrubs, and evergreen trees such as black spruce and tamarack.

Buttressed - The swollen or enlarged bases of trees developed in response to wet conditions or prolonged inundation.

Calcareous - Containing calcium carbonate, calcium, or lime that typically causes an alkaline condition.

Concentric - A series of circles, each progressively smaller, nested inside one another.

Detritus - Any non-living plant or animal material or debris.

Drained, effectively - A condition where ground or surface water has been removed by artificial means to the point that an area no longer meets the wetland hydrology criterion.

Drawdown – Process of partially or completely dewatering a wetland with pumps or other mechanical devices. The purpose of a drawdown is to manage vegetation and wildlife.

Drift line - An accumulation of water-carried debris along a topographical contour of the land surface or on vegetation that provides direct evidence of prior inundation and often indicates the directional flow of flood waters.

Ecological integrity - A term used to describe intact ecosystems that are diverse, productive, and otherwise function normally.

Ecoregion - An ecological region that has broad similarities to other regions with respect to soil, topography, and dominant vegetation.

Ecosystem - A community of plants and animals and the physical environment they inhabit, e.g., wetlands, rivers, upland. The ecosystem reflects the interaction among soil, climate, vegetation, and animal life.

Emergent aquatic plants - Rooted plants growing in shallow water with a portion of their stems and leaves growing above the water surface.

Endangered - Any species that is in danger of extinction throughout all or a significant portion of its range.

Environmental impact statement (EIS) - Written reports prepared to assess the environmental impacts of, and alternatives to, actions that may significantly affect the environment. The EIS is required by the National Environmental Policy Act.

Erosion - The process by which soil particles are detached and transported by water, ice, wind, and gravity down slope or to some downstream point.

Eutrophication - Process by which a body of water becomes highly productive either due to natural causes or excessive inputs of pollution rich in dissolved nutrients.

Evapotranspiration - Conversion of liquid water to vapor both by evaporation and by transpiration of the water by plants growing thereon.

Facultative Plant Species (FAC) - Plant species that are estimated to occur in wetlands approximately 34-66% of the time.

Facultative Upland Plant Species (FACU) - Plant species that are estimated to occur in wetlands approximately 1-33% of the time.

Facultative Wetland Plant Species (FACW) - Plant species that are estimated to occur in wetlands approximately 67-99% of the time.

Fen - A type of peatland that receives mineral-rich inputs of ground or surface water and is dominated by sedges and other grass-like vegetation.

Field tiles (Drainage Tiles) - Perforated plastic or clay pipes that are buried under the surface of the ground to facilitate drainage.

Flooded - A condition in which the soil surface is temporarily covered with water from any source, such as streams overflowing their banks, runoff from adjacent or surrounding slopes, inflow from high tides, or any combination of sources.

Floodplain - That part of a lake or river basin lying between the shoreline and the uplands subject to submergence during a high water stage.

Flora - Plant life.

Function - Any biological, chemical, or ecological process that a wetland performs, such as nutrient removal, wildlife habitat support, and sediment trapping.

Gleyed - Distinctive blueish-gray soil color which develops under conditions of poor drainage, resulting in reduction of iron and other elements.

Ground water - Water that seeps below the surface of the ground and fills interconnected pores in soil and cracks in rocks.

Habitat - The environment in which the requirements of a specific plant or animal are met.

Headwaters - For regulatory (Section 404) purposes, the point on a non-tidal stream above which the average annual flow is less than five cubic feet per second.

Herb - Nonwoody (herbaceous) plants including grasses and grass-like plants, forbs, ferns, fern allies, and nonwoody vines. For the purposes of wetland delineation, seedlings of woody plants that are less than three feet in height are also considered herbs.

276

Hummock - A mound standing above the soil level of the immediate area, usually overgrown with vegetation.

Hydric soil - A soil that is saturated, flooded, or ponded long enough during the growing season to develop anaerobic conditions in the root zone.

Hydrologic regime - The sum total of water that occurs in an area on average during a given period.

Hydrology - The science dealing with the properties, distribution, and circulation of water.

Hydroperiod - The duration of a particular flooding event. The period during which surface water remains on a wetland.

Hydrophyte or hydrophytic vegetation - Literally, water-loving vegetation. Any macrophyte that grows in water, or on a substrate that is at least periodically deficient in oxygen as a result of excessive water content; plants typically found in wetlands and other aquatic habitats.

Indicator - An event, entity, or condition that typically characterizes a prescribed environment or situation; indicators determine or aid in determining whether or not certain circumstances exist or criteria are satisfied.

Infiltration - The downward movement of water from the atmosphere into soil and rock formations.

Interdunal swale - A type of wetland usually dominated by grass-like vegetation that occurs between sand dunes and beach ridges along the Great Lakes shoreline.

Inundation - A condition in which water from any source temporarily or permanently covers a land surface.

Invasive - Specie that tends to spread.

Macrophyte - Any plant species that can be readily observed without the aid of optical magnification, including all vascular plant species or bryophytes (e.g. *Sphagnum* spp.), as well as large algae (e.g. *Chara* spp., and *Fucus* spp.).

Marl - A mixture of clay and the carbonates of calcium and magnesium, from precipitation, shells, and limestone. Common substrate underlying wetlands in the Great Lakes basin, especially in the north.

Marsh - A frequently or continually inundated wetland characterized by emergent herbaceous vegetation adapted to saturated soil conditions.

Mineral soil - Any soil consisting primarily of mineral (sand, silt, and clay) material, rather than organic matter.

Mitigation - Mitigation includes avoiding impacts, minimizing impacts, rectifying impacts, reducing impacts over time, and compensating for impacts. Compensatory mitigation covers creation, restoration, or enhancement of adverse impacts to wetlands.

Mitigation banking - An offsite wetland area created to mitigate for a number of independent wetland development conversions. Under mitigation banking, a developer need not produce the compensatory wetland values but instead can purchase them from another entity that has produced and banked them for this purpose.

Mottles - Spots or blotches of different color or shades of color interspersed within the dominant matrix color in a soil layer.

Muck - Dark colored, finely textured, well-decomposed organic soil material.

Mud flats - The bare flat bottoms of lakes and wetlands exposed by a drop in water level. A mud bar is exposed by accretion of sediments.

Nonhydric soil - A soil that has developed under predominantly aerobic conditions.

Nonpoint source pollution - A diffuse form of pollution that is carried to waterbodies, particularly during rain events. Nonpoint source pollution is typically associated with land use activities such as agriculture, construction, and forestry.

Nonwetland - Any area that has sufficiently dry conditions that hydrophytic vegetation, hydric soils, and/or wetland hydrology are lacking, including former wetlands that have been effectively drained (synonymous with Upland).

Normal circumstances - Refers to the soil, vegetation, hydrology, and climate conditions (in other words, environmental conditions) that are usually present.

Nutrient - Any mineral, compound, or element that promotes biological growth or development.

Obligate Upland Plant Species (UPL) - Plant species that are estimated to occur in wetlands less than 1% of the time.

Obligate Wetland Species (OBL) - Plant species that are estimated to occur in wetlands more than 99% of the time.

Oligotrophic - Lacking in plant nutrients and having an abundance of dissolved oxygen.

Organic soils - Soils whose properties are dominated by organic materials; commonly contain more than 50 percent organic matter by volume and at least 20 percent by weight.

Oxidation-reduction - A complex of biochemical reactions that influence the valence state of elements and their ions. Long periods of soil saturation during the growing season tend to elicit anaerobic conditions that shift the overall process to a reducing condition.

Oxidized root channels - Iron oxide concretions (orange or red-brown in color) that form along the length of a root channel in wetland conditions. Oxidized rhizospheres serve as a common field indicator of wetland hydrology in mineral soils.

Palustrine wetlands - A wetland not a part of a main lake and not subject to the main lake's intensive wave or current affects.

277

Peat - A low-density, slightly decomposed fibrous organic soil composed largely of plant material.

Peatland - A generic term used to refer to peat accumulating wetlands, such as fens and bogs.

Perched - Wetland system in which soils do not allow water to pass through them to the ground water.

Perennial (plant) - Living for more than one year.

Permeability - The quality of the soil that enables water to move downward through the profile, measured as the number of inches per hour that water moves downward through the saturated soil.

Piezometer - A shallow well used to measure ground water fluctuations.

Plant community - The various plant species that share a single habitat or environment.

Propagules - The structure of an organism involved in dispersal and reproduction, as in seeds or spores of plants.

Rhizosphere - The zone of a soil in which interactions between living plant roots and micro-organisms occur; root zone.

Riparian - Adjacent to a body of water; a person who resides on a shoreline property.

Sapling - Woody vegetation between 0.4 and 5.0 inches in diameter at breast height and greater than or equal to 20 feet in height, not including woody vines.

Sapropel - A gaseous product of decomposition from organically rich bottom sediments. Sapropel is formed under anaerobic conditions and has the fetid odor of hydrogen sulfide. It is common in marshes.

Saturated - A condition in which virtually all voids (pores) between soil particles are temporarily or permanently filled with water.

Sedimentation - The process of nutrients and sediments entering waterbodies and wetlands.

Shrub - Woody vegetation usually greater than 3 feet but less than 20 feet tall, including multi-stemmed, bushy shrubs and small trees and saplings.

Soil horizon - A layer of soil or soil material approximately parallel to the land surface and differing from adjacent layers in physical, chemical, and biological properties or characteristics (e.g., color, structure, and texture).

Staff gauge - A fixed point in a body of water from which measurements of the surface water level are taken.

Stewardship (land) - To care for and manage natural land in a way that maintains its ecological integrity for the benefit of present and future generations.

Submergent vegetation - Plants that have their stems and leaves below the water surface. They may have some flowering parts above.

Substrate - The surface beneath a wetland in which organisms grow or to which organisms are attached.

Swamp - A forested wetland.

"Takings" - The unconstitutional denial of an individual's rights to use his or her property. Refers to the Fifth Amendment of the U.S. Constitution and similar provisions in other constitutions, which prohibit governments from "taking" private property for public use unless they pay just compensation.

Threatened - Any species likely to become endangered within the foreseeable future throughout all or a significant portion of its range.

Transpiration - The process in plants by which water is released into the gaseous environment (atmosphere).

Tree - A woody plant 5 inches or greater in diameter at breast height and 20 feet or taller.

Upland - Any area that does not qualify as a wetland because the associated hydrologic regime is not sufficiently wet to elicit development of vegetation, soil, and/or hydrologic characteristics associated with wetlands.

Values - Those aspects of wetlands that are deemed worthy, desirable, or useful to humans. Wetland values emanate from their functions. Perceived wetland values arise from their functional ecologic process but are determined by human perceptions, the location of a particular wetland, the human population pressures on it, and the extent of the resource. See also "Function."

Vernal pool - Shallow, intermittently flooded wet meadow, generally dry for most of the summer and fall.

Water table - The depth or level below which the ground is saturated with water.

Watershed - The region drained by or contributing water to a stream, lake, or other body of water.

Wetland boundary - The point on the ground at which a shift from wetland to upland occurs.

Wetland delineation - The process by which the boundaries of a particular wetland are defined.

278

Wetland determination - The process by which an area is identified as a wetland or non-wetland.

Wetland hydrology - In general terms, inundation or prolonged soil saturation for a duration sufficient to support wetland vegetation or foster the development of hydric soils (approximately 14 days or more during the growing season in the temperate zone).

Wetland indicator status - One of five categories which provide an estimate of the percentage of time a particular plant species would occur in a wetland. Indicator statuses include Obligate Wetland, Facultative Wetland, Facultative, Facultative Upland, and Obligate Upland and are defined elsewhere in this glossary.

Zone of influence - The area contiguous to a ditch, channel, or other drainage structure that is directly drained by it.

Zooplankton – Animal microorganisms, such as small crustaceans, rotifers, and protozoans floating in the water. They graze on phytoplankton and each other.